# Linear and Interface Circuits Applications

## Volume 1

## Amplifiers, Comparators, Timers, and Voltage Regulators

D.E. Pippenger and E.J. Tobaben
Linear Applications

Contributors
C.L. McCollum
Field Applications Engineering
Linear Product Engineering

### TEXAS INSTRUMENTS

# Contents

## Section 3
### Operational Amplifier and Comparator Applications

## Section 4
### Video Amplifiers

**Section 5**
**Voltage Regulators**

## Section 6
## Switching Power Supply Design

### Section 7
### Integrated Circuit Timers

# List of Illustrations

# List of Tables

# Section 1

# Introduction

The technology of incorporating microprocessors and other logic circuits on a single integrated circuit chip has heralded the computer age. Accompanying this technology have been linear and interface circuits to provide the variety of functions required for these complex computer devices to communicate with each other and external systems. The broad range of integrated circuits available today can be divided into two general classes; logic and nonlogic. This is the first in a new series of application books that address the nonlogic devices.

The books have been divided into basically independent sections for eace of use. Each section covers a product category, beginning with the basic theory of that product, followed by the key characteristics of devices in that category, and then applications of the devices.

The primary objective is to assist the user in understanding the operating principles and characteristics of the wide variety of devices. By understanding the devices the user can solve one of the most common application problems — selecting the proper device for a particular application. Some theory is discussed; however emphasis is placed on demonstrating operating characteristics of devices and their potential uses in circuits. Obviously presentation of all possible circuits is beyond the scope of any book. The circuit examples selected for this book have accrued from numerous customer inquiries and related laboratory simulations. In many cases they are solutions to actual customer design problems. However, the circuits are presented only as examples to stimulate your thinking on how the devices could be used to solve your specific design requirements. In each case, a data book or data sheet should be referred to for complete device characteristics and operating limits.

In order to more easily present up-to-date information, additional volumes are planned for this series of application books. This volume discusses operational amplifiers, comparators, video amplifiers, voltage regulators and timers. Volume 2 will present information on display drivers and data line drivers, receivers, and transceivers. Volume 3 will provide information on peripheral drivers, data acquisition circuits, and special functions.

As an overview of the device numbering system, Table 1-1 shows the meaning of the various characters in Texas Instruments Linear and Interface circuit device numbers. Texas Instruments devices that are direct alternate sources for other manufacturers' parts carry the original part number including its prefix. Alternations in device characteristics from the original data sheet specfciations, generally to improve performance, results in a new number with the appropriate SN55, SN75, or TL prefix. The type of package is also included in the device number. Table 1-2 lists the package suffixes and their definitions.

## Table 1-1. Linear and Interface Circuits

**XXX XXXXX XX**

Package Type
(See Table 1-2)

| ORIGINAL MANUFACTURER | PREFIX | DEVICE NUMBER | TEMP* RANGE |
|---|---|---|---|
| TI | TL | XXXC | COM |
| | | XXXI | IND |
| | | XXXM | MIL |
| | SN | 75XXX | COM |
| | | 55XXX | MIL |
| NATIONAL | LM | 1XXX | MIL |
| | | 2XXX | IND |
| | | 3XXX | COM |
| | ADC | XXXX | COM |
| | DS | 78XX | MIL |
| | | 88XX | COM |
| RAYTHEON | RC | 4XXX | COM |
| | RM | 4XXX | MIL |
| SIGNETICS | NE | 5/55XX | COM |
| | SA | 5/55XX | AUTO |
| | SE | 5/55XX | MIL |
| | N8T | XX | COM |
| FAIRCHILD | uA | 7XXXC | COM |
| | | 7XXXI | IND |
| | | 7XXXM | MIL |
| | uA | 9XXX | COM |
| MOTOROLA | MC | 13/33XX | IND |
| | | 14/34XXX | COM |
| | | 15/35XX | MIL |
| SPRAGUE | UCN | XXX | COM |
| | UDN | XXXX | COM |
| | ULN | XXXX | COM |
| AMD | AM | XXXXXM | MIL |
| | | XXXXXC | COM |
| SILICON GENERAL | SG | 15XX | MIL |
| | | 25XX | IND |
| | | 35XX | COM |
| PMI | OP- | XX | COM |

*Temperature ranges:

COM = 0°C to 70°C

IND = −25°C to 85°C

AUTO = −40°C to 85°C

MIL = −55°C to 125°C

## Table 1-2. Packages

| TYPE | PACKAGE DESCRIPTION |
|---|---|
| N | Plastic DIP |
| NE, NG | Plastic DIP, copper lead frame |
| NF | Plastic DIP, 28 pin, 400 mil |
| NT | Plastic DIP, 24 pin, 300 mil |
| P | Plastic DIP, 8 pin |
| D | Plstic SO, small outline |
| J | Ceramic DIP |
| JD | Ceramic DIP, side braze |
| JG | Ceramic DIP, 8 pin |
| FE, FG | Ceramic chip carrier, rectangular |
| FH, FK | Ceramic chip carrier, square |
| FN | Plastic chip carrier, square |
| KA | TO-3 metal can |
| KC | TO-220 plastic, power tab |
| LP | TO-226 plastic |
| U | Ceramic flatpack, square |
| W, WC | Ceramic flatpack, rectangular |

# Section 2

# Operational Amplifier and Comparator Theory

## OPERATIONAL AMPLIFIER THEORY

In l958, the age of the integrated circuit was ushered in by Jack Kilby of Texas Instruments. From the two hand-built circuits which he fabricated, the variety and quantity of integrated circuits have mushroomed at an ever increasing rate. One type of integrated circuit is the operational amplifier that is characterized by its high gain and versatility. Because of its versatility and ease of application, the operational amplifier has become one of the most widely used linear integrated circuits. Operational amplifiers are designed to be used with external components to provide the desired transfer functions.

The rapid evolution and versatility of the operational amplifier is shown by its initial development and use. One of the two hand-built integrated circuits which Jack Kilby built was a phase shift oscillator, the first linear integrated circuit. This was soon followed by the introduction of the uA702 and SN523 operational amplifiers. Even with their lack of short-circuit protection and their requirements for complex compensation they quickly gained acceptance. Among the improved designs which quickly followed was the uA741 single operational amplifier which required no external compensation. Conversely, the uA748 was designed for compensation by external components to change the frequency response for applications requiring wider bandwidth and higher slew rate.

Operational amplifier capabilities and versatility are enhanced by connecting external components to change the operating characteristics. Typical operational amplifier characteristics include frequency response, signal phase shift, gain and transfer function. The external components are placed in one or more feedback networks and/or the circuits that terminate the input.

To adequately evaluate the potential of an operational amplifier for a specific application, an understanding of operational amplifier characteristics is required. Figure 2-1 represents an equivalent operational amplifier circuit and its parameters. The parameters illustrated in Figure 2-1 are as follows:

- Input bias currents ($I_{IB1}$ and $I_{IB2}$) — the current flowing into both operational amplifier inputs. In an ideal condition, $I_{IB1}$ and $I_{IB2}$ are equal.
- Differential input voltage ($V_{DI}$) — the differential input voltage between the noninverting ( + ) input and the inverting ( − ) input.

- Input offset voltage ($V_{IO}$) — an internally generated input voltage identified as the voltage that must be applied to the input terminals to produce an output of 0 V.
- Input resistance ($R_I$) — the resistance at either input when the other input is grounded.
- Output voltage ($V_O$) — normal output voltage as measured to ground.
- Output resistance ($R_O$) — resistance at the output of the operational amplifier.
- Differential voltage gain ($A_{VD}$) or open-loop voltage gain ($A_{OL}$) — the ratio of the input voltage to the output voltage of the operational amplifier without external feedback.
- Bandwidth (BW) — the band of frequencies over which the gain ($V_O/V_{DI}$) of the operational amplifier remains within desired limits.

The generator symbol Ⓖ in Figure 2-1 represents the output voltage resulting from the product of the gain and the differential input voltage ($A_{VD} V_{DI}$).

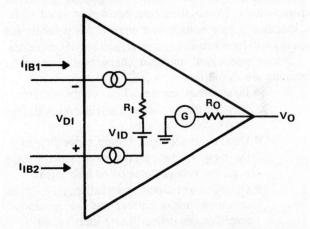

**Figure 2-1. Operational Amplifier Equivalent Circuit**

An ideal operational amplifier (see Figure 2-2) provides a linear output voltage that is proportional to the difference in voltage between the two input terminals. The output voltage will have the same polarity as that of the noninverting ( + ) input with respect to the voltage at the inverting ( − ) input. When the noninverting input is more positive than the inverting input, the output voltage will have a positive amplitude. When the noninverting input is more negative than the inverting input, the output voltage will have a negative amplitude.

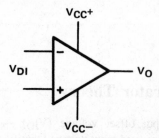

**Figure 2-2. Ideal Operational Amplifier**

An operational amplifier having no external feedback from output to input is described as being in the open-loop mode. In the open-loop mode, the characteristics of the ideal operational amplifier are as follows:

Differential gain = $\rightarrow \infty$
Common-mode gain = 0
Input resistance = $\rightarrow \infty$
Output resistance = 0
Bandwidth = $\rightarrow \infty$
Offset and drift = 0

## MAJOR PERFORMANCE CHARACTERISTICS

The detailed and specific performance characteristics of a particular operational amplifier can be found on the appropriate data sheet. An operational amplifier data sheet will normally provide many nongeneric electrical characteristics. The electrical characteristics provided are for a specified supply voltage and ambient temperature and usually will have minimum, typical, and maximum values.

Major operational amplifier characteristics and their meaning are as follows:

- Input offset current ($I_{IO}$) — the difference between the two input bias currents when the output voltage is zero.
- Common-mode input voltage range ($V_{ICR}$) — the range of the common-mode input voltage (i.e., the voltage common to both inputs).
- Output short-circuit current ($I_{OS}$) — the maximum output current that the operational amplifier can deliver into a short circuit.
- Output voltage swing ($V_{OPP}$) — the maximum peak-to-peak output voltage that the operational amplifier can produce without saturation or clipping occurring. This characteristic is dependent upon output load resistance.
- Large-signal differential voltage gain ($A_{VD}$) — the ratio of the ouput voltage swing to the input voltage swing when the output is driven to a specified large-signal voltage (typically $\pm 10$ V).
- Slew rate (SR) — the time rate of change of the closed-loop output voltage with the operational amplifier circuit having a voltage gain of unity (1).
- Supply current ($I_{CC}$) — The total current that the operational amplifier will draw from both

power supplies when unloaded (per amplifier for multiunit packages).

- Common-mode rejection ratio (CMRR) — a measure of the ability of an operational amplifier to reject signals that are present at both inputs simultaneously. The ratio of the common-mode input voltage to the generated output voltage and is usually expressed in decibels (dB).

The preceding paragraphs have discussed basic operational amplifier characteristics. The following paragraphs will provide more detailed information. The specific characteristics that will be discussed are as follows:

- Gain and frequency response
- Difference of input resistance
- Influence of input offset voltage
- Input offset compensation
- Input offset voltage temperature coefficient
- Influence of input bias current
- Influence of output resistance
- Input common-mode range
- Common-mode rejection ratio (CMRR)
- Slew rate
- Noise
- Phase margin
- Output voltage swing
- Feed-forward compensation

**Gain and Frequency Response**

Unlike the ideal operational amplifier, a typical operational amplifier has a finite differential gain and bandwidth. Because many of the ideal operational amplifier characteristics cannot be achieved, the characteristics of a typical amplifier differ significantly from those of the ideal amplifier. The open-loop gain of a TL321 operational amplifier is shown in Figure 2-3. At low frequencies, open-loop gain is constant. However, at approximately 6 Hz it begins to roll off at the rate of $-6$ dB/octave (an octave is a doubling in frequency and decibels are a measure of gain

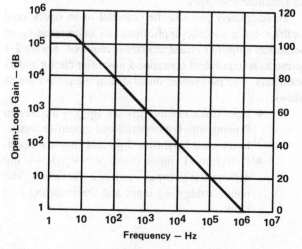

**Figure 2-3. TL321 Operational Amplifier Bandwidth**

calculated by $20 \log_{10} V_O/V_I$). The frequency at which the gain reaches unity is called unity gain bandwidth and referred to as B1.

When a portion of the output signal is fed back to the input of the operational amplifier, the ratio of the output to input voltage is called closed-loop gain. Closed-loop gain is always less than the open-loop gain. Because gain error is proportional to the ratio of closed-loop gain to open-loop gain, a very high value of open loop gain is desirable.

## Gain-Bandwidth Product

When selecting an operational amplifier for a particular application, gain-bandwidth product is one of the primary factors to consider. The product of closed-loop gain and frequency response (expressed as bandwidth, BW, remains constant at any point on the linear portion of the open-loop gain curve (see Figure 2-4).

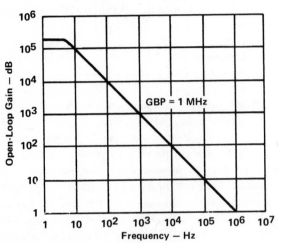

Gain-Bandwidth Product = Closed-Loop Gain X Frequency Response

## Figure 2-4. Bandwidth for Operational Amplifier TL321

The bandwidth is the frequency at which the closed-loop gain curve intersects the open-loop curve as shown in Figure 2-4. The bandwidth may be obtained for any desired closed-loop gain by drawing a horizontal line from the desired gain to the roll-off intersection of the open-loop gain curve. In a typical design, a factor of 1/10 or less of the open loop gain at a given frequency should be used. This ensures that the operational amplifier will function properly with minimum distortion. When the voltage gain of an operational amplifier circuit is increased, the bandwidth will decrease.

## Influence of the Input Resistance

The influence of the input resistance can be determined with Kirchhoff's law. By applying Kirchhoff's law to the circuit in Figure 2-5, we can use the following equations:

$$I_1 = I_2 + I_3 \text{ or}$$

$$\frac{V_I - V_{DI}}{R1} = \frac{V_{DI} - V_O}{R2} + \frac{V_{DI}}{R_I}$$

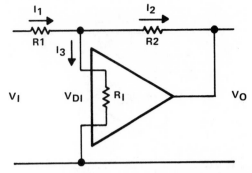

## Figure 2-5. Influence of the Input Resistance

If the open-loop gain is infinite, the differential input voltage will be zero and the value of input resistance (if it is not zero) will have no influence. Since $V_{DI} = V_O/A_{VD}$, the following equations apply:

$$\frac{V_I - \dfrac{V_O}{A_{VD}}}{R1} = \frac{\dfrac{V_O}{A_{VD}} - V_O}{R2} + \frac{\dfrac{V_O}{A_{VD}}}{R_I}$$

Therefore:

$$\frac{V_I}{V_O} = \frac{1}{A_{VD}} + \frac{1}{\dfrac{R2}{R1} A_{VD}} + \frac{R1}{R_I A_{VD}} - \frac{1}{\dfrac{R2}{R1}}$$

or:

$$\frac{V_I}{V_O} = -\frac{1}{\dfrac{R2}{R1}} + \frac{1}{\dfrac{R2}{R1} A_{VD}} + \frac{1}{A_{VD}}\left(1 + \frac{R1}{R_I}\right)$$

The previously listed equations indicate that the input resistance (unless it is small relative to R1) will have little or no effect on the ratio of output voltage to input voltage. Therefore, the closed-loop gain for typical applications is independent of the input resistance.

## Influence of Input Offset Voltage

The input offset voltage ($V_{IO}$) is an internally generated voltage and may be considered as a voltage inserted between the two inputs (see Figure 2-6). In addition, it is a differential input voltage resulting from the mismatch of the operational amplifier input stages.

The effect on currents $I_1$ and $I_2$ can be determined by the following equations:

$$\frac{V_I - V_{IO}}{R1} = \frac{V_{IO} - V_O}{R2}$$

If the input voltage ($V_I$) is zero, the equation is as follows:

$$\frac{-V_{IO}}{R1} = \frac{V_{IO} - V_O}{R2}$$

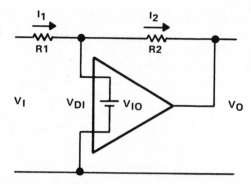

**Figure 2-6. Influence of Input Offset Voltage**

The output voltage is the output offset voltage ($V_{OO}$). The following equation can be used to determine $V_{OO}$:

$$V_{OO} = \left(\frac{R2}{R1} + 1\right) V_{IO}$$

The value of the input offset voltage can be found by dividing the output offset voltage by the closed-loop gain.

## Input Offset Compensation

An ideal operational amplifier has zero input offset voltage and no drift. However, because of the mismatch of input transistors and resistors on the monolithic circuit, typical operational amplifiers have a low but definite offset voltage. Most operational amplifiers have provisions for connecting an external potentiometer so that the input offset can be adjusted to zero. The exact method used and total resistance of the null adjustment potentiometer is dependent upon the type of operational amplifier circuit. A general-purpose internally compensated operational amplifier (a uA741) may require a 10 kΩ potentiometer. A BIFET or externally compensated operational amplifier may require a 100 kΩ potentiometer. Recommended input offset voltage null adjustment circuits are usually shown in the data sheet.

Methods of nulling the input offset voltage are shown in Figures 2-7 and 2-8. When the offset null pins (N1 and N2) are connected to the emitter of the constant-current

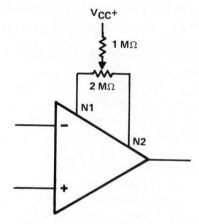

**Figure 2-8. Null Pins Connected to Collectors**

generators, a circuit similar to that shown in Figure 2-7 is used. When the null pins are connected to the collectors of the constant-current generator, a circuit similar to that shown in Figure 2-8 is used.

Actual resistor values depend upon the type of operational amplifier used. Consult the appropriate data sheet for complete input offset nulling procedures.

## Input Offset Voltage Temperature Coefficient

Input offset voltage temperature coefficient (offset voltage drift) is specified in volts per degree Celsius. The amount of drift that occurs with temperature variations is directly related to how closely matched the input characteristics are when the device is manufactured. BIFET input devices (such as the TL080 family) typically have 10 to 12 μV/°C. The LinCMOS™ operational amplifier family has from 0.7 to 5 μV/°C depending upon the bias mode selected.

## Influence of Input Bias Current

Both input bias current ($I_3$) and the normal operating currents ($I_1$ and $I_2$) flow through resistors R1 and R2 (see Figure 2-9). A differential input voltage equal to the product of $I_3(R1R2)/R1 + R2$ is generated by this current. The differential input (which is similar to input offset voltage)

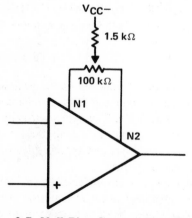

**Figure 2-7. Null Pins Connected to Emitters**

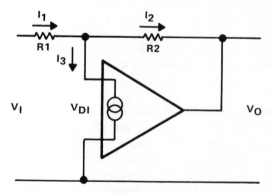

**Figure 2-9. Influence of Input Bias Current**

LinCMOS is a trademark of Texas Instruments

also appears as a component of the output that is amplified by the system gain. Methods of correcting for the effects of input bias current are discussed later.

## Influence of Output Resistance

The influence of output resistance is illustrated by Figure 2-10. Output current can be expressed by the following equation:

$$I_O = I_2 + I_L \text{ and } I_2 + I_1 = \cfrac{V_O}{\cfrac{R2R_L}{R2 + R_L}}$$

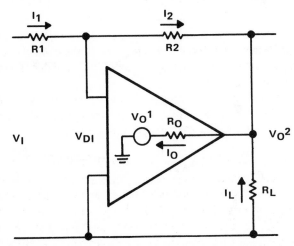

**Figure 2-10. Influence of Output Resistance**

If $V_O1$ is the output voltage of the equivalent ideal amplifier, and $V_O2$ is the output voltage of the actual device, then $V_O2$ can be determined by the following equation:

$$V_O2 = V_O1 - R_O I_O = V_O1 - \cfrac{R_O V_O2}{\cfrac{R2R_L}{R2 + R_L}}$$

For the ideal case $V_O1 = V_{DI}A_{VD}$; therefore:

$$V_O2 = V_{DI}A_{VD} - R_O \left[ \cfrac{V_O2}{\cfrac{R2R_L}{R2 + R_L}} \right]$$

## Input Common-Mode Range

The input common-mode range may be defined as the maximum range of the input voltage that can be simultaneously applied to both inputs without causing cutoff, clipping, or saturation of the amplifier gain stages. The input stage must be capable of operating within its specifications over the dynamic range of output swing. If it cannot, the amplifier may saturate (or latch-up) when the input limits

are exceeded. Latch-up occurs most often in voltage-follower stages where the output voltage swing is equal to the input voltage swing and the operational amplifier is driven into saturation. The specified common-mode voltage range of the input stage must exceed the maximum peak-to-peak voltage swing at the input terminals or the input stage may saturate on peaks. When saturation occurs, an inverting stage no longer inverts. The negative feedback becomes positive feedback and the stage remains in saturation.

## Common-Mode Rejection Ratio (CMRR)

The common-mode rejection ratio may be defined as the ratio of the differential signal gain to the common-mode signal gain and is expressed in decibels.

$$\text{CMRR (dB)} = 20 \ (\log_{10}) \ \cfrac{\cfrac{V_O}{V_I}}{\cfrac{V_O}{V_{CM}}}$$

$$\text{or} \ \frac{\text{(differential signal gain)}}{\text{(common-mode signal gain)}}$$

An ideal operational amplifier responds only to differential input signals and ignores signals common to both inputs. In a typical circuit, however, operational amplifiers have a small but definite common-mode error. Common-mode rejection is important to noninverting or differential amplfiers because these configurations see a common-mode voltage. Depending upon the type of device, dc rejection ratios may range from 90 dB to 120 dB. Generally, bipolar operational amplifiers have higher rejection ratios than FET-input amplifiers.

## Influence of Voltage and Current Drift

Input offset voltage, input bias current, and differential offset currents may drift with temperature. Although it is relatively easy to compensate for the effects of these characteristics themselves, correcting for their drift with temperature variations is difficult. However, there is some limited control offered by the design over any drift characteristics. When drift tendencies are expected to be a design problem, device type, construction, and application should be considered.

## Slew Rate

The slew rate may be defined as the maximum rate of change of the output voltage for a step voltage applied to the input (see Figure 2-11). Slew rate is normally measured with the amplifier in a unity gain configuration. Both slew rate and gain bandwidth product are measures of the speed of the operational amplifier.

Slew-rate limiting is accomplished by the limiting of the operational amplifier internal circuit ability to drive capacitive loads. Capacitance limits the slewing ability of the operational

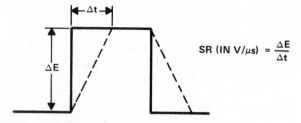

$$SR \ (IN \ V/\mu s) = \frac{\Delta E}{\Delta t}$$

NOTE: Solid line is a square-wave input. Broken line is slewed output.

**Figure 2-11. Effect of Slew Rate**

amplifier at high frequencies. When the current available to charge and discharge the capacitance becomes exhausted, slew-rate limiting occurs.

### Noise

Although not specifically stated as one of the primary characteristics of the ideal operational amplifier, noise-free operation is desirable. Typical operational amplifiers degrade the input signal by adding noise components. Noise components are usually random and determine the ultimate lower limit of signal-handling capability. Noise is usually specified on the data sheet as equivalent input noise, and like the other input factors, is increased by the gain of the stage. There are several potential sources of noise in an operational amplifier. The most common are thermal noise caused by the two source resistances (this noise exists within an ideal operational amplifier), internal noise current, and noise-voltage generators. Under normal audio applications the noise-voltage will be the dominant source of amplifier noise. As the source resistance is increased, the effect of noise-current increases until (at high source resistance) noise current and the bias compensation resistor noise together are the dominant components of amplifier input noise. In specifications, these two parameters are detailed separately. Noise voltage is specified at a low source resistance. Noise current is specified at a high source resistance. Both $V_n$ and $I_n$ are given in terms of density. These are measured with a narrow-bandwidth filter (1 Hz wide) at a series of points across a useful spectrum of the amplifier. Data is usually given in terms of noise voltage versus frequency. Practical data or curves on data sheets are normally given as the following:

$$V_n = e_n/\sqrt{F \ (Hz)}$$

NOTE: Typically a frequency and source resistance will be given in the test conditions included in the device data sheet.

In general, low-input-current operational amplifiers (FET) or low-bias-current bipolar operational amplifiers will have lower noise current and tend to be quieter at source impedances above 10 kΩ. Below 10 kΩ, the advantage swings to bipolar operational amplifiers which have lower input voltage noise. When the source impedance is below 10 kΩ,

actual source resistance is composed mostly of generator resistance. The noninverting operational amplifier configuration has less noise gain than the inverting configuration for low signal gains and, thus, high signal-to-noise ratio. At high gains, however, this advantage diminishes.

### Phase Margin

Phase margin is equal to 180° minus the phase shift at the frequency where the magnitude of the open-loop voltage gain is equal to unity. Phase margin is measured in degrees and must be positive for unconditional stability. Figure 2-12 illustrates a typical circuit used to measure phase margin.

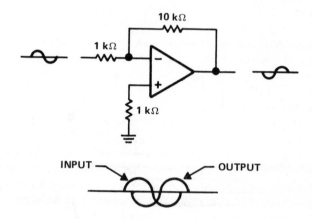

**Figure 2-12. Phase Margin Measurement Circuit**

If the phase difference between the input and output waveform is 120°, 180° minus 120° phase difference leaves 60° as the phase margin. Phase difference may or may not be given on the data sheet. Phase margin will normally be from 50° to 70° on commercially available operational amplifiers. When phase margin decreases to 45°, the operational amplifier becomes unstable and may oscillate.

### Output Voltage Swing ($V_{OPP}$)

$V_{OPP}$ is the peak-to-peak output voltage swing that can be obtained without clipping or saturation. Peak-to-peak swing may be limited by loading effects, operational amplifier frequency capability, load resistance, and power supply used. Load resistances given on the data sheet are usually 2 kΩ or 10 kΩ. With load resistances of 2 kΩ or less, the output decreases due to current limiting. Normally, this will not damage the operational amplifier as long as the specified power-dissipation limits of the package are not exceeded. However, the open-loop gain will be reduced because of excessive loading.

### Feed-Forward Compensation

The TL080 through TL084 BIFET operational amplifiers have been developed by Texas Instruments through state-of-the-art semiconductor technology. The BIFET process allows optimum circuit design with the fabrication of bipolar and FET transistors on a common substrate. This process, along with ion-implanted FET inputs, produces an almost ideal operational amplifier family which typically exhibits a higher input impedance than that obtainable with conventional manufacturing technology. High input impedance and the FET's inherently low input bias currents make the BIFET family ideal for numerous instrumentation and audio amplifier applications.

The TL080 provides for externally controlled compensation on pins 1 and 8. This is an advantage over the internally compensated version (TL081) because it allows the user to obtain slew rates from a typical 12 V/$\mu$s (for nominal compensation of 12 pF) to 30 V/$\mu$s (for a compensation of 3 pF). This increased slew rate is also reflected in the small signal response where the rise time is decreased from 0.1 $\mu$s to less than 50 ns. The power bandwidth can be extended to greater than 1 MHz. This greatly increases the potential for large-signal wide-bandwidth applications and for filters with frequencies at or above 1 MHz. The unity gain bandwidth is identical to the normal compensation mode but the first pole frequency is extended above 10 kHz; thus, gain accuracy is maintained at higher frequencies.

In the feed-forward circuit (see Figure 2-13), a 100 k$\Omega$ resistor is shown in parallel with a 3 pF capacitor in the negative feedback loop. A 500 pF feed-forward capacitor is connected from pin 1 to the inverting input of the TL080. The high-frequency response increases from approximately 6 kHz to over 200 kHz. Figure 2-14 is the feed-forward compensation curves.

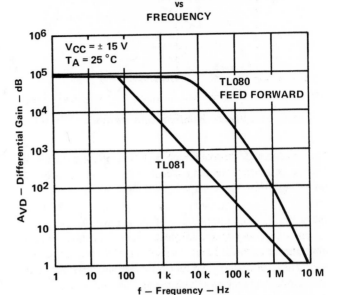

Figure 2-14. Feed-Forward Compensation Curves

## BASIC OPERATIONAL AMPLIFIER CIRCUITS

Operational amplifiers, because of their variable characteristics and wide range of adaptablility, can be configured to perform a large number of functions. Operational amplifier applications are frequently limited more by the imagination than by their functional limitations or operating parameters. The basic operational amplifier circuits that are discussed in this section are as follows:

- Noninverting Amplifier
- Inverting Amplifier
- DC Output Offset Amplifier
- Summing Amplifier
- Differentiator
- Active Filter
- Voltage Follower
- Differential Amplifier
- Integrator
- Unity-Gain Active Filter
- Band-Reject Active Filter
- Low-Pass Active Filter

### NONINVERTING OPERATIONAL AMPLIFIER

A noninverting amplifier circuit provides an amplified output that is in phase with the circuit input. Figure 2-15 illustrates a basic noninverting operational amplifier circuit. In the circuit shown in the figure, the output is in phase with the input at low frequencies.

In this circuit, the input signal is applied to the noninverting ($+$) input of the amplifier. A resistor (R1), which is usually equal to the resistance of the input element, is connected between ground and the inverting ($-$) input of

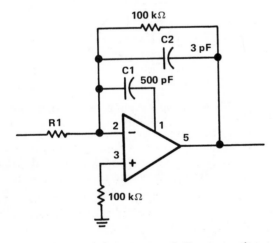

Figure 2-13. Feed-Forward Compensation

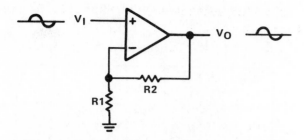

**Figure 2-15. Basic Noninverting Amplifier Circuit**

the amplifier. A feedback loop is connected from the output of the amplifier, through feedback resistor R2, to the inverting input. The voltage gain of a noninverting amplifier circuit is always greater than unity (1). For practical purposes, the input impedance of the noninverting amplifier circuit is equal to the intrinsic input impedance of the operational amplifier.

The output voltage of the noninverting amplifier circuit can be determined by the following equation:

$$V_O = \left[1 + \frac{R2}{R1}\right](V_I)$$

The voltage gain of the noninverting amplifier circuit can be determined by the following equation:

$$A_V = \frac{V_O}{V_I} = 1 + \frac{R2}{R1}$$

## INVERTING AMPLIFIERS

An inverting amplifier circuit, as illustrated in Figure 2-16, provides an output that is 180 degrees out of phase with the input signal.

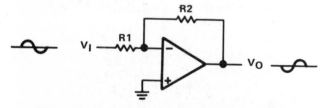

**Figure 2-16. Basic Inverting Amplifier Circuit**

In this circuit, the input signal is applied through a resistor (R1) to the inverting input (−) of the operational amplifier. The noninverting input (+) is connected to ground. A feedback loop is connected from the output, through feedback resistor R2, to the inverting input. The voltage gain of an inverting amplifier circuit can be less than, equal to, or greater than unity (1). Resistor R1 determines the input impedance of the inverting amplifier circuit. The input impedance is much lower than for a noninverting amplifier circuit.

The output voltage for an inverting amplifier can be determined by the following equation:

$$V_O = \left[-\frac{R2}{R1}\right](V_I)$$

NOTE: The minus sign in the equation indicates the 180° phase reversal.

The voltage, or closed-loop, gain can be determined by the following equation:

$$A_{CL} = \frac{V_O}{V_I} = -\left[\frac{R2}{R1}\right]$$

## DC OUTPUT OFFSETS

When the input voltage to an operational amplifier is zero, the ideal output voltage is also zero. However, the ideal condition cannot be realistically achieved because of dc offset. DC offset may be caused by the internal input offset and input bias currents. It may also be caused by an input signal offset voltage. With no signal into the amplifier shown in Figure 2-17, input bias current flows through resistors R1 and R2. Because of the voltage drop across R1 and R2, these input currents will produce an offset voltage. Since the noninverting input is grounded, the voltage appears as input offset and is amplified by the operational amplifier.

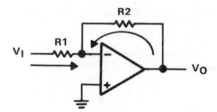

**Figure 2-17. Inverting Amplifier with Input Bias Currents**

The method commonly used to correct for a dc offset condition is to place an additional resistor (R3) between the noninverting input and ground as shown in Figure 2-18.

The value of resistor R3 is calculated as the parallel combination of R1 and R2 as follows:

$$R3 = \frac{R1R2}{R1 + R2}$$

A voltage is developed across R3 that is equal to the voltage across the parallel combination of R1 and R2. Ideally, the voltages appear as common-mode voltages and are cancelled. However, in a typical operational amplifier, the bias currents are not exactly equal. Because of this difference, a small dc offset voltage remains.

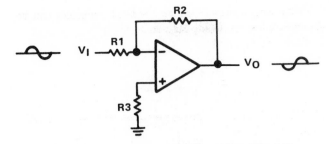

**Figure 2-18. Inverting Amplifier with DC Offset Correction**

The remaining source of output offset voltage is due to the internal input offset voltage. This may be nulled in several ways. The most common method is to connect a potentiometer across the offset null terminals available on many operational amplifiers. Depending upon the type of circuit and chip construction, the center arm is connected to the $V_{CC}+$ rail or $V_{CC}-$ rail. The terminals on the operational amplifier used for this purpose are usually labeled N1 and N2. For complete information on a specific device, consult the appropriate data sheet.

## VOLTAGE FOLLOWER

The voltage or source follower is a unity-gain, noninverting amplifier with no resistor in the feedback loop (see Figure 2-19). The output is exactly the same as the input. The voltage follower has a high input impedance which is equal to the operational amplifier intrinsic input impedance.

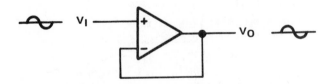

**Figure 2-19. Basic Voltage Follower Circuit**

The function of the voltage follower circuit is identical to a emitter follower for a bipolar transistor or a source follower on an FET transistor. The main purpose of the circuit is to buffer the input signal from the load. The input impedance is high and the output impedance is low.

## SUMMING AMPLIFIER

If several input resistors are connected to the inverting input of the operational amplifier, as shown in Figure 2-20, the result is an amplifier which sums the separate input voltages.

The output voltage of the summing amplifier circuit can be determined by the following equation:

$$V_O = -R4\left(\frac{V_{I1}}{R1} + \frac{V_{I2}}{R2} + \frac{V_{I3}}{R3}\right)$$

If feedback resistor R4 and input resistors R1, R2, and R3 are made equal, the output voltage can be determined by the following equation:

$$V_O = -(V_{I1} + V_{I2} + V_{I3})$$

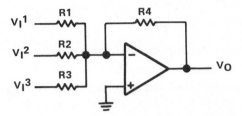

**Figure 2-20. Basic Summing Amplifier**

## DIFFERENCE AMPLIFIER

In a difference amplifier circuit, input voltages $V_{I}1$ and $V_{I}2$ are applied simultaneously to the inverting and noninverting inputs of the operational amplifier (see Figure 2-21).

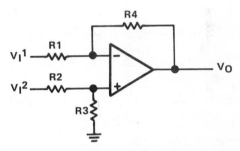

**Figure 2-21. Basic Difference Amplifier Circuit**

When all four resistors are equal, the output voltage is equal to the difference between $V_{I}1$ and $V_{I}1$. This circuit is called a unity-gain analog subtractor. Mathematically, the output voltage is stated as follows:

$$V_O = V_{I}2 - V_{I}1$$

## DIFFERENTIATOR

The operational amplifier differentiator is similar to the basic inverting amplifier circuit except that the input component is a capacitor rather than a resistor (see Figure 2-22).

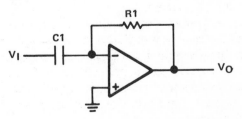

**Figure 2-22. Basic Differentiator Circuit**

The output voltage of the differentiator circuit can be determined by the following equation:

$$V_O = -R1C1 \frac{\Delta V_I}{\Delta t}$$

In this equation $\Delta V_I / \Delta t$ is the change in input voltage divided by a specified time interval. A problem with the basic differentiator circuit is that the reactance of input capacitor C1 ($1/2\pi fC1$) varies inversely with frequency. This causes the output voltage to increase with frequency and makes the circuit susceptible to high-frequency noise. To compensate for this problem, a resistor is connected in series with the capacitor on the inverting input (see Figure 2-23).

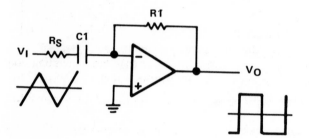

**Figure 2-23. Differentiator with High Frequency Noise Correction**

However, this circuit functions as a differentiator only on input frequencies which are less than those which can be determined by the following equation:

$$fC1 = \frac{1}{2\pi R1C1}$$

The time constant (R1C1) should be approximately equal to the period of the input signal to be differentiated. In practice, series resistor $R_S$ is approximately 50 $\Omega$ to 100 $\Omega$.

## INTEGRATOR

An operational amplifier integrator circuit can be constructed by reversing the feedback resistor and input capacitor in a differentiator circuit (see Figure 2-24).

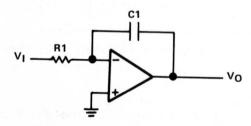

**Figure 2-24. Basic Integrator Circuit**

The resistor (R1) is the input component and the capacitor (C1) is the feedback component. However, if the low-frequency gain of the circuit is not limited, the dc offset

(although small), would be integrated and eventually saturate the operational amplifier. A more practical integrator circuit is shown in Figure 2-25.

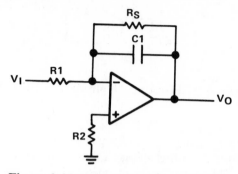

**Figure 2-25. Typical Integrator Circuit**

In this circuit, a shunt resistor ($R_S$) is connected across feedback capacitor C1 to limit the low-frequency gain of the circuit. The dc offset (due to the input bias current) is minimized by connecting resistor R2 between the noninverting input and ground. Resistor R2 is equal to the parallel combination of R1 and shunt resistor $R_S$. The shunt resistor helps limit the circuit low-frequency gain for input frequencies greater than those determined by the following equation.

$$fC1 = \frac{1}{2\pi R_S C1}$$

## ACTIVE FILTERS

Filters are often thought of as discrete networks consisting of resistors, capacitors, and inductors (passive components). Because the components are passive, the energy from a passive filter is always less than the energy applied by the input signal. The attenuation (or insertion losses) limit the effectiveness of passive filters and make some applications impractical. However, resistors and capacitors can be combined with operational amplifiers to form active filters which operate without signal loss.

Depending upon the circuit type, low-pass filters as well as high-pass, bandpass, or band-reject filters can be designed with a roll-off characteristic of 6 to 50 dB or greater per octave. Some of the more common active filters that use operational amplifiers are discussed in the following paragraphs.

### Unity-Gain Active Filters

The unity-gain active filter is the simplest to design. It combines an operational amplifier connected in a unity gain configuration with RC filter networks. It can be either a low-pass filter [Figure 2-26(a)], or a high-pass filter [Figure 2-26(b)], depending upon the positions of its discrete resistors and capacitors.

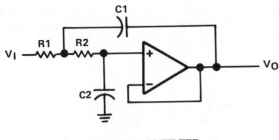

(a) LOW-PASS FILTER

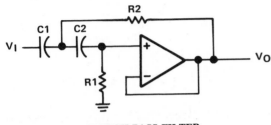

(b) HIGH-PASS FILTER

**Figure 2-26. High-Pass and Low-Pass Filter Circuits**

The −3 dB (cutoff) frequency of the filter can be determined from the following equations:

Low-frequency cutoff $\quad f_0 = \dfrac{1}{2\pi\ C2\sqrt{R1R2}}$

High-frequency cutoff $\quad f_0 = \dfrac{1}{2\pi\ R2\sqrt{C1C2}}$

The Q of the circuit can be calculated using the following formulas for a low or high pass filter:

Low-pass filter $\qquad Q = 1/2\sqrt{C1/C2}$
High-pass filter $\qquad Q = 1/2\sqrt{R1/R2}$

These formulas are valid for a value of Q greater than 10.

## Low-Pass Active Filters

Figure 2-27 illustrates the response curve typical of a low-pass active filter using a general-purpose operational amplifier. Outside the passband, the attenuation is computed at 12 dB per octave. However, at high frequencies the attenuation of the filter is less than predicted. In simple theory, the operational amplifier is considered to be perfect, and, for a typical general-purpose operational amplifier, this perfection proves to be acceptable up to 100 kHz. However, above 100 kHz the output impedance and other characteristics of the amplifier can no longer be ignored. The combined effect of these factors causes a loss of attenuation at high frequencies. General-purpose operational amplifiers are most effective in the audio frequency range. For higher frequency applications, a broad band amplifier such as the LM318 or TL291 should be used.

When the frequency spectrum of the input signal is especially wide, the high-frequency rejection characteristic must be considered. This is true when the input to the filter

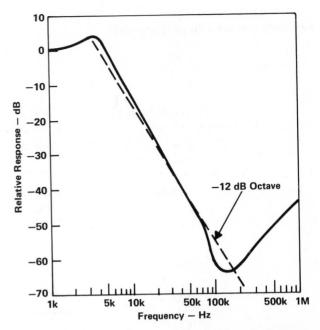

**Figure 2-27. Response Curve of a Low-Pass Active Filter**

is a rectangular signal. Figure 2-28 shows the response of a low-pass active filter to a 1-MHz square-wave signal.

The high-frequency-cutoff problem is resolved by using a simple RC filter ahead of the active filter. The combination of an RC filter and an active filter having superior low-frequency performance will significantly improve high-frequency cutoff. In addition, an impedance adapter should be inserted between the two filters shown in Figure 2-29.

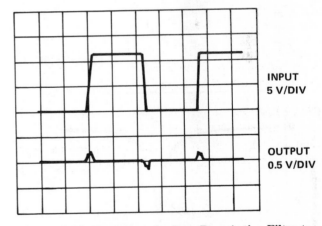

**Figure 2-28. Response of a Low-Pass Active Filter to High Frequency Signals**

## Band-Reject Active Filters

In addition to the previously described functions, an active filter may be used to perform a band-reject function. A filter with a band-reject characteristic is frequently referred to as a notch filter. A typical circuit using a uA741 in unity-gain configuration for this type of active filter is shown in Figure 2-30.

The filter response curve shown in Figure 2-31 is a second-order band-reject filter with a notch frequency of

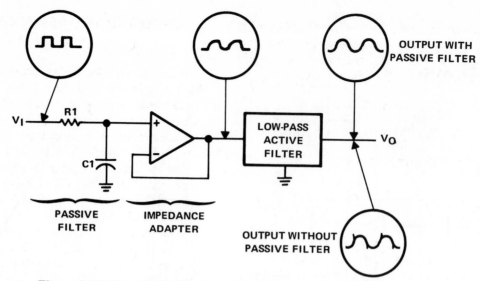

**Figure 2-29. Use of a Passive Filter Preceding an Active Filter**

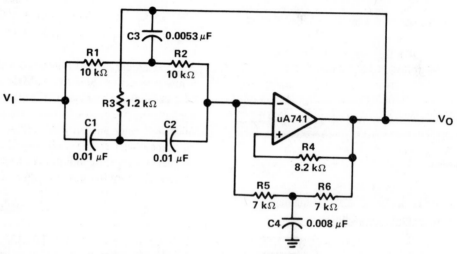

**Figure 2-30. Band-Reject Active Filter**

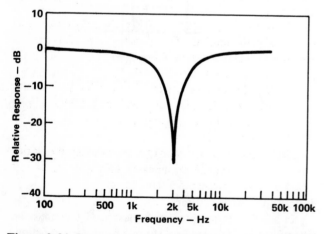

**Figure 2-31. Response Curve of Band-Reject Active Filter**

3 kHz. The resulting Q of this filter is about 23, with a notch depth of −31 dB. Although three passive T networks are used in this application, the operational amplifier has become a sharply tuned low-frequency filter without the use of inductors or large-value capacitors.

**Bandpass Active Filters**

A bandpass filter permits a range of frequencies to pass while attenuating frequencies above and below this range. The center frequency ($f_o$) is the frequency at which the maximum voltage gain occurs. The bandwidth of this type of filter is the difference between the upper and lower frequencies at the points where the voltage gain is 0.707 times the maximum value, or 3 dB lower than the response at the center frequency. As shown in Figure 2-32 $f_L$ is called the lower 3-dB frequency and $f_H$ is called the upper 3-dB frequency. Bandwidth is determined by the following equation:

$$\text{Bandwidth} = f_H - f_L$$

The bandpass filter bandwidth and center frequency are related to each other by the Q, which is defined as follows:

$$Q = \frac{f_o}{f_H - f_L} \quad \text{or} \quad \frac{f_o}{BW}$$

Bandpass filter responses like those shown in Figure 2-32 can be built with operational amplifiers. The filter circuit shown in Figure 2-33 uses only one operational amplifier and is most often used for Q's of 10 or less.

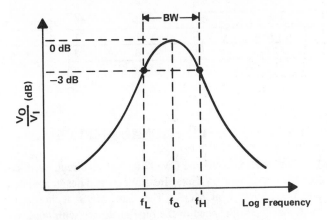

Figure 2-32. Active Bandpass Filter Response Curve

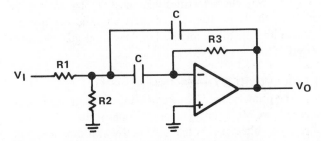

Figure 2-33. Active Bandpass Filter

Given the center frequency ($f_O$), the Q, and the desired gain (G), choose a convenient value of capacitance C. For typical audio filters, C is often 0.01 to 0.1 $\mu$F. The component values are easy to find from the following equations.

$$R1 = \frac{Q}{2\pi f_O\, GC}$$

$$R2 = \frac{Q}{(2Q^2 - G)2\pi f_O\, C}$$

$$R3 = \frac{2Q}{2\pi f_O\, C}$$

Best performance is obtained when the gain is somewhat greater than the square root of the Q. For instance, if the filter is designed for a Q of 16, then the gain should be greater than four.

# CHOOSING THE RIGHT OPERATIONAL AMPLIFIER

The operational amplifier, because of its versatility and ease of application, is the most widely used linear integrated circuit today. Because of this useful linear building block, many electronic circuits are much less complex. Due to the popularity of the operational amplifier, many different types are available that offer a variety of features. Which device to use for a specific application is a question that must be answered. If the characteristics of the selected device are not adequate, total system performance may be less than desired. If the selected device is too complex for the job, system cost may be increased unnecessarily. The following paragraphs provide a summary of the various types of operational amplifiers. To assist in the selection of the most effective operational amplifier for a specific application, the features and key applications are presented.

## GENERAL-PURPOSE OPERATIONAL AMPLIFIERS — BIPOLAR

Since their inception, many operational amplifier designs have used bipolar transistors as the differential amplifier pair at the operational amplifier inputs. Because these input transistors operate from constant-current sources, an additional pair of matched transistors are used to obtain closely matched base-emitter voltages for a predictable ratio of currents for the constant-current generators. Phase-shift is controlled by frequency compensation that is internal to the amplifier. Amplfier phase-shift must be less than 135° at the frequency where the open-loop gain curve and closed-loop gain curve intersect. In bipolar operational amplifiers, the phase-shift is typically set with an internal capacitance of approximately 30 pF. The output stage should be designed to have a wide range of voltage swing with medium current capability.

The bipolar operational amplifier is usually operated in a class-B configuration. The key features of a bipolar operational amplifier are as follows:

Input impedance of $10^6$ $\Omega$.

Typical slew rates from 0.5 to 1 V/$\mu$s.

Typical unity-gain bandwidth of 1 MHz.

Noise levels of approximately 25 to 30 nV/$\sqrt{\text{Hz}}$.

Table 2-1 is a selection guide showing the major parameters to be considered in choosing bipolar operational amplifiers for a particular circuit design.

### Table 2-1. Bipolar Operational Amplifier Comparison Chart

| PARAMETER | DEVICE | | | | | | | | | UNITS |
|---|---|---|---|---|---|---|---|---|---|---|
| | OP-07 | 741 | TL321 | SE5534A | LM358 | LM318 | MC1458 | RC4136 | RC4558 | |
| $V_{IO}$ | 30 | 1 | 2 | 0.5 | 2 | 2 | 1 | 0.5 | 0.5 | mV |
| $I_{IO}$ | 0.5 | 20 | 5 | 10 | 5 | 30 | 20 | 5 | 5 | nA |
| $I_B$ | ±1.2 | 80 | 45 | 400 | 45 | 150 | 80 | 40 | 40 | nA |
| SR | 0.2 | 0.5 | 0.5 | 6 | 0.5 | 70 | 0.5 | 1 | 1 | V/µs |
| B1 | 0.6 | 1 | 1 | 10 | 1 | 15 | 1 | 3 | 3 | MHz |

†Test conditions are $V_{CC}$ = ±15 V. All values are typical.

‡Unity-gain bandwidth

## BIFET OPERATIONAL AMPLIFIERS

BIFET operational amplifiers combine JFET input transistors with bipolar transistors in a monolithic integrated circuit. The ion-implantation process used in making BIFET devices results in closely matched transistors. This permits true class-AB operation in the output stage which results in near zero crossover distortion and low total harmonic distortion.

In addition to high input impedance ($10^{12}$ Ω) and input bias currents in the picoampere range, most BIFET operational amplfiers have slew rates of approximately 13 V/µs and a typical unity-gain bandwidth of 3 MHz. However, BIFET operational amplifiers have higher offset voltages and input noise than bipolar operational amplifiers.

Some BIFET operational amplifiers are power-adjustable. This allows the user to select (with an external resistor) the operating current levels. While this causes a tradeoff with power dissipation, it gives greater control over slew rate or signal bandwidth. An example of such a device is the TL066 BIFET operational amplifier. The TL066 can be adjusted for a no-signal supply current of 5 to 200 µA. Slew rate and bandwidth will also change depending upon the level of operating current. Except for the adjustable feature, the TL066 is similar to the TL061. The key application for power adjustable operational amplifiers is in battery-operated and telecommunication equipment where power consumption is an important factor. Table 2-2 is a selection guide listing the major parameters to be considered when choosing a BIFET operational amplifier for a particular application.

### Table 2-2. BIFET Operational Amplifier Comparison Chart

| PARAMETER | DEVICE SERIES | | | | UNITS |
|---|---|---|---|---|---|
| | TL080 | TL070 | TL060 | TL087 | |
| $V_{IO}$ | 5 | 3 | 3 | 0.1 | mV |
| $I_B$ | 30 | 30 | 30 | 60 | pA |
| NOISE | 25 | 18 | 42 | 18 | nV/Hz |
| SR | 13 | 13 | 3.5 | 13 | V/µs |
| B1 | 3 | 3 | 1 | 3 | MHz |

Test conditions are $V_{CC}$ = ±15 V. All values are typical.

## LinCMOS™ OPERATIONAL AMPLIFIERS

The linear silicon-gate CMOS integrated circuit process was first developed by Texas Instruments and designated by the trademark LinCMOS. The LinCMOS technology combines the high speed of the bipolar device with the low power, low voltage, and high input impedance of the CMOS device. The LinCMOS device provides better offset and voltage swing characteristics than most bipolar devices. In addition, the LinCMOS device overcomes the stability and bandwidth limitations imposed on linear designs by metal-gate CMOS.

### ULTRASTABLE OFFSETS

The primary disadvantage of using conventional bipolar metal-gate CMOS for linear applications is the unavoidable threshold-voltage shifts that take place with time and with changes in temperature and gate voltage. These shifts (caused by the movement of sodium ions within the device transistor) are frequently more than 10 mV/V of applied gate voltage. However, LinCMOS technology overcomes this problem by replacing the metal gates with phosphorus-doped polysilicon gates that bind the sodium ions. The result is linear integrated circuits with low (2 to 10 mV) input-offset voltages that vary no more than a few microvolts from their original values.

The TLC251 and TLC271 series of general-purpose operational amplfiers have low input offset voltages that typically vary only 0.1 µV per month and 0.7 µV per degree Celsius. The extremely low offset voltage can be reduced even further by using the offset null pins on the device. Unlike metal-gate CMOS devices, the input-offset voltage of LinCMOS devices is not sensitive to input-overdrive voltages.

### WIDE BANDWIDTHS

In addition to providing stable offset voltages, LinCMOS technology produces integrated circuits with bandwidths that are two to three times wider than those of metal-gate CMOS devices. This occurs because the silicon gate in LinCMOS transistors is formed during the same processing step that forms the source and drain. As a result, the source, gate, and drain are self-aligned. In contrast, metal gates are formed after the source and drain regions are diffused, necessitating a built-in overlap to ensure source, gate, and drain alignment.

The self-aligned gate of LinCMOS transistors results in a gate-drain capacitance that is approximately one-seventh that of typical metal-gate CMOS integrated circuits. This enhances the bandwidth and speed of LinCMOS devices.

The TLC251 and TLC271 operational amplifiers offer a 2.3 MHz bandwidth, 60-ns rise-time with 25% overshoot, and a slew rate of 4.5 V/$\mu$s. These speeds are better than most bipolar operational amplifiers, approach those of BIFET operational amplifiers, and are several times faster than their metal-gate CMOS counterparts.

## ADVANTAGES OF LinCMOS OPERATIONAL AMPLIFIERS

The TLC251 and TLC271 series operational amplifiers provide a low input offset voltage (10 mV maximum) that remains highly stable over time and temperature and is not sensitive to input-overdrive voltages. They are also available with tightened, guaranteed input offset voltages.

The TLC251 and TLC271 series operational amplifiers can be adjusted for low-, medium- or high-bias operation. This is accomplished by connecting the bias-select pin to $V_{DD}$ for low bias, to ground for high bias, or to 1/2 $V_{DD}$ for medium bias. By providing a choice of bias conditions, the TLC251 and TLC271 allow users to select between ac performance and power consumption to meet a wide range of circuit requirements. When operated in high-bias with $V_{DD}$ equal to 10 V, these devices draw 100 $\mu$A of $I_{DD}$ for 10-mW power dissipation and feature 4.5-V/$\mu$s slew rate and 2.3-MHz bandwidth. In the low bias mode with $V_{DD}$ equal to 10 V and $I_{DD}$ equal to 10 $\mu$A (100 $\mu$W power dissipation), the devices have a slew rate of 0.04 V/$\mu$s and a bandwidth of 100 kHz. In low-bias, and at 1 V, the TLC251 consumes just 10 $\mu$W making it the ideal choice for battery-operated applications. The bias-select pin can be driven with a logic signal from a microprocessor, allowing the operational amplifier performance to be software-controlled.

Additional features of the TLC251 and TLC271 include a common-mode rejection ratio of 88 dB and a low input-noise voltage of 30 to 70 nV/$\sqrt{\text{Hz}}$ (depending upon whether the device is operating in high, medium, or low bias).

These capabilities make the TLC251 and TLC271 suited for a wide range of applications. These applications include active filters, transducer interfacing, current drivers, voltage-to-current converters, long-interval timers, and many types of amplifiers. The TLC251 and TLC271 series are particularly suited for low-power designs and instrumentation amplifiers that require stable offsets.

When using the TLC251 or TLC271 LinCMOS devices for design, the following characteristics must be considered:
- Supply Voltage, $V_{DD}$
  TLC251 . . . . . . . . . . . . . . . . . 1 V to 16 V
  TLC271 . . . . . . . . . . . . . . . . . . . 4 V to 16 V
- True Single Supply or a Maximum of $\pm 8$ V
- Adjustable Supply Current, $I_{DD}$
  Low Bias = 10 $\mu$A typical
  Medium Bias = 150 $\mu$A typical
  High Bias = 1000 $\mu$A typical

- Extremely Low Input Bias and Offset
  Currents: 1 pA Typical
- Low Input Offset Voltage: 3 mV typical
- Ultra Stable Input-Offset Voltage:
  0.1 $\mu$V/Month Typical
- Noise: 30 nV/Hz Typical
- Slew Rate, SR
  High Bias . . . . . . . . . . . . . 4.5 V/$\mu$s typical
  Medium Bias . . . . . . . . . . . 0.6 V/$\mu$s typical
  Low Bias . . . . . . . . . . . . . 0.04 V/$\mu$s typical
- Bandwidth, BW
  High Bias . . . . . . . . . . . . . . . . . . 2.3 MHz
  Medium Bias . . . . . . . . . . . . . . . . 0.7 MHz
  Low Bias . . . . . . . . . . . . . . . . . . 0.1 MHz

## COMPARATORS

A basic comparator is similar to a differential amplifier operating in the open-loop mode. Because of high gain, the output is normally saturated in either the high state or the low state depending upon the relative amplitudes of the two input voltages. With these conditions, the comparator provides a logic-state output which is indicative of the amplitude relationship between two analog input signals.

In typical applications, a comparator provides an indication of the relative state of the two input signals. Figure 2-34 illustrates a basic comparator and its transfer function.

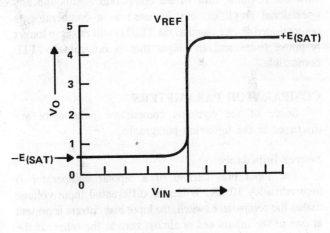

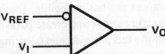

**Figure 2-34. Basic Comparator and Transfer Function**

In the circuit in Figure 2-34, if a reference voltage is applied to the inverting input and an unknown potential to the noninverting input, the output will reflect the relationship between the two inputs. When $V_I$ is more negative that $V_{REF}$, the device output will be in saturation at a logic low level. When $V_I$ becomes more positive than $V_{REF}$, the output will change states and become saturated at a logic high level.

Because comparators are normally used to drive logic circuits, the output must change states as rapidly as possible. High open-loop gain, wide bandwidth and slew rate are key factors in comparator speed. Operation in the open-loop mode (no feedback), with minimum or no frequency compensation, results in maximum gain-bandwidth product for best performance. Most comparators operate in this manner.

The ideal comparator has the same characteristics as the ideal operational amplifier. Those characteristics are as follows:

- Differential Gain = → ∞
- Common-Mode Gain = 0
- Input Impedance = → ∞
- Output Impedance = 0
- Bandwidth = → ∞
- Offset Voltage and Current = 0

Initially operational amplifiers were used in the open-loop mode to perform comparator functions. However, devices designed specifically for this operation resulted in improvements in recovery time, switching speed, and output levels. Since the comparator amplifier stage is usually followed by a TTL logic stage, output logic-state levels normally match those required by TTL loads.

Circuits designed as a comparator use none of the phase/frequency compensation usually required for operational amplifier stabilization with feedback. In fact, these compensation components are detrimental because they slow the response time of the comparator. Although any operational amplifier may be used as a comparator, a compensated device (such as the TL071) will result in longer response times and an output that is not directly TTL compatible.

## COMPARATOR PARAMETERS

Some of the common comparator parameters are discussed in the following paragraphs.

### Source Impedance

The input bias current of a bipolar comparator is approximatley 10 μA. When the differential input voltage makes the comparator switch, the input bias current is present at one of the inputs and is almost zero at the other. If the source impedances are not negligible, feedback will lower the gain of the comparator and create parasitic oscillations. Figure 2-35 shows this phenomenon occuring with a TL810. The comparator is driven by a ramp voltage at a rate of 1 mV/μs as represented by the center waveform. The upper output waveform shows the response of the comparator with a source impedance of 50 Ω. The lower output waveform represents the response of the same comparator with a source impedance of 10 kΩ. The initial switching occurs sooner with a high source impedance because the bias current characteristics produce an additional offset voltage. However, the subsequent oscillations make this circuit configuration unusable with low-slew-rate input signals.

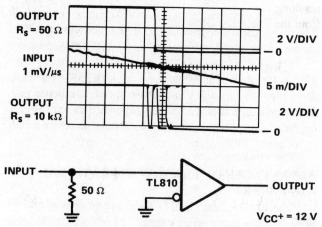

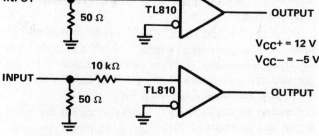

**Figure 2-35. Influence of Source Impedance**

### Differential Voltage Gain

Differential voltage gain ($A_{VD}$) determines the sensitivity and threshold accuracy of a comparator. In the ideal comparator, the gain would be infinite and an extremely small voltage applied between the two inputs would cause a change in the output. In actual practice, the gain is not infinite and some minimum voltage variation at the input is required to obtain a change in the output. The ratio of the variation of output voltage to that of input voltage is the voltage gain of the comparator. The voltage gain of the comparator may be expressed by the following equation:

$$A_{VD} = \frac{\Delta V_O}{\Delta V_I}$$

The quantity $\Delta V_O$ (the difference between the high and low states of the output) is normally set at 2.5 V to ensure matching between the comparator and a TTL load. For example, if the TL810 has a minimum $A_{VD}$ of 12,500, then (for an output swing of 2.5 V) $\Delta V_{I(min)}$ = 2.5 V/12,500, or 0.2 mV.

### Output Characteristics

Although some comparators have a full TTL fanout capability of 10 or greater, others have a fanout that is limited to one TTL load. An evaluation of the output circuits should indicate the basic limiting factors and how maximum performance can be obtained.

In the active pull-down mode [see Figure 2-36(a)], the output low-level sink current ($I_{OL}$) is limited. The emitter of Q2 is clamped at one base-emitter voltage drop or −0.7 V with Q3 providing another base-emitter voltage drop. The resulting low-level output current ($I_{OL}$) may be calculated from the following equation:

$$I_{OL} = \frac{V_{CC} - 2\,V_{BE}}{1.77\ k\Omega}$$

$$= \frac{-6\ V + 1.4\ V}{1.77\ k\Omega} = -2.6\ mA$$

The resulting value is near the typical value for this device. The minus sign indicates a sink current. The corresponding $V_{OL} = V_E\ (Q2) + V_{CE(SAT)}(Q2)$ or $(-0.7\ V + 0.2\ V) = -0.5\ V$, which is the typical data sheet value.

In a logic low-level ouput state, the TL810 can handle one standard TTL gate with its maximum requirement of $-1.6\ mA$. Increased fanout capability can be obtained by connecting an external resistor between the comparator output and the negative supply.

In the active pull-up mode, the typical high-level output voltage ($V_{OH}$) is 3.2 V for the TL810. The voltage at the base of the pull-up transistor [Q1, Figure 2-36(b)] is defined by the following equation:

$$V_{OH} + V_Z + V_{BE(Q1)}$$

Where:

$$V_Z = 6.2\ V$$
$$V_{BE(Q1)} = 0.7\ V$$

The base vaoltage is $(3.2 + 6.2 + 0.7)$, 10.1 V. The resulting base drive is determined by the following equation:

$$I_b = \frac{V_{CC+}\ -\ V_B}{R_b}$$

$$= \frac{12\ V\ -\ 10.1\ V}{3.9\ k\Omega}\ 0.488\ mA$$

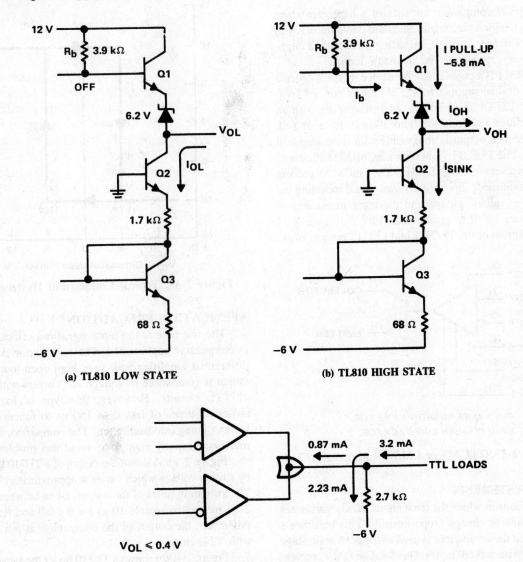

(a) TL810 LOW STATE

(b) TL810 HIGH STATE

(c) TL811 FANOUT OF 2

Figure 2-36. Comparator Output Configurations

Assuming a typical saturated $h_{FE}$ of 12, the resulting pull-up drive capability is (0.488 mA) (12) or 5.8 mA. Only part of the 5.8-mA drive is available to the external circuit. Since the current sink is not turned off during the logic-high output condition, the remainder of the current will be shunted through the pull-down circuit. For TL810, the resulting $I_{OH}$ level available for external drive will be the difference between the pull-up drive of 5.8 mA and the pull-down sink of 2.6 and is 3.2 mA [Figure 2-36(c)]. The 3.2 mA is adequate because the logic high level ($I_{OH}$) required is only 40 μA per TTL load. Similar calculations for the TL811 comparator yield an $I_{OL}$ level of 0.87 mA and an $I_{OH}$ of 4.3 mA. For example, a fanout capability of 2 requires an $I_{OL}$ level of 3.2 mA. With the TL811 [see Figure 2-36(c)], a 2.7-kΩ resistor is connected between the output and the negative supply. The resulting $I_{OL}$ is 3.2 mA at a 0.4-V maximum $V_{OL}$. The effective $I_{OH}$ capability, therefore, is reduced to 1.19 mA at a minimum $V_{OH}$ of 2.4 V.

## STANDARD COMPARATORS

The typical comparator consists of a high-gain stage followed by a logic-state output. Standard comparators with many performance features, including strobes and high-output current capabilities, are available today.

The LM311 is a popular bipolar device that will operate from single or dual supplies from 5 V to 30 V (or ± 15 V). The LM311 has an uncommitted output transistor with an available emitter and collector. This allows source or sink output drive. The output is compatible with most standard logic levels. The TLC311, built with LinCMOS technology, is an improved version of the LM311. The LinCMOS process allows common-mode input levels down to and including the negative $V_{CC}$ rail or ground and the input impedance is increased from $10^6$ Ω to greater than $10^{12}$ Ω. Figure 2-37 is a basic diagram of the TLC311 and LM311 comparators.

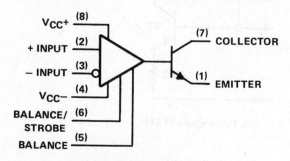

PIN NUMBERS SHOWN ARE FOR
8-PIN DUAL-IN-LINE PACKAGE.

**Figure 2-37. TLC311 or LM311 Comparator**

## USE OF HYSTERESIS

Applications in which the input signal slowly varies can cause the ouput to change proportionally. This becomes a problem when the comparator is used to trigger a logic stage requiring fast rise and fall inputs. One solution to the problem is the introduction of positive feedback. This causes a fast or Schmitt trigger action. This action is accomplished by feeding a portion of the output signal back to the noninverting input. Depending upon the amount of positive feedback, a new trip-level will be introduced after each transition. The result is two (rather than one) threshold points. These are called the upper threshold point (UTP) and lower threshold point (LTP). the difference between these two points is the hysteresis. A comparator with hysteresis is shown in Figure 2-38.

A typical hysteresis loop diagram for this type of circuit is shown in Figure 2-39.

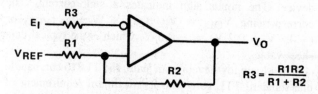

**Figure 2-38. Comparator with Hysteresis**

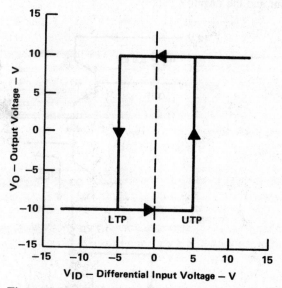

**Figure 2-39. Typical Comparator Hysteresis Loop**

## APPLICATION PRECAUTION

The rise time of the input signal is a critical parameter in comparator applications. The comparator is basically a differential amplifier with very high open-loop gain. The output is compatible in voltage and current with the inputs of TTL circuits. However, this type of logic requires switching times of less than 150 ns to function correctly without going into oscillation. The comparator input signal must vary rapidly enough to avoid this problem.

Figure 2-40(a) shows the output of a TL710 being driven by a ramp voltage which varies at approximately 0.1 mV/μs. The switching times of the output, taken between 0.8 V and 2 V, are approximately 10 μs for the fall and rise times. In this mode, the output of the comparator is not compatible with TTL circuits.

Figure 2-40(b) shows a TL810 under the same conditions as described for the TL710. With a higher gain than the TL710, the switching speed for the TL810 is also higher,

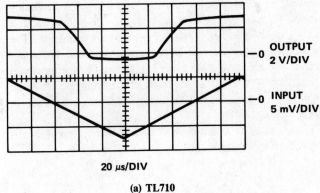

**(a) TL710**

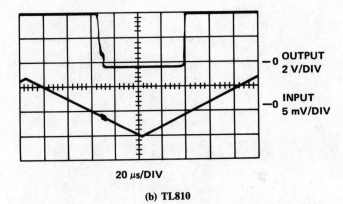

**(b) TL810**

**Figure 2-40. Response of a TL710 and a TL810 to a Ramp Input**

When these input conditions are not being met, some positive feedback must be added or a Schmitt trigger configuration must be designed (see Figure 2-41) to accelerate the switching speed. However, the resulting hysteresis makes the comparator less voltage sensitive.

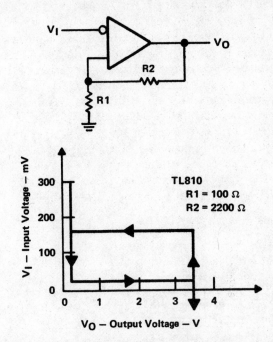

**Figure 2-41. Use of Hysteresis to Prevent Oscillations**

and the rise time is compatible with TTL circuits. However, some oscillation is present during the periods of switching. This occurs because the input signal remains in the high-gain linear range of the comparator for an excessive period of time. For the output of a comparator to be good, the input must force the output to vary between 0.8 V and 2 V in 150 ns or less.

When the minimum gain ($A_{VD}$) of the comparator is known, the input signal must vary at a minimum rate determined by the following equation:

$$\frac{2\ V - 0.8\ V}{150\ ns \times A_{VD}}$$

For the TL710, the minimum rate is determined as follows:

$$\frac{2\ V - 0.8\ V}{150\ ns \times 500} = 16\ mV/\mu s$$

For the TL810, the minimum rate is determined as follows:

$$\frac{2\ V - 0.8\ V}{150\ ns \times 8000} = 1.0\ mV/\mu s$$

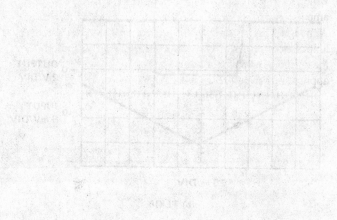

# Section 3

# Operational Amplifier and Comparator Applications

## OPERATIONAL AMPLIFIER APPLICATIONS

### GENERAL APPLICATIONS

This section contains information on several specific circuits which will assist the reader in designing circuits which can be applied to a variety of applications. The specific functions which these operational amplifiers perform include: amplification, measurement, control, sensing, and regulation. Although specific applications are given for each operational amplifier circuit, sufficient information is presented to allow the design of circuits for additional applications. The specific applications circuits discussed in this section are as follows:

- Optical Sensor to TTL Interface
- Bridge-Balance Indicator
- High-Input-Impedance Differential Amplifier
- Low-Voltage Shunt Limiter
- Schmitt Triggers
- PTC Thermistor Automotive Temperature Indicator
- Accurate 10-Volt Reference
- Precision Large Signal Voltage Buffer

### OPTICAL SENSOR TO TTL INTERFACE CIRCUIT

This optical sensor to TTL interface circuit is designed to detect a low light level at the sensor, amplify the signal, and provide a TTL-level output. When the optical sensor detects low-level light (ON condition), its output is small and must be amplified. Because of this small output, an operational amplifier with very low input bias current and high input resistance must be used to detect the ON condition of the sensor and provide an amplified output.

Figure 3-1 is an optical sensor to TTL interface circuit. When connected as shown in the figure, operational amplifier OP-07 meets all of the previously stated characteristics. When sensor TIL406 is in the ON condition, its output is assumed to be 250 nA (allowing a safety margin). This results in a 250-mV signal being applied to the noninverting input of amplifier OP-07. Because of the circuit configuration, the OP-07 provides a gain of 100 and its output is in positive saturation. The OP-07 output level is applied to a loading network that provides the basic TTL level. Because an optoelectronic circuit may operate at slow speeds, it may be

| CONDITION | TIL406 CURRENT | OUTPUT LOGIC |
|-----------|----------------|--------------|
| LIGHT ON  | ≈ 3 μA         | 0            |
| LIGHT OFF | ≈ 3 nA         | 1            |

necessary to connect an SN7513 Schmitt-trigger device on the output of the load network to shape the TTL output signal.

### BRIDGE-BALANCE INDICATOR

A bridge-balance indicator provides an accurate comparison of two voltages by indicating their degree of balance (or imbalance).

A common bridge, referred to as a Wheatstone bridge, consists of two impedance divider networks as shown in Figure 3-2. Generally one side of the bridge consists of known impedances (one of which is usually adjustable) resulting in a known voltage (E1). The other side of the bridge may consist of combined known and unknown impedances resulting in an unknown voltage E2. The unknown impedance might be varied by a system condition (speed, temperature, etc.). A sensitive voltmeter is used to detect the balance of E1 and E2. For example, the bridge may be used to control motor speed, temperature, or physical position. The accuracy of this type of control is dependent on how close to zero difference, or the null point a deviation can be detected.

Detecting small variations near the null point is difficult with the basic Wheatstone bridge alone. Amplification of voltage differences near the null point will improve circuit accuracy and ease of use. The bridge-balance indicator circuit (Figure 3-3) replaces the meter shown in Figure 3-2 and provides the gain required near the null-point for improved accuracy. An OP-07 operational amplifier is used as the gain element in this circuit.

In this application, the 1N914 diodes in the feedback loop result in high sensitivity near the point of balance (R1/R2 = R3/R4). When the bridge is unbalanced the amplifier's closed-loop gain is approximately $R_F/r$, where r is the parallel equivalent of R1 and R3. The resulting gain equation is $G = R_F(1/R1 + 1/R3)$. During an unbalanced condition the voltage at point A is different from that at point B. This difference voltage ($V_{AB}$), amplified by the gain factor G, appears as an output voltage. As the bridge approaches a balanced condition (R1/R2 = R3/R4), $V_{AB}$ approaches zero. As $V_{AB}$ approaches zero the 1N914 diodes in the feedback loop lose their forward bias and their resistance increases, causing the total feedback resistance to increase. This increases circuit gain and accuracy in detecting a balanced condition. Figure 3-4 shows the effect of approaching balance on circuit gain. The visual indicator used at the output of the OP-07 could be a sensitive voltmeter or oscilloscope.

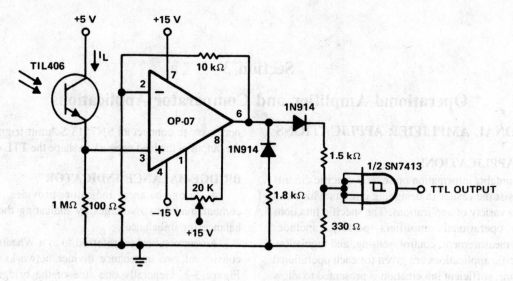

**Figure 3-1. Optical Sensor to TTL Interface Circuit**

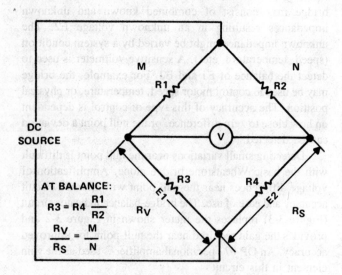

**Figure 3-2. Wheatstone Bridge Circuit**

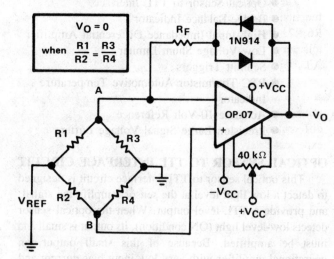

**Figure 3-3. Bridge-Balance Indicator Circuit**

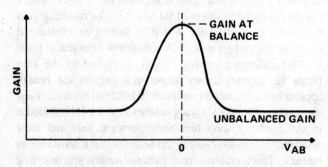

**Figure 3-4. Gain as a Function of $V_{AB}$**

## HIGH-INPUT-IMPEDANCE DIFFERENTIAL AMPLIFIER

One of the most useful applications of an operational amplifier is the differential-input dc amplifier configuration shown in Figure 3-5.

Operational amplifiers A1 and A2 are connected in a noninverting configuration with their outputs driving amplifier A3. Operational amplifier A3 could be called a subtractor circuit which converts the differential signal floating between points X and Y into a single-ended output voltage. Although not mandatory, amplifier A3 is usually operated at unity gain and R4, R5, R6 and R7 are all equal.

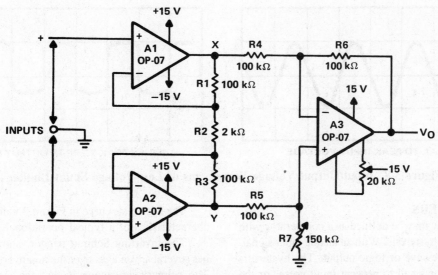

**Figure 3-5. High-Input-Impedance Differential Amplifier**

The common-mode-rejection of amplifier A3 is a function of how closely the ratio R4:R5 matches the ratio R6:R7. For example, when using resistors with 0.1% tolerance, common-mode rejection is greater than 60 dB. Additional improvement can be attained by using a potentiometer (slightly higher in value than R6) for R7. The potentiometer can be adjusted for the best common-mode rejection. Input amplifiers A1 and A2 will have some differential gain but the common-mode input voltages will experience only unity gain. These voltages will not appear as differential signals at the input of amplifier A3 because, when they appear at equal levels on both ends of resistor R2, they are effectively canceled.

This type of low-level differential amplifier finds widespread use in signal processing. It is also useful for dc and low-frequency signals commonly received from a transducer or thermocouple output, which are amplified and transmitted in a single-ended mode. The amplifier is powered by ±15-V supplies. It is only necessary to null the input offset voltage of the output amplifier A3.

## LOW VOLTAGE SHUNT LIMITER

In some circuits, it is necessary to symmetrically limit or clip the peak output voltage of an amplifier stage. Limiting may be required to prevent overdriving a following amplifier stage. This type of circuit is also used in volume compressor and amplitude leveler designs.

The limiting function may be accomplished by several methods. Figure 3-6 shows a simple back-to-back diode limiter.

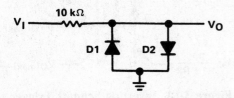

**Figure 3-6. Simple Back-to-Back Shunt Limiter**

If standard small signal diodes such as 1N914 are used for D1 and D2, ±0.6 V would be available at the limiter output. If germanium diodes are used for D1 and D2, ±0.4 V will be the output voltage. Limiting may also be accomplished utilizing resistor/zener diode networks. The low-voltage shunt limiter shown in Figure 3-7 is useful when the signal level must be limited at a very low level, such as several hundred millivolts. Such levels are, of course, below the range of conventional diodes, so alternate methods are necessary to accomplish limiting at these levels.

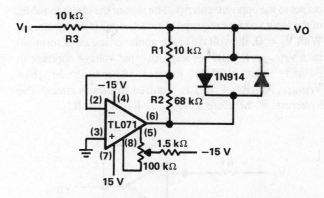

**Figure 3-7. Low-Voltage Shunt Limiter**

In this circuit, the operational amplifier is used to shift the apparent threshold of a conventional 1N914 silicon diode. The output voltage limit can be adjusted to any fraction of the diode voltage. This circuit divides the signal level, even when below the threshold, because of the feedback through resistor R2. As an example, assume a 10-V peak-to-peak input sine-wave signal at a frequency of 1 kHz. With the values shown the output will be a 150-mV peak-to-peak square wave as shown in the scope photos in Figure 3-8.

3-3

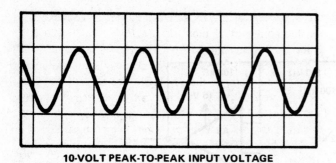

**10-VOLT PEAK-TO-PEAK INPUT VOLTAGE**

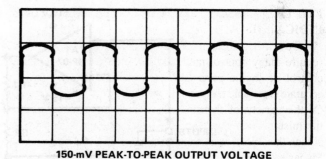

**150-mV PEAK-TO-PEAK OUTPUT VOLTAGE**

**Figure 3-8. Input/Output Voltage Waveforms of Low-Voltage Shunt Limiter**

## SCHMITT TRIGGERS

A Schmitt trigger may be defined as a comparator with positive feedback, or hysteresis. With an analog input signal, the output is a squarewave or logic output. The hysteresis may be made large or small to prevent input noise, or the unwanted portion of the input signal, from appearing at the output. These types of circuits are very useful as the input section to data line receivers. They may also be used as level detectors, threshold detectors, pulse generators, and pulse shapers.

A voltage-follower Schmitt trigger can be constructed by connecting a positive feedback loop around an operational amplifier as shown in Figure 3-9. The feedback bias is connected to the noninverting input, maintaining it as a voltage level proportional to the output which is latched at either the $V_{CC+}$ or $V_{CC-}$ supply level. An input voltage $V_I$ may be applied to overcome the feedback and force the output to the opposite polarity. The sum of the absolute values of the input voltages required to switch states is the hysteresis. With $V_I = 0$, the voltage at the noninverting input terminal is $\pm V_{O(max)} R1/(R1 + R2)$. An input voltage opposite in polarity and slightly greater in magnitude than $V_{O(max)} R1/(R1 + R2)$ is required to switch states. The hysteresis is therefore $2 V_{O(max)} R1/(R1 + R2)$.

The hysteresis curve in Figure 3-9 illustrates the transfer characteristics of a typical operational amplifier.

The inverting Schmitt trigger, shown in Figure 3-10, has several advantages over the noninverting Schmitt trigger. The primary advantage is that the signal input current, because it flows only through R3, is independent of the output and feedback. Therefore, the input may be from a current or voltage source and must generate only enough voltage across R3 to result in switching. The input thresholds are $\pm V_{O(max)} R2/(R1 + R2)$. This circuit may be used to convert analog signals to standard logic levels. A positive voltage pulse of sufficient amplitude will switch the output negative. It will remain negative until a negative input pulse is applied causing the output to switch back to the positive state. This is similar to the operation of a set-reset type flip-flop. Operational amplifiers respond slowly for some switching applications. If additional speed is required, use externally compensated amplifiers. Very low value (1 to 2 pF) frequency-compensation capacitors will enhance switching speeds considerably and allow data rates as high as 1 MHz. A device recommended for this application is the TL070.

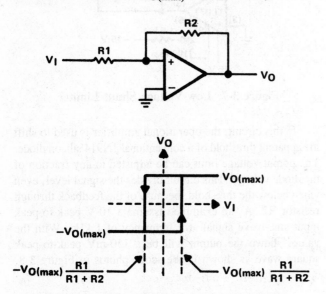

**Figure 3-9. Voltage-Follower Schmitt Trigger**

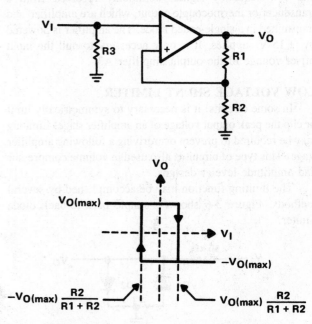

**Figure 3-10. Inverting Schmitt Trigger**

## PTC THERMISTOR AUTOMOTIVE TEMPERATURE INDICATOR

To reach maximum efficiency, present day automobiles require many control methods. For example, temperature control of engine parts and fluids is essential. However, accurate electronic temperature measurements are not simple. Of the variety of thermocouples, resistance sensors, and thermistors available, the positive-temperature-coefficient silicon thermistor is an excellent choice for this application. Planar technology using the spreading-resistance principle allows this integrated circuit to be built. The TSP102 has a positive resistance temperature coefficient of 0.7%/°C and has very close resistance tracking from unit to unit. Nominally it is about 1 kΩ resistance at 25°C and changes from 500 Ω at −40°C to 1900 Ω at 120°C.

The example circuit (Figure 3-11) is used to indicate two different water temperature trip points by turning on LEDs when the temperatures are reached. The circuit is constructed around the LM2904 dual operational amplfier which was designed mainly for the automotive industry.

The circuit is powered from the 12-V auto system. The 1N5239 zener diode supplies a regulated 9.1 V to operate the circuit. The thermistor is in series with a 10-kΩ resistor from ground to the positive 9.1-V point. The top of the thermistor is tied to both noninverting inputs of the LM2904. The voltage at these inputs will change as the thermistor resistance changes with temperature. Each inverting input on the LM2904 has a reference, or threshold trip point, set by a 10-kΩ resistor and a 2-kΩ potentiometer in series across

the 9.1-V regulated voltage. When this threshold is exceeded on the noninverting input of LM2904, the TIL220 LED lights. In this circuit, the FAN ON trip point was set at 70°C. This occurs with approximately 1.3 V on the inverting input of the top section of the LM2904. The OVERHEAT trip point was set at 95°C. This condition exists when the bottom section of the LM2904 has approximately 1.44 V on the inverting input. The two trip points can be recalibrated or set to trip at different temperatures by adjusting the 2-kΩ potentiometer in each section. In addition to being used as warning lights as shown here, circuits can be added to turn on the fan motor or activate a relay.

Other types of thermistors and temperature sensors manufactured by other companies can be used with this type of circuit.

## ACCURATE 10-VOLT REFERENCE

A stable 10-V reference is a valuable asset for calibrating oscilloscopes and other laboratory equipment. The 10-V reference was selected because it can be used in decade fashion (multiplied or divided by 10). One of the major requirements for a laboratory reference is not only initial accuracy but long-term stability. This requires precision low-drift components. An OP-07 bipolar operational amplifie was chosen because it has low offset and long-term stability. The offset voltage drift is approximately 0.3 µV/°C. The OP-07 is excellent because of its low noise and high-accuracy amplification of very low-level signals. Figure 3-12 illustrates an accurate 10-V reference circuit.

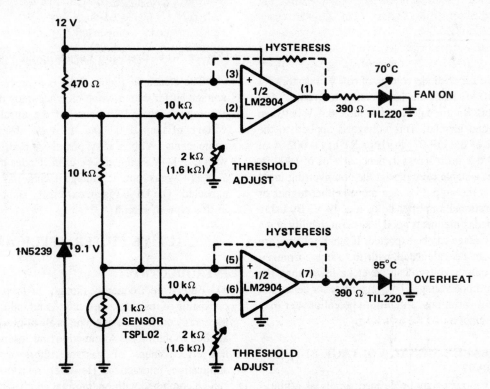

**Figure 3-11. PTC Sensor Automotive Temperature Control Circuit**

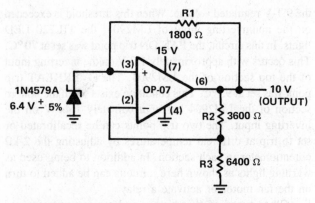

**Figure 3-12. Accurate 10-Volt Reference Circuit**

The accuracy of the circuit can be enhanced by using precision resistors. The 1N4579A zener diode was chosen because of its 0.0005%/°C temperature coefficient. The resistor values were calculated from the following formulas:

$$R1 = \frac{10\text{ V} - V_Z}{2 \times 10^{-3}}$$

Where:

$$V_Z = \text{Zener Voltage}$$

$$R2 = \frac{10\text{ V} - V_Z}{1 \times 10^{-3}}$$

$$R3 = \frac{V_Z}{1 \times 10^{-3}}$$

Assuming a zener diode voltage of 6.4 V, resistors R2 and R3 total 10 kΩ from the 10-V output to ground. The values of R2 and R3 are calculated to have 6.4 V between their junction and ground. This voltage is applied to the inverting input of the OP-07. Resistor R1 has 0.002 A of current and a 3.6 V drop across it, hence a value of 1800 Ω. This establishes a stable reference at the noninverting input of the OP-07. If the output voltage moves either higher or lower, the operational amplifier holds it at 10 V. By using the recommended components good long-term stability at the desired output voltage can be expected. If other voltages are needed, they can be calculated with the same formulas. However, the output voltage can never be lower than the reference zener diode voltage. To compensate for zener and other component variations, a multiturn potentiometer may be used at the junction of R2 and R3.

## PRECISION LARGE-SIGNAL VOLTAGE BUFFER USING AN OP-07

A voltage follower may be defined simply as a unity-gain noninverting amplifier. There is no feedback resistance. A basic voltage follower is shown in Figure 3-13.

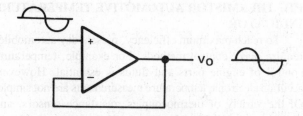

**Figure 3-13. Basic Voltage-Follower Circuit**

For the basic voltage-follower circuit, the output voltage is an exact reproduction of the input voltage. The input impedance is equal to the operational amplifier intrinsic input impedance. The output impedance for the voltage-follower circuit is, for all practical purposes, equal to the operational amplifier output impedance.

The primary purpose of the voltage-follower circuit is to buffer an input signal from its load. The input impedance is high and the output impedance is low. The function of an operational amplifier voltage follower is identical to the cathode, emitter, and source followers for vacuum tubes, bipolar transistors, and field-effect transistors, respectively. A complete voltage-follower circuit using an OP-07 is shown in Figure 3-14.

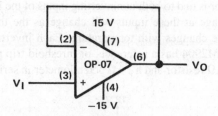

**Figure 3-14. Precision Large-Signal Voltage Follower**

The circuit in Figure 3-14 is a precision large-signal voltage buffer with a worst-case accuracy of 0.005%. This accuracy is possible because of the ultralow input-offset voltage of the OP-07 and the total absence of external components. With ±15-V power supplies, an input signal with a ±14-V swing can be used. Under these conditions, a peak-to-peak output voltage swing of ±13 V can be expected. The OP-07 is an extremely stable device for use in this type of circuit.

## ACTIVE FILTER APPLICATIONS

### INTRODUCTION

Filters are frequently thought of as passive networks consisting of resistors, capacitors, and inductors. Therefore the energy out of a passive filter is always less than the energy applied to the input. Attenuation and insertion losses limit the effectiveness of passive filters and make some applications impractical. However, resistors and capacitors can be combined with operational amplifiers to form active filters.

In an active filter the amplifier may add energy to the system, resulting in both filtering and some power gain. Other advantages of active filters include low output impedance, cascaded stages without gain loss, and the capability of generating filtering functions having relatively high Q at low frequencies without inductors. In low-frequency applications, the inductors required for passive filters are generally cumbersome as well as difficult and costly to build. On the other hand, only a few easily used components are needed for active filters in these applications.

Depending on the circuit type; low-pass, high-pass, band-pass, or band-reject filters can be designed with a roll-off characteristic from 6 to 50 dB or greater per octave. An active filter offers several advantages over a passive (LC) filter.

1. No insertion loss. The op amp can provide gain if needed.
2. Cost. Active filter components are more economical than inductors.
3. Tuning. Active filters are easily tuned and adjusted over a wide range without altering the desired response.
4. Isolation. Active filters have good isolation due to their high input impedance and low output impedance, assuring minimal interaction between the filter and its load.

## ACTIVE BAND-PASS FILTER

A band-pass filter passes a specific range of frequencies while preventing the passage of all others. Passive LC band-pass filters have been used for many years but the tuning procedures are difficult. These difficulties include removing or adding turns to the inductor and the need for specific capacitor values. Although a passive LC filter uses only inductors and capacitors, an active band-pass filter uses an op amp plus a few resistors and capacitors, but it is physically

smaller and requires less PC board space. The primary disadvantage of using an active filter is that it requires a power supply for the op amp.

The circuit in Figure 3-15 is a two-pole active filter using a TL081 op amp. This type of circuit is usable only for Qs less than 10. The gain of this stage is nominally or slightly larger than the square root of the Q. For example, with a Q of five, the gain chosen would be slightly over two.

The component values for this filter are easily calculated from the following equations. Assume you want to build a filter with a center frequency of 800 Hz. R2 is a potentiometer about twice the calculated value, which is then adjusted to set the resonant frequency precisely. This larger than calculated resistance value is used to compensate for the tolerance of the other resistor and capacitor values. A capacitor value of 0.01 $\mu$F to 0.1 $\mu$F is often used for filters in the audio range.

$$R1 = \frac{Q}{2\pi fGC}$$

$$R2 = \frac{Q}{(2Q^2 - G)\, 2\pi fC}$$

$$R3 = \frac{2Q}{2\pi fC}$$

$$R4 = R3$$

Where

$$f = \text{filter center frequency (800 Hz)}$$
$$Q = 5$$
$$G = 2 \text{ (Gain)}$$
$$C = 0.01 \ \mu F$$

$$R1 = \frac{Q}{2\pi fGC}$$

$$= \frac{5}{(6.28)\,(800)\,(2)\,(0.01 \times 10^{-6})}$$

$$= 49,761 = 50 \ k\Omega$$

$$R2 = \frac{Q}{(2Q^2 - 2)\, 2\pi fC}$$

$$= \frac{5}{(50 - 2)\,(6.28)\,(800)\,(0.01 \times 10^{-6})}$$

$$= 2073 = 2.2 \ k\Omega$$

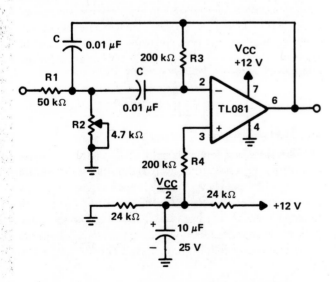

**Figure 3-15. Two Pole Active Band-Pass Filter**

$$R3 = \frac{2Q}{2\pi fC}$$

$$= \frac{10}{(6.28)\ (800)\ (0.01 \times 10^{-6})}$$

$$= 199{,}045 = 200\ \text{k}\Omega$$

$$R4 = R3 = 200\ \text{k}\Omega$$

Figure 3-16 shows the frequency response of this filter.

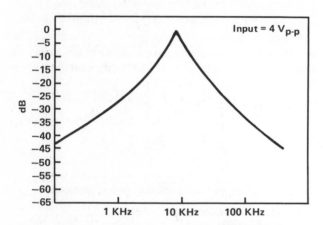

**Figure 3-16. Active Band-Pass Filter Response Curve**

## HIGH- AND LOW-PASS ACTIVE FILTERS

Among the many types of filter circuits, the "Butterworth" filter is often the best overall choice because it has the flattest passband and reasonable overshoot. It also has a characteristic that sets all cascaded sections to the same frequency, which makes voltage control and wide-range tuning easier. Complex filters are normally built using first and second-order networks. A first-order section is not very useful by itself as a filter because all you can control is the center frequency and impedance level. In a second-order section, it is possible to control the impedance level, the center frequency, and another feature called damping, or its inverse, Q. Damping, or Q, sets the peaking or drop of the response near the cutoff frequency.

The simplest second-order low-pass filter is the voltage-controlled-voltage-source (VCVS) circuit shown in (Figure 3-17). In this circuit the capacitors have very little effect at low frequencies, which results in an essentially flat low frequency response. At high frequencies the capacitors separately shunt the signal to low-impedance points, one to ground and one to the output. This two-step shunting causes the response at high frequencies to fall off as the square of the frequency; hence the name, second-order section. The performance starts out flat at low frequencies and falls at 12 dB/octave, or 40 dB/decade past the cutoff frequency.

The most common approach for selecting the values of the two resistors and capacitors in the filter section is to make

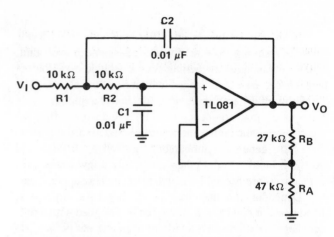

**Figure 3-17. Second Order Low-Pass Filter**

R1 and R2 equal, and C1 and C2 equal. The cutoff frequency is simply:

$$f_O = \frac{1}{2\pi RC}$$

This is called an "equal-component" low-pass filter. The passband gain is fixed at 1.586 (+4 dB) for a second-order Butterworth response, and is the only gain that will permit this circuit to function properly. The cutoff point will be 3 dB from the passband gain of +4 dB, 4+1 dB.

Since the op amp is in the noninverting mode, the feed back resistor $R_B$ must be 0.586 times the value of the input resistor $R_A$ for a voltage gain of 1.586. To build a low-pass Butterworth filter with a cutoff frequency of 1500 Hz you choose the component values in the following manner. Let $R_A = 47$ k$\Omega$. $R_B$ would be $R_A \times 0.586$ or about 27 k$\Omega$. If we let the capacitor value be 0.01 $\mu$F, the resistors will be selected by the formula:

$$R1 = \frac{1}{2\pi f_O C}$$

$$= \frac{1}{(6.28)\ (1500)\ (0.01 \times 10^{-6})}$$

$$= 10{,}617\ \Omega = R2$$

The nearest standard value would be 10 k$\Omega$.

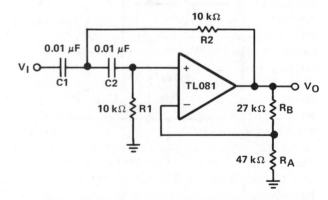

**Figure 3-18. Second Order High-Pass Filter**

Simply interchanging the position of the resistors and capacitors as shown in Figure 3-18 produces a high-pass active filter with the same cutoff frequency. The passband gain is also 1.586, or +4 dB. Figure 3-19 shows the response curves of both of these filters.

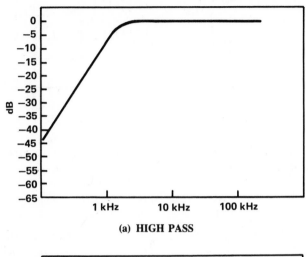

(a) HIGH PASS

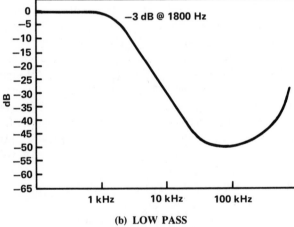

(b) LOW PASS

**Figure 3-19. Active Filter Response**

## MULTIPLE-FEEDBACK BAND-PASS FILTERS

The basic multiple-feedback band-pass filter is useful for Qs up to about 15 with "moderate" gain. Band-pass circuits normally have lower damping and higher Q values than the usual low-pass or high-pass responses. In fact, these circuits are progressively harder to build and tune as the damping goes down and the Q goes up. Experience has shown that a high-performance, high-Q band-pass active filter cannot be built with a single op amp. Component-tolerance problems, sensitivity problems, or severe gain restrictions provide insurmountable barriers as you try to increase the circuit Q of single op amp circuits beyond a certain point. Therefore, single op amp versions of this filter may be used only for low-Q applications (Qs in the 2 to 5 range). Fortunately, Q values of 2 to 5 are ideal for many audio applications, including equalizers and tone controls. Higher Q circuits find use at IF and RF frequencies.

Figure 3-20 shows a single-stage, multiple-feedback band-pass filter where the op amp is connected in the inverting mode. Resistor R3 from the output to the inverting input sets the gain and the current through the frequency-determining capacitor, C1. Capacitor C2 provides feedback from the output to the junction of R1 and R2. C1 and C2 are always equal in value. Resistor R2 may be made adjustable in order to adjust the center frequency which is determined from:

$$fo = \frac{1}{2\pi C}\left[\frac{1}{R3} \times \frac{R1 + R2}{R1R2}\right]^{1/2}$$

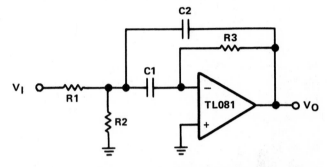

**Figure 3-20. Single Stage Feedback Band-Pass Filter**

When designing a filter of this type it is best to select a value for C1 and C2, keeping them equal. Typical audio filters have capacitor values from 0.01 $\mu$F to 0.1 $\mu$F which will result in reasonable values for the resistors. We will design a filter for 10 kHz and assume a Q of 3 and a stage gain of 2. The three resistors values are then determined from the following equations:

$$R1 = \frac{Q}{2\pi fCG} = 2388.5$$

or 2.4 k$\Omega$ (nearest standard value)

$$R2 = \frac{Q}{2\pi fC\,(2Q^2 - G)} = 298.5$$

or 300 $\Omega$ (nearest standard value)

$$R3 = \frac{Q}{\pi fC} = 9554$$

or 10 k$\Omega$ (nearest standard value)

Where

$$G = 2$$
$$Q = 3$$
$$C = 0.01\ \mu F$$
$$f = 10\ kHz$$

As previously stated, a single-stage active filter of this type results in low Qs (2 to 5). Filters which provide a very narrow passband must have a much higher Q than possible with a single section using one op amp. This may

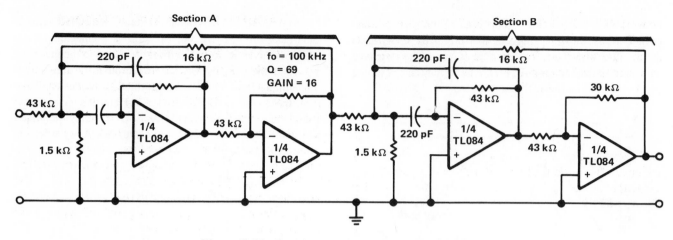

**Figure 3-21. Positive Feedback Band-Pass Filter**

be achieved by using several cascaded stages. Another method to achieve higher Q is the use of positive feedback. Figure 3-21 shows a positive-feedback band-pass filter using four op amps which make up two sections.

While looking rather complex at first, this circuit may be analyzed by examining each filter section separately. The complete filter is comprised of two identical sections, section "A" and section "B". Each section uses an op amp connected as a multiple-feedback band-pass filter as we have described in the preceding paragraphs. This is followed by a second op amp used as a phase inverter to achieve positive feedback to the input of the first op amp. This stage has a gain of only 0.7. While the 16 kΩ positive feedback resistor gives us a gain of about 10.7, it is reduced to about 7.5 due to the 0.7 gain of the phase inverter stage. The resulting overall gain of section "A" is 4.

When section B is cascaded to section A we have the complete two stage (4 op amp) filter with an overall gain of 16 and Q of 69. The scope photo in Figure 3-22 shows the bandwidth of both stages cascaded. The measured bandwidth with an $f_O$ of 100 kHz is 2.3 kHz at the $-3$ dB or half-power points.

## TWIN-T NOTCH FILTER

A notch filter is used to reject or block a frequency or band of frequencies. These filters are often designed into audio and instrumentation systems to eliminate a single frequency, such as 60 Hz. Perhaps the best-known passive notch filter is the "twin-T" filter. The circuit is shown in Figure 3-23.

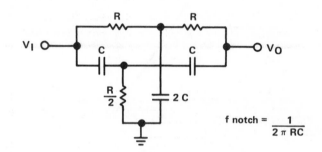

$$f \text{ notch} = \frac{1}{2 \pi RC}$$

**Figure 3-23. Twin-T Notch Filter**

If the six components are carefully matched, theoretically you can obtain an almost infinite rejection at the null frequency. Commercial grade components (5%—10% tolerance) produce a null depth of at least 30 to 40 dB.

When this twin-T network is combined with a TL081 op amp in a circuit, an active filter can be implemented as shown in Figure 3-24. Notice the added resistor capacitor

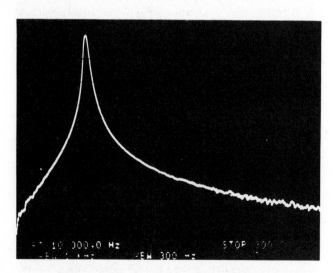

**Figure 3-22. Band-Pass Filter Response**

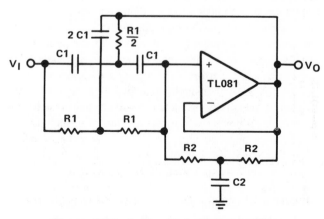

**Figure 3-24. Active Twin-T Notch Filter**

network (R2, C2), effectively in parallel with the original twin-T network, on the input of the filter. These networks set the Q of the filter. The op amp is basically connected as a unity-gain voltage follower. The Q is found from:

$$Q = \frac{R2}{2R1} = \frac{C1}{C2}$$

Let's now design a 60-Hz notch filter with a Q of 5 using the circuit in Figure 3-24. It is usually best to pick the C1 capacitor value and calculate the resistor R1. Let C1 = 0.22 $\mu$F.

$$f_n = \frac{1}{2\pi RC}$$

$$R = \frac{1}{2\pi f_n C} = \frac{1}{(6.28)\,(60)\,(0.22 \times 10^{-6})}$$

$$R1 = 12,063 \text{ or } 12 \text{ k}\Omega$$

Next calculate R2 in the Q network.

$$Q = \frac{R2}{2R1}$$

$$R2 = Q \times 2R1 = 5 \times 24 \text{ k}\Omega = 120 \text{ k}\Omega$$

$$R2 = 120 \text{ k}\Omega$$

Finally, calculate C2 from the equation.

$$Q = \frac{C1}{C2}$$

$$C2 = \frac{C1}{Q} = \frac{0.22\ \mu F}{5} = 0.044\ \mu F$$

C2 = 0.047 $\mu$F (nearest standard value)

Standard 5% resistors and 10% capacitors produce a notch depth of about 40 dB as shown in the frequency response curve (Figure 3-25).

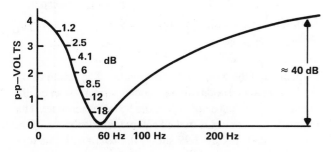

**Figure 3-25. 60 Hz Twin-T Notch Filter Response**

## AUDIO OP AMP APPLICATIONS

### MIKE PREAMP WITH TONE CONTROL

Microphones may be classified into two groups: high-impedance ($\approx 200$ k$\Omega$) with high-voltage output and low-impedance ($\approx 200$ $\Omega$) with low-voltage output. The output from a high-impedance microphone can be amplified simply and effectively with a standard inverting or noninverting operational amplifier configuration. However, high-impedance microphones are more susceptible to stray RF and 60-Hz noise. They have a fairly flat frequency response but are usually restricted to short cable lengths (10 feet or less). Long cables result in a high frequency roll-off characteristic caused by the cable capacitance.

Low-impedance microphones also have a flat frequency response but their low output levels impose rather stringent noise requirements on the preamp. The preamp shown in Figure 3-26 operates from a low-impedance, unbalanced, two-wire microphone where one of the wires is ground. The circuit consists of the LM318 preamp and the tone control circuitry.

The LM318 op amp is operated as a standard noninverting amplifier. Resistor R1 (47 k$\Omega$) provides an input path to ground for the bias current of the noninverting input. The combination of R2 (560 $\Omega$) and C2 (10 $\mu$F) provide a frequency roll-off below 30 Hz. At 30 Hz and above the gain is relatively flat at about 50 dB, set by the ratio R3/R2. R3 (220 k$\Omega$) furnishes negative feedback from the output to the inverting input of the op amp. C3 (1.0 $\mu$F electrolytic) ac couples the preamp to the tone control section.

The top half of the tone control section is the bass control. The bottom half controls the treble frequency response. These tone controls (R5 and R8) require audio taper (logarithmic) potentiometers. The 50-k$\Omega$ potentiometer on the output can be used to set the output or gain of the preamp. Figure 3-27 shows the bass and treble responses of the circuit.

### TL080 IC PREAMPLIFIER

A preamplifier is needed to amplify the signal generated by a tape head or phonograph cartridge. It is also common to include, with the preamplifier, a means of altering the bass and treble frequency response. The "purist" may want the amplifier to be "flat", which means no change from the input's frequency response. This condition should occur with both bass and treble controls at midposition. Sometimes it may be necessary to compensate for the effects of room acoustics, speaker response, etc. Also there is simply a matter of personal taste; one person may prefer music with heavier bass; another may prefer stronger treble.

Active tone control circuits offer some advantages: they are inherently symmetrical in boost and cut operation and have very low total harmonic distortion (THD) because they are incorporated in the negative feedback loop.

The circuit shown in Figure 3-28, is a form of the so-called "Americanized" version of the Baxandall negative-feedback tone control. At very low frequencies the reactance

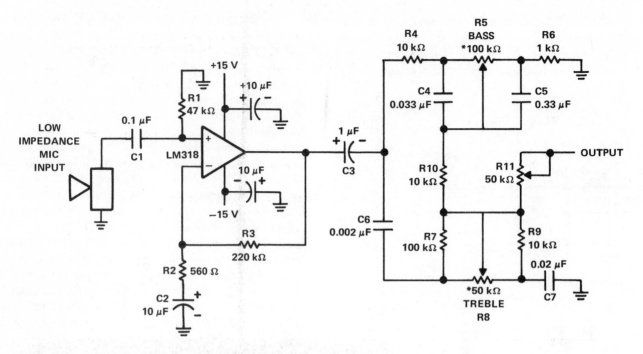

*THE TONE CONTROLS ARE AUDIO TAPER (LOG) POTENTIOMETERS.

**Figure 3-26. Mike Preamp With Tone Control**

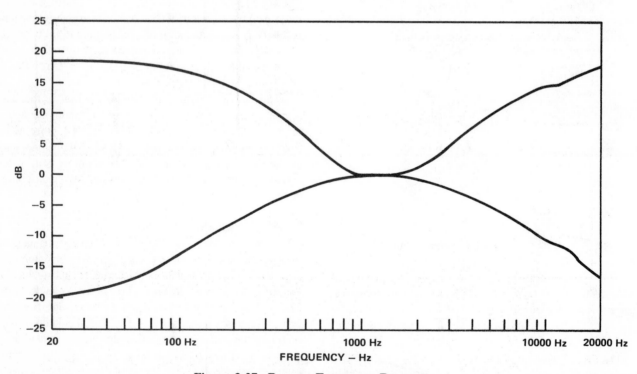

**Figure 3-27. Preamp Frequency Response**

of the capacitors is large enough that they may be considered open circuits, and the gain is controlled by the bass potentiometer. At low to middle frequencies the reactance of the 0.03 μF capacitors decreases at the rate of 6 dB/octave, and is in parallel with the 100 kΩ bass potentiometer; so the effective impedance is reduced correspondingly, thereby reducing the gain. This process continues until the 10-kΩ resistors, which are in series with the bass pot become dominant and the gain levels off at unity. The action of the treble circuit is similar and becomes effective when the reactance of the 0.003-μF capacitors becomes minimal. This complete tone control is in the negative feedback loop of the second TL080. Figure 3-29 shows the bass and treble tone control response. The response curves were run with 1.0 V equal to "0" dB as the "flat" response line.

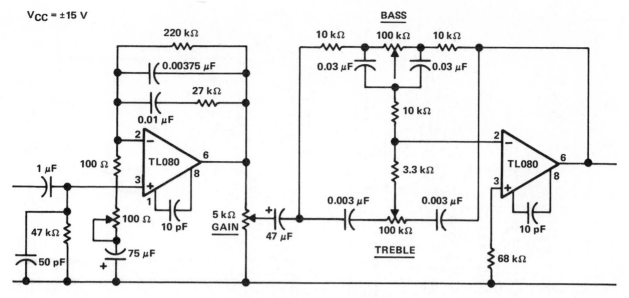

Figure 3-28. IC Preamplifier

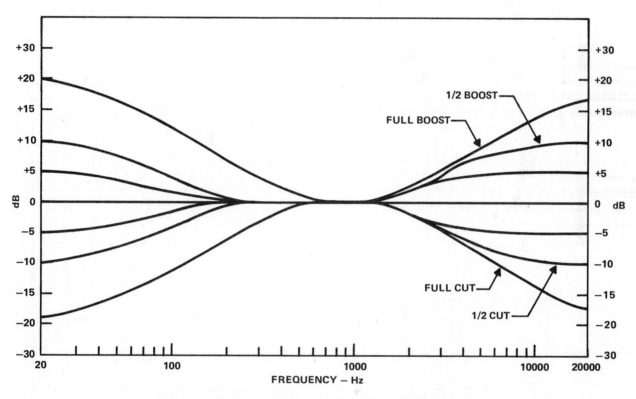

Figure 3-29. Bass and Treble Tone Control Response

The first TL080 is a preamp with a 100-Ω adjustable gain change pot. This gives a gain adjustment of about 6 dB for matching to the output of a particular pick-up or tape head. The negative feedback loop of this TL080 contains the gain setting and frequency compensation components.

## AUDIO DISTRIBUTION AMPLIFIER

Sometimes there is a need for a preamplifier to receive the output from a single audio input device such as a microphone and drive several audio power amplifiers. This could be done most easily with a shielded cable to each

amplifier from the originating preamplifier. However, if this were done by simply paralleling the shielded cables and connecting them to the preamp, the result could be an oscillating preamp stage or degraded high-frequency response due to the heavy capacitive loading.

A simple solution to this problem is the three channel output distribution amplifier using a single TL084 as shown in Figure 3-30. The first stage is capacitively coupled with a 1.0-μF electrolytic capacitor. The inputs are at 1/2 $V_{CC}$ rail or 4.5 V. This makes it possible to use a single 9-V supply. A voltage gain of 10 (1 MΩ /100 kΩ ) is obtained

3-13

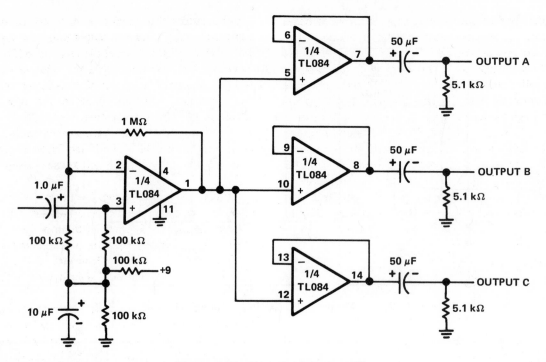

**Figure 3-30. Distribution Amplifier**

in the first stage, and the other three stages are connected as unity-gain voltage followers. Each output stage independently drives an amplifier through the 50-$\mu$F output capacitor to the 5.1-k$\Omega$ load resistor.

As shown in the response curve (Figure 3-31), the response is flat from 10 Hz to 30 kHz. Sinewave distortion begins at about 0.45 $V_{PP}$ input with 5.5 $V_{PP}$ output at 1 kHz. The total supply current is about 9 mA at a maximum input of 0.45 $V_{PP}$. The TL070 and TL080 family of op amps

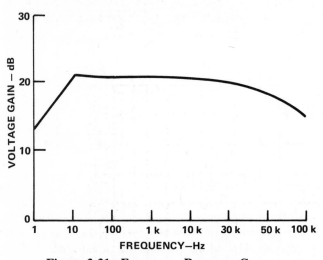

**Figure 3-31. Frequency Response Curve**

operate in true class-AB and therefore offer zero crossover distortion. The absence of crossover distortion can be noted in the scope photos (Figure 3-32). At a frequency of 1.0 kHz and with 3.0 $V_{PP}$ output the total harmonic distortion is 0.14%.

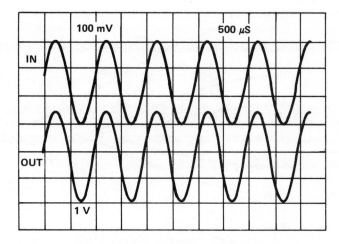

**Figure 3-32. Amplifier Waveforms**

## AUDIO POWER AMPLIFIER

Most audio amplifier circuits today are voltage output devices which apply a voltage to the terminals of the speaker. Large changes in speaker impedance with frequency yield poor frequency response with the high-frequency output falling off rapidly as the speaker impedance increases. It should be noted that the speaker cone displacement is proportional to the current in the voice coil rather than the voltage across the speaker terminals. The current is the primary mover of the voice coil.

The single speaker amplifier circuit shown in Figure 3-33 uses current feedback rather than the more popular voltage feedback. As shown, the feedback loop is from the junction of the speaker terminal and a 0.5-$\Omega$ resistor, to the inverting input of the NE5534. Sensing the current through the speaker and feeding it back provides better speaker damping than obtainable with voltage-drive systems.

Note the unusual grounded output pin on the NE5534 op amp. When the input to the amplifier is positive, the power supply supplies current through the TIP32 and the load to ground. Conversely, with a negative input the TIP31 supplies current through the load to ground. The gain in this case is set to about 15 (gain = SPKR 8 Ω /0.5 Ω feedback). The 0.22-μF capacitor across the speaker rolls off its response beyond the frequencies of interest. Using the 0.22-μF capacitor specified, the amplifier output is 3 dB down at 90 kHz where the speaker impedance is about 20 Ω. The Quiescent output stage collector current is determined by the

130-Ω resistors that connect each transistor base to the appropriate supply rail, the output transistor $V_{BE}$, and the 1-Ω emitter resistors. To set the recommended class "A" output collector current, adjust the value of either 130-Ω resistor. An output current of 50 to 100 mA will provide a good operating midpoint between the best crossover distortion and power dissipation.

The 0.1 μ bypass capacitors on each rail may be mylar or ceramic disk. The 2.0 μF should be a nonpolarized capacitor while the 0.22 μF across the speaker should be mylar.

Figure 3-34 shows the frequency response of the amplifier with a 2.0-μF input capacitor. This response is very flat with the −3.0-dB point on the low frequency end at 45 Hz. The −3.0-dB point at the high frequency end occurs at 80 kHz. Total Harmonic Distortion (THD) is 0.01% at 6.25 W rms output into an 8-Ω load with ±18 V on the supply rails.

This amplifier circuit uses few components, has low total harmonic distortion, excellent frequency response and is easily duplicated. It works well up to 12 W peak output before clipping is noted. The TIP31 and TIP32 output transistors are complementary power transistors in the TO-220 package. Both transistors are rated at 3.0 A continuous collector current.

## OSCILLATORS AND GENERATORS

### AUDIO OSCILLATOR CIRCUIT DESCRIPTION

A Wein bridge oscillator can be used to produce sinewaves with very low distortion level. The Wein bridge oscillator produces zero phase shift at only one frequency (f = 1/2 πRC) which will be the oscillation frequency. In the configuration shown in Figure 3-35. stable oscillation can occur only if the loop gain remains at unity at the oscillation frequency.

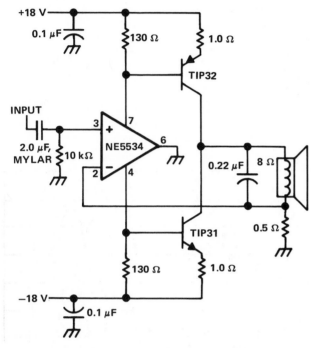

Figure 3-33. Audio Power Amplifier

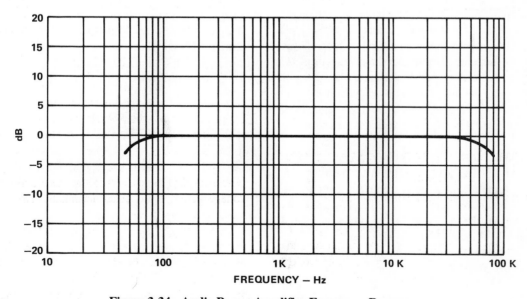

Figure 3-34. Audio Power Amplifier Frequency Response

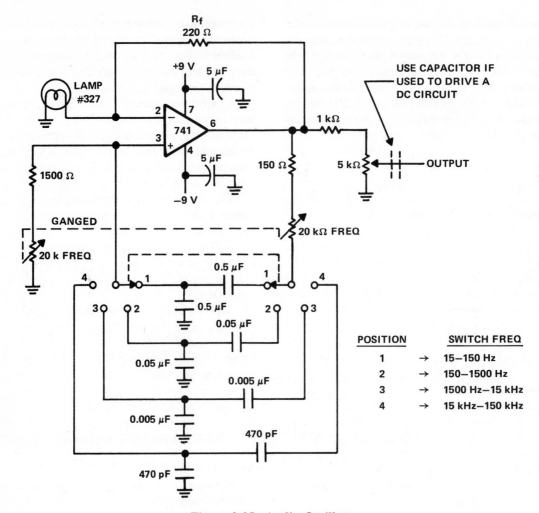

**Figure 3-35. Audio Oscillator**

| POSITION | | SWITCH FREQ |
|---|---|---|
| 1 | → | 15–150 Hz |
| 2 | → | 150–1500 Hz |
| 3 | → | 1500 Hz–15 kHz |
| 4 | → | 15 kHz–150 kHz |

The circuit achieves this control by using the positive temperature coefficient of a small lamp to regulate gain($R_f/R_{LAMP}$) as the oscillator attempts to vary its output. This is a classic technique for achieving low distortion that has been used by numerous circuit designers for about 40 years. The smooth limiting action of the bulb, in combination with the Wein network's near-ideal characteristics, yields very high performance. In this circuit a 741 op amp is used with ±9 V power supplies. The tungsten lamp is a type #327 miniature which has a standard bayonet base. This lamp is rated at 28.0 V and 40 mA. For mass production of these oscillators, the lamps are burned in for a predetermined number of hours to stabilize the characteristics of the filament.

The oscillator shown here has four frequency bands covering about 15 Hz to 150 kHz. The frequency is continuously variable within each frequency range with ganged 20-kΩ potentiometers. The oscillator draws only about 4.0 mA from the 9-V batteries. Its output is from 4 to 5 V with a 10-kΩ load and the $R_f$ (feedback resistor) is set at about 5% below the point of clipping. As shown, the center arm of the 5-kΩ output potentiometer is the output terminal. It should be noted that if you couple the oscillator to a dc type circuit, a capacitor should be inserted in series with the output lead.

## THE BASIC MULTIVIBRATOR

A basic multivibrator may be constructed using an operational amplifier and a few external components, as shown in Figure 3-36. When this circuit is turned on, the natural offset of the devices serves as an automatic starting voltage. Assume the output voltage $V_O$ goes positive and the positive feedback through R2 and R1 forces the output to saturate. The high-voltage level at $V_O$, then charges C through R3 until the voltage at the inverting input exceeds that at the noninverting input. As the inverting input exceeds

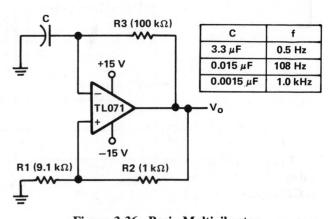

| C | f |
|---|---|
| 3.3 μF | 0.5 Hz |
| 0.015 μF | 108 Hz |
| 0.0015 μF | 1.0 kHz |

**Figure 3-36. Basic Multivibrator**

the noninverting input level, the output switches to the negative saturation voltage. This action starts the capacitor discharging toward the new noninverting input level. When the capacitor reaches that level the op amp switches back to the positive saturation voltage, and the process starts again.

With the TL071 the positive and negative output levels are nearly equal, resulting in a 50% duty cycle. The total time period of one cycle will be

$$t_T = 2 \ (R3)C \ \ln (1 + 2R1/R2)$$

## LinCMOS™ OP AMP APPLICATIONS

### MICROPHONE PREAMPLIFIER

It is sometimes necessary to have a microphone preamplifier mounted in the mike head. Obviously, the preamplifier should be as small as possible, battery operated and consume a small amount of power. In the past this was accomplished with bipolar and FET op amps. The primary disadvantage of these circuits is the comparatively large physical size of both the amplifier and power source. Another major factor is relatively large power consumption, which requires frequent battery replacement. The most obvious next choice would be a CMOS op amp. While this approach seems logical at first, it has some disadvantages. A metal-gate CMOS op amp can be operated from a low-voltage supply and has low power consumption; but, it suffers from input-offset voltage instability. This input-offset drift is due primarily to the differential input signals at the op amp input terminals. The LinCMOS op amp overcomes these problems. In addition, it has the advantage of low power comsumption and low voltage operation (down to 1.0 V).

A microphone preamplifier using a LinCMOS op amp is illustrated in Figure 3-37. This unit comes complete with its own battery, and is small enough to be put in a small mike case. The amplifier illustrated was designed to be operated from a 1.5-V mercury cell battery at low supply currents.

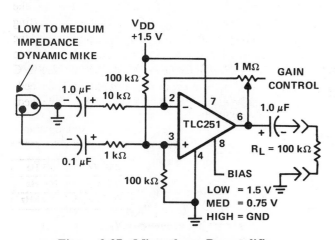

**Figure 3-37. Microphone Preamplifier**

This preamplifier will operate at very low power levels and maintain a reasonable frequency response as well. The TLC251 operated in the low bias mode (operating at 1.5 V)

draws a supply current of only 10 $\mu$A and has a $-3$-dB frequency response of 27 Hz to 4.8 kHz. With pin 8 grounded, which is designated as the high bias condition, the upper limit increases to 25 kHz. Supply current is only 30 $\mu$A under those conditions.

If improved higher frequency performance is desired, the $V_{DD}$ may be increased. For example, when using a 5-V supply the frequency response is from 27 Hz to 11 kHz for the low bias, and from 27 Hz to 220 kHz for the high bias modes respectively. Operating in the high bias mode at 5-V $V_{DD}$ the amplifier requires a supply current of less than 500 $\mu$A. Frequency response for the amplifier is shown in Figure 3-38.

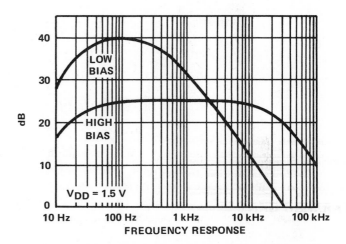

**Figure 3-38. Preamplifier Frequency Response**

### POSITIVE PEAK DETECTOR

Peak detectors measure and hold the maximum value of a fluctuating voltage. The purpose of the circuit in Figure 3-39 is to hold the peak of the input voltage on capacitor C1, and read the value, $V_O$, at the output of U2. Op amps U1 and U2 are connected as voltage followers. When a signal is applied to $V_I$, C1 will charge to this same voltage through diode D1. This positive peak voltage on C1 will maintain $V_O$ at this level until the capacitor is reset (shorted). Of course, higher positive peaks will raise this level while lower peaks will be ignored. C1 can be reset manually with a switch, or electronically with an FET that is normally off.

The capacitor specified for C1 should have low leakage and low dielectric absorption. Diode D1 should also have low leakage. The op amps selected for use in a peak detector should be immune to instability due to capacitive loading, and have high output drive and slew rate. They should also have very low input bias currents and extremely high input impedance. The TLC251 meets these requirements well. The TLC251 allows the reading of low-level signals near ground because its input-common-mode range includes the negative connection to the power supply. Peak values of negative polarity signals may be detected by reversing D1.

LinCMOS is a trademark of Texas Instruments.

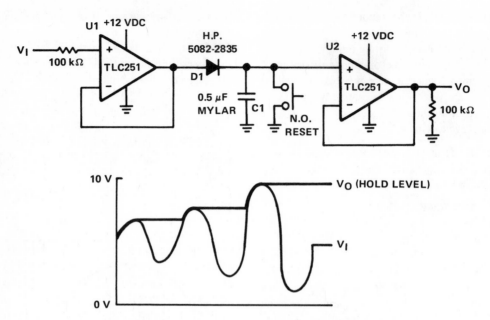

Figure 3-39.  Positive Peak Detector and Waveform

## INSTRUMENTATION METER DRIVER

Instrumentation amplifier circuitry which has incorporated low-cost general-purpose op amps provides the designer with economical, quality performance options. Improved instrumentation amplifier circuits are possible because of the development of op amps using junction FETs. These op amps have improved input impedance characteristics and ac performance compared with general purpose bipolar devices. Metal gate CMOS op amps have reduced the power required and will operate at voltages as low as 2 V.

Because the input offset voltage of a metal gate CMOS circuit changes with varying differential input voltage levels, there are severe drawbacks in using this technology for op amps. LinCMOS technology overcomes these disadvantages. LinCMOS devices do not have an input offset shift with differential input voltage and can operate satisfactorily down to 1.0 V supply. TLC271 LinCMOS op amps are used in the instrumentation amplifier illustrated in Figure 3-40 because of their unique features. Some of these features are:

- Operate at low voltages
- Input signal operation close to $-V_{CC}$ rail
- Reasonable ac performance at low power
- Provide the high input impedance characteristic of FET input devices
- Offset stability
- High CMRR
- Power/performance adjustment for desired performance levels while maintaining the lowest possible power requirement.

The TLC271 operational amplifiers (the first monolithic devices to combine these characteristics) allow the construction of a $\pm 5$-V instrumentation amplifier with reasonable ac performance. Some of the important features of Figure 3-40 which should be pointed out are:

- Three op amps U1, U2, and U3 are connected

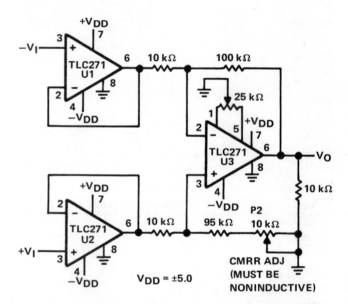

Figure 3-40.  TLC Low Power Instrumentation Amplifier

in the basic instrumentation amplifier configuration.

- Operating from $\pm 5$ V, pin 8 of each op amp is connected directly to ground and provides the ac performance desired in this application (high bias mode).
- Two adjustment pots are used. P1 is for offset error correction and P2 allows adjustment of the input common mode rejection ratio.
- The high input impedance allows metering of signals from sources of several megohms without loading. The resulting circuit frequency response is 200 kHz at $-3$ dB and has a slew rate of 4.5 V/$\mu$s. This is a significant improvement over general bipolar performance. The signal response and speed characteristics are

particularly significant in light of the low supply voltage and supply currents. Total supply current is 670 μA per supply.

● Output error voltages of less than 1% are experienced over the 0 °C to 70 °C operating range.

## A STABLE TWO-VOLT LOGIC ARRAY POWER SUPPLY

The popularity of logic gate array devices has emphasized the need for closely regulated low-voltage power supplies. Typical power requirements for these devices are +2.0 V at approximately 250 mA per array. A major requirement for many systems is the ability of the power supply to operate over a wide range of input voltages, particularly from 5 V or less to minimize losses. Regulation to within ±5% and good ripple rejection are also desirable in most applications.

Several types of three-terminal adjustable series pass regulators or shunt regulators are capable of providing regulation at 2 V. For example the LM317 will provide 2 V with a minimum number of external components. Good regulation is possible with this device when supply voltages are in excess of 5 V. LM317 operating characteristics will begin to deteriorate at 5 V or less because of insufficient input to output differential voltage.

Adjustable zeners such as the TL431 will operate at low voltage levels. However, they do not produce enough output current to be useful as a regulator in this application.

Combining a TL431, to provide an accurate reference; an op amp, for accurate output level control; with a power pass transistor is very effective (Figure 3-41). However, this configuration puts some rather severe constraints on the op amp used, as shown below:

1. It should be a device capable of operating below 5 V and handling high input, common-mode

voltages (up to 2 V when operating from a single 3.5-V supply)

2. Accommodate varying differential input voltage without adversely affecting input offset stability.

3. Provide adequate output drive current while maintaining a low operating current for maximum circuit efficiency.

The TLC271 is such a device.

In the application discussed here the TLC271 must operate from a single supply that can be as low as 3.5 V. A temperature compensated voltage reference is provided by the TL431 and coupled to the inverting input of the TLC271. The power supply output of 2.0 V is sensed and fed back to the TLC271's noninverting input. This results in a commmon-mode input level of about 2.0 V which can easily be handled by the TLC271 even when operating from a single 3.5-V supply. The TLC271's high-bias, open-loop gain of approximately 96 dB (at a $V_{CC}$ of 3.5 V) provides control of the output drive transistors with minimum error. Most of the no-load supply current required is drawn by the 110 Ω load shunt at the 2-V output (20 mA). The supply's total no-load current with a 15-V input is less than 30 mA.

The circuit's stability is excellent for both input voltage and output current variations. Maximum variation of output voltage, with input voltage swings from 3.5 V to 15 V, is less than 5%. Ripple rejection with a 2-V input swing at 120 Hz was over 60 dB. Variation in output voltage from no load to full load is less than 0.5%. The capability of the TLC271 to operate from a 3.5-V supply and handle 2-V common-mode input signals without input clipping or distortion, coupled with the inherent input offset stability of the Silicon Gate CMOS process, makes this kind of performance possible.

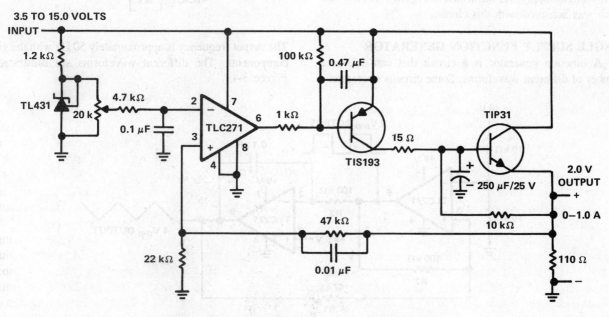

**Figure 3-41. TLC271 Logic Array Power Supply**

## TLC271 TWIN-T NOTCH FILTER

The theory of a bipolar twin-T notch filter was discussed in the section under Active Filter Applications. That twin-T filter required ± 15-V power supplies. This filter however, can be powered with a single 5-V supply. Active filters built with LinCMOS op amps will operate well at low frequencies from a single low-voltage supply. They also require minimum space because of their low component count. The 60-Hz filter illustrated in Figure 3-42 has only one op amp, three resistors, and three small capacitors.

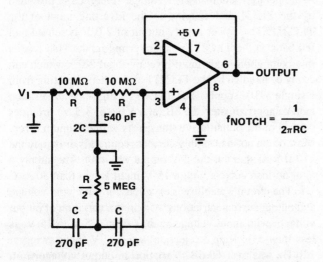

**Figure 3-42. Twin-T Notch Filter for 60 Hz**

$$f_{NOTCH} = \frac{1}{2\pi RC}$$

If the resistors and capacitors are carefully matched, you theoretically obtain almost complete rejection of the 60-Hz null frequency. The TLC271 has an input bias current of about 1 pA and will not generate adverse offset voltages even though the source impedance is 20 MΩ. Low–level 60–Hz ripple will also be attenuated due to the TLC271's capability of handling input signals at the ground rail while operating from a single supply. As illustrated in Figure 3-43, a 39-dB notch was achieved with this circuit.

## SINGLE SUPPLY FUNCTION GENERATOR

A function generator is a circuit that can deliver a number of different waveforms. Some circuits operate at a

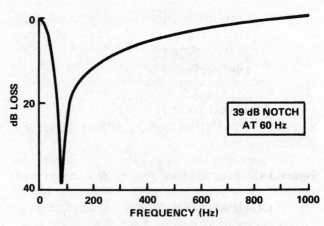

**Figure 3-43. TLC271 Twin-T Notch Filter Frequency Response**

fixed frequency while others have the capability of varying their frequencies over a wide range. The example circuit shown in Figure 3-44 has both square-wave and triangle-wave output.

The left section is similar in function to a comparator circuit that uses positive feedback for hysteresis. The inverting input is biased at one-half the $V_{CC}$ voltage by resistors R4 and R5. The output is fed back to the noninverting input of the first stage to control the frequency. The amplitude of the square wave is the output swing of the first stage, which is 8 V peak-to-peak.

The second stage is basically an op amp integrator. The resistor R3 is the input element and capacitor C1, is the feedback element. The ratio R1/R2 sets the amplitude of the triangle wave, as referenced to the square-wave output. For both waveforms, the frequency of oscillation can be determined by the equation:

$$fo = \frac{1}{4R3C1} \left[ \frac{R2}{R1} \right]$$

The output frequency is approximately 50 Hz with the given components. The different waveforms are illustrated in Figure 3-45.

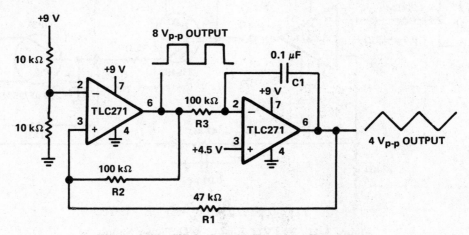

**Figure 3-44. Single Supply Function Generator**

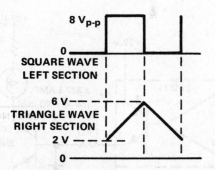

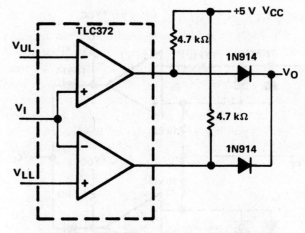

**Figure 3-46. Basic Window Comparator**

**Figure 3-45. Function Generator Output Waveforms**

## COMPARATOR APPLICATIONS

### WINDOW COMPARATOR

As the name implies, a window detector is a specialized comparator circuit designed to detect the presence of a voltage between two prescribed limits that is, within a voltage "window". A window comparator is useful in test and production equipment to select components that are within a specific set of limits.

This circuit is implemented by logically combining the outputs of two single-ended comparators. One indicates an input greater than the lower limit, and the other an input less than the upper limit. If both comparators indicate a true condition, the output is true. If either input is not true, the output is not true. A basic window comparator circuit is illustrated in Figure 3-46.

In this circuit, the outputs of the two comparators are logically combined by the 1N914 diodes. When the input voltage is between the upper limit ($V_{UL}$) and the lower limit ($V_{LL}$) the output voltage is zero; otherwise it equals a logic high level. The output of this circuit can be used to drive a logic gate, LED driver or relay driver circuit. The circuit shown in Figure 3-47 shows a 2N2222 npn transistor being driven by the window comparator. When the input voltage to the window comparator is outside the range set by the $V_{UL}$ and $V_{LL}$ inputs, the output changes to positive, which turns on the transistor and lights the LED indicator.

The TLC372 features extremely high input impedance (typically greater than $10^{12}$ $\Omega$) which allows direct interfacing with high-impedance sources. The outputs are n-channel open-drain configurations, and can be connected to achieve positive-logic wired-AND relationships. While these devices meet the 2000 V ESD (electrostatic discharge) specification, care should be exercised in handling the chips because exposure to ESD may result in a degradation of the device performance. If the input signal will exceed the common-mode voltage, it is good design practice to include protective input circuitry to the comparators. Clamp diodes and/or series resistors, as shown in Figure 3-48, could be used for this purpose.

### COMPARATOR INTERFACE CIRCUITS

A comparator is a useful building block in signal conditioning circuits as well as in instrumentation and control circuits. Once the inputs to the comparator have been correctly matched and connected, the comparator must interface with any additional output circuitry to perform functions such as: energizing a relay, lighting a lamp or driving another type of logic circuit.

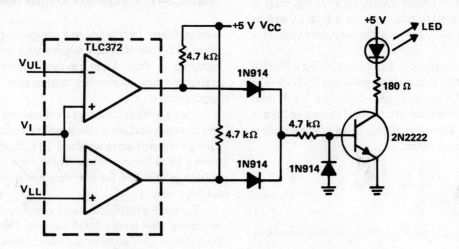

**Figure 3-47. Window Comparator with LED Indicator**

3-21

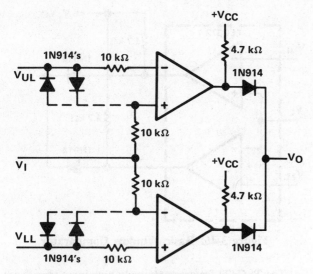

**Figure 3-48. Input Protection Circuitry**

Figure 3-49 shows three similar output interface circuits which can be used to drive a lamp, a relay, and an LED. All three circuits utilize the popular LM311 comparator and 2N2219/2N3904 family of discrete transistors. A resistor in series with the transistor base should be used in circuits of this type in order to limit the current. Although it is possible to directly drive some small lamps and relays from the output of the comparator, it is advisable to use a buffer transistor as illustrated. The output buffer will minimize loading on the comparator to preserve its gain and drift characteristics, and provide a higher output current.

Figure 3-49(a) is a circuit which can be used to turn on a 28-V lamp. A 100-Ω resistor must be included in series with the lamp. The purpose of this resistor is to limit the cold lamp inrush current. Lower voltage lamps of up to 150-mA current rating can be driven by reducing the lamp supply voltage appropriately.

Figure 3-49(b) illustrates a relay driver circuit. The relay is connected in series with the transistor collector terminal and the 24-V supply. The 1N914 diode across the relay clamps the back EMF voltage generated when the relay is turned off. Lower voltage relays can be driven as well as the relay illustrated here, provided the maximum current is less than 150 mA.

Figure 3-49(c) illustrates an LED driver, using a 2N3904 transistor switch rather than the high-powered 2N2219. The TIL220 is a red LED and has approximately a 1.7-V drop in the forward-bias condition at a forward current of 20 mA with a $V_{CC}$ of 5 V. The value of the current limiting resistor is calculated as shown below.

$$R = \frac{5 \text{ V} - 1.7 \text{ V}}{0.020 \text{ A}} = 165 \text{ ohms}$$

The next higher standard value is 180 Ω which has been used in this circuit.

A comparator output may interface with digital logic. If the comparator operates from a single 5-V supply, there

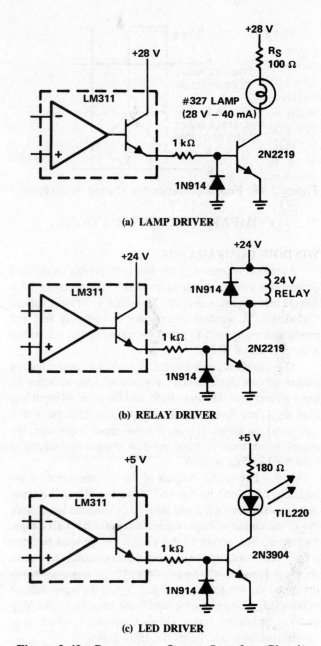

(a) LAMP DRIVER

(b) RELAY DRIVER

(c) LED DRIVER

**Figure 3-49. Comparator Output Interface Circuits**

is no problem. Interfacing to a comparator that is operating from +15-V supplies may require some level shifting and/or clamping to drive logic circuits. Figure 3-50 illustrates graphically how to interface comparators to different level logic circuits.

Figure 3-50(a) illustrates a comparator with a single 5-V power supply and has a 10-kΩ pull-up resistor on the output. This circuit will drive standard TTL logic circuits or low-level CMOS logic circuits. These logic circuits require a maximum of 0.8 V for low state and a minimum of 2.4 V for high state.

Figure 3-50(b) illustrates a comparator circuit capable of driving high-level CMOS circuits. This circuit operates from dual +15-V supplies and uses a 100-kΩ pull-up resistor on the output. High-level CMOS logic requires a maximum of 4.0 V for a low state and a minimum of 11.0 V for a high state.

Figure 3-50(c) illustrates how a three-state output is produced by following the comparator with a hex-bus driver such as the SN74367. In this circuit the comparator has a 10-kΩ pull-up resistor on its output and sends TTL logic signals to the input of the hex buffer. The output of the hex buffer is controlled by the input control pin's logic level. When this pin is low the device is enabled and the output is TTL logic. When the input control pin is high there is no output from the device and the output looks like a high impedance.

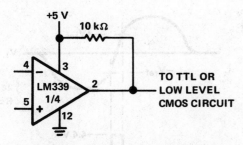

(a) TTL AND LOW-LEVEL CMOS DRIVER

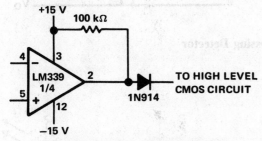

(b) HIGH-LEVEL CMOS DRIVER

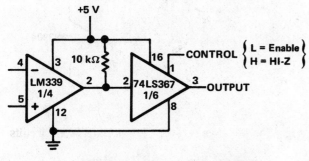

(c) 3-STATE BUS DRIVER (TTL OUTPUT)

**Figure 3-50. Comparator Logic Interface Circuits**

## LM393 ZERO-CROSSING DETECTOR

A zero-crossing detector is sometimes called a zero-level detector or a Schmitt trigger. In operation, a zero-crossing detector determines if an input voltage to the comparator is greater or less than zero. In response to this determination, the output voltage of the comparator can assume only two possible states. The output state may be high or low depending upon which comparator input (plus or minus) is used to detect the incoming signal.

A single comparator may be used as a simple crossover detector, but this can allow several sources of error. These errors may be caused by the input bias and offset currents of the comparator. Temperature may also affect the zero-crossing voltage points. This basic zero-crossing detector also will have another drawback called chatter which is due to noise on the input signal. Chatter can be reduced by adding hysteresis or positive feedback. These provide noise immunity and prevent the output from "chattering" between states as the input voltage passes through zero.

An improved circuit is illustrated in Figure 3-51. This zero-crossing detector of this type uses a dual LM393 comparator, and easily controls hysteresis by the reference levels which are set on the comparator inputs.

The circuit illustrated is powered by ±10-V power supplies. The input signal can be an ac signal level up to +8 V. The output will be a positive going pulse of about 4.4 V at the zero-crossover point. These parameters are compatible with TTL logic levels.

The input signal is simultaneously applied to the noninverting input of comparator A and the inverting input of comparator B. The inverting input of comparator A has a +10-mV reference with respect to ground, while the noninverting input of comparator B has a −10-mV reference with respect to ground. As the input signal swings positive (greater than +10 mV), the output of comparator "A" will be low while comparator "B" will have a high output. When the input signal swings negative (less than −10 mV), the reverse is true. The result of the combined outputs will be low in either case. On the other hand, when the input signal is between the threshold points (±10 mV around zero crossover), the output of both comparators will be high. In this state the output voltage will be one-half the 10 V ($V_{CC+}$) less the 0.6-V diode drop at the junction of the two 10-kΩ resistors (approximately +4.4 V). This circuit is very stable and immune to noise. If more hysteresis is needed, the ±10-mV window may be made wider by increasing the reference voltages. The 1N914 diode in series with the outputs allows a positive going pulse at the crossover point. This circuit "squares" the input signal into positive rectangular output pulses whose pulse width corresponds to the input zero crossings.

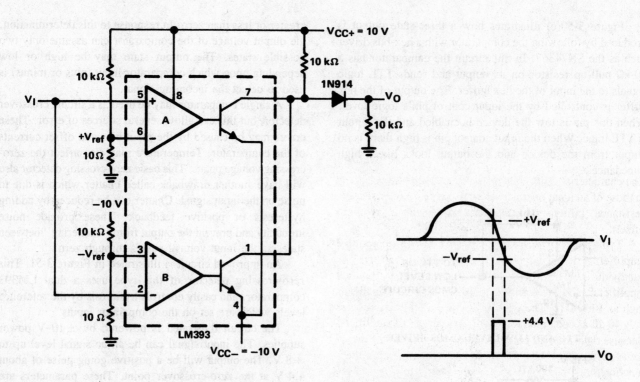

**Figure 3-51. LM393 Zero-Crossing Detector**

# Section 4

# Video Amplifiers

## VIDEO AMPLIFIER THEORY

The characteristics of an ideal video amplifier are identical to those of an ideal operational amplifier (i.e., infinite input resistance, infinite gain, zero output resistance, and zero offset).

Typical performance differences between operational amplifiers and video amplifiers are bandwidth and gain. The bandwidth averages 100 kHz for typical operational amplifiers. However, video amplifiers have bandwidths as high as 100 MHz. The gain for a video amplifier averages only 40 dB as compared to 100 dB for operational amplifiers. Because their internal phase shift does not permit the use of negative feedback to control gain, most video amplifiers function only in the open-loop mode. Video amplifiers have a limited output voltage swing. For high-frequency operation, the output voltage swing is limited to a few volts. Table 4-1 lists general characteristics of some video amplifiers which are currently available.

The input stage of most video amplifiers consists of a basic emitter-coupled differential transistor pair connected to a constant-current source transistor. Most early video amplifiers consisted of these three transistors combined with a few integrated resistors and diodes. In addition, all component terminals were brought out for external interconnection. A typical video amplifier configuration is illustrated in Figure 4-1. The bias input voltage can be adjusted to provide symmetrical output voltage swing with respect to ground.

Video amplifier characteristics are similar to those of operational amplifiers and comparators. However, the following definitions are specifically applicable to video amplifiers.

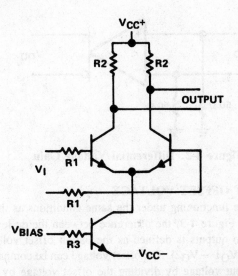

**Figure 4-1. Basic Video Amplifier Circuit**

### VOLTAGE GAIN

Video amplifiers have a differential type of input and output modes. Voltage gain is defined as the ratio between the change in differential output voltage to the change in differential input voltage as stated in the following equation (see Figure 4-2):

$$A_{VD} = \frac{V_{OD}}{V_{ID}}$$

### COMMON-MODE OUTPUT VOLTAGE

With the inputs grounded, the outputs of a video amplifier are at dc levels with respect to ground. The average of the two dc output voltages is the common-mode output

**Table 4-1. Video Amplifier Selection Guide**

| DEVICE | CHARACTERISTICS | DESCRIPTION |
|---|---|---|
| uA733, TL733 | −3 dB bandwidth, 90 MHz | Differential video amplifier. Selectable amplification of 10, 100, or 400. |
| NE592, SE592 | −3 dB bandwidth, 90 MHz | Differential video amplifier. Selectable amplification of 100 or 400. Adjustable gain from 0 to 400. Adjustable passband. |
| TL592 | −3 dB bandwidth, 90 MHz | Differential video amplifier. Adjustable gain from 0 to 400. Adjustable passband. |
| MC1445 | −3 dB bandwidth, 50 MHz | 2-Channel-input video amplifier. Gate controlled. 16-dB minimum gain. Broadband noise, typically 25 V. |

voltage, $V_{OC}$, and can be determined by the following equation (see Figure 4-2):

$$V_{OC} = \frac{V_O1 + V_O2}{2}$$

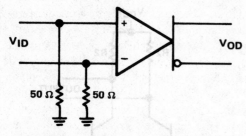

**Figure 4-2. Differential Voltage Gain**

## OUTPUT OFFSET VOLTAGE

While functioning under the same conditions as those shown in Figure 4-3, the difference between the dc levels at the two outputs is defined as the output offset voltage ($V_{OO} = V_O1 - V_O2$). The offset voltage can be compared to the input voltage by dividing the offset voltage by the differential voltage gain of the amplifier.

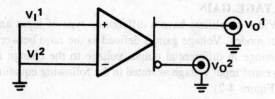

**Figure 4-3. Common-Mode And Offset Voltages**

Video amplifiers have no provision for adjusting the dc input offset voltage. In circuits where this will cause problems, capacitive coupling is used on both the inputs and outputs to block the dc component and prevent its affecting the amplified signal. Figure 4-4 illustrates the single-ended and differential coupling methods.

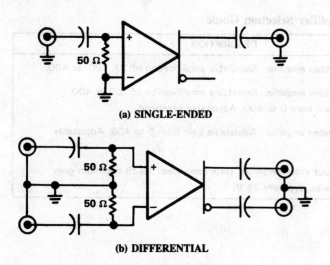

**(a) SINGLE-ENDED**

**(b) DIFFERENTIAL**

**Figure 4-4. Coupling Methods**

## WIRING PRECAUTIONS

The mechanical layout of the video amplifier is very important. All leads should be as short as possible. When using a printed circuit board, conductors should be wide and as short as possible. This helps provide low resistance and low inductance connections. In addition, stray signal coupling from the input to the output is minimized.

Grounding is the most important wiring precaution. As with all high frequency circuits, a ground plane and good grounding techniques should be used. The ground plane should connect all areas of the pattern side of the printed circuit board that are not otherwise used. The ground plane provides a low-resistance low-inductance common return path for all signal and power returns. The ground plane also reduces stray signal pick up.

Each power supply lead should have a bypass capacitor to ground as near as possible to the amplifier pins. A $0.1$-$\mu$F capacitor is normally sufficient. In very high-frequency and high-gain circuits, a combination of a $1$-$\mu$F tantalum capacitor in parallel with a 470-pF ceramic capacitor is a suitable bypass.

Single point grounding should be used in cases where point-to-point wiring is used or a ground plane is not used. The input signal return, the load signal return, and the power supply common should all be connected at the same physical point. This eliminates ground loops or common current paths which may cause signal modulation or unwanted feedback.

When designing video amplifier circuits, resistor values from 50 $\Omega$ to 100 $\Omega$ should be used for input terminations. Resistors in this range improve circuit performance by reducing the effects of device input capacitance and input noise currents.

## OSCILLOSCOPE/COUNTER PREAMPLIFIER

A circuit containing a single NE592A video amplifier (the only active component) can be used to increase the sensitivity of an older oscilloscope or frequency counter.

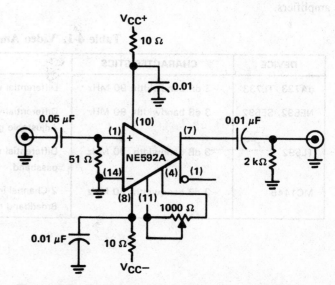

**Figure 4-5. Oscilloscope/Counter Preamplifier Circuit**

Figure 4-5 shows a circuit which will provide a $20 \pm 0.1$ dB voltage gain from 500 kHz to 50 MHz. The low-frequency response of the amplifier may be extended by increasing the value of the 0.05-$\mu$F capacitor connected in series with the input terminal. This circuit will yield an input-noise level of approximately 10 $\mu$V over a 15.7 MHz bandwidth.

The gain can be calibrated by adjusting the potentiometer connected between pins 4 and 11 (gain adjust terminals). These pins go directly to the emitter terminals of the two npn differential input amplifiers. The 1000-$\Omega$ potentiometer (a cermet type trimmer) can be adjusted for an exact voltage gain of 10. This preserves the scale factor of the instrument. The usual precautions of short leads and wide area ground planes for low-inductance ground systems, should result in good high-frequency response. A compact assembly package for an oscilloscope/counter preamplifier can be made by forming a small piece of sheet copper or brass into a the shape of a U.

## NE592 FILTER APPLICATIONS

The NE592 is a two-stage differential-output wideband video amplifier. It has a voltage gain of 0 to 400 that can be adjusted by one external resistor. The input stage is designed so that by adding a few external reactive elements between the gain-select terminals (pins 4 and 11), the circuit can function as a high-pass, low-pass, or band-pass filter. This feature makes the circuit ideal for use as a video or pulse amplifier in communications, magnetic memories, display and video recorder systems. Figure 4-6 illustrates the basic filter circuit. This circuit has a 50-$\Omega$ input termination and a 50-$\Omega$ output termination and uses a $\pm 6$-V power supply. The 50-$\Omega$ output termination allows interfacing to the spectrum analyzer.

Figure 4-7 illustrates the results when five different reactive elements are placed across the gain select terminals (pins 4 and 11). The parametric values and condition of each circuit, as well as the scope photos, are shown.

## MC1445 BALANCED MODULATOR

A balanced modulator can be obtained by connecting an MC1445 operational amplifier as shown in Figure 4-8. The internal differential amplifiers are connected in a manner which cross couples the collectors (see Figure 4-9).

When the carrier level is adequate to switch the cross-coupled pair of differential amplifiers, the modulation signal (which has been applied to the gate) will be switched, at the carrier rate, between the collector loads. When switching occurs, it will result in the modulation being multiplied by a symmetrical switching function. If the modulation gate remains in the linear region, only the first harmonic will be present. To achieve good harmonic suppression of the modulation input, the input level must remain in the linear region of the gate.

To balance the MC1445 modulator, equal gain must be achieved in the two separate channels. In Figure 4-10 (the composite gate characteristic for both channels) the equal gain point is at 1.3 V. The midpoint of the linear region of channel B is at 1.2 V. To remain in the linear region, the modulation input must be restricted to approximately 200 mV peak-to-peak. Because the gate bias point is sensitive to the amount of carrier suppression, a high-resolution (10-turn) potentiometer should be used.

In Figure 4-11, the top trace shows the 1 MHz carrier being modulated by a 1 kHz signal. The output is 750 mV peak-to-peak. The bottom trace shows the 600 mV peak-to-peak 1 kHz modulating signal. When functioning under these conditions, a carrier rejection of 38 dB should be obtained.

## MC1445 FREQUENCY SHIFT KEYER

To construct a frequency shift keyer with an MC1445, apply a signal to each differential amplifier input pair. When the gate voltage is changed from one extreme to the other, the output may be switched alternately between the two input signals (see Figure 4-12).

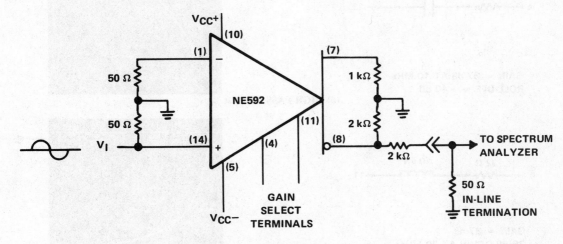

**Figure 4-6. Basic Filter Circuit**

When the gate level is high (1.5 V), a signal applied between pins 5 and 6 (channel A) will be passed and a signal applied between pins 3 and 4 (channel B) will be suppressed.

The reverse situation will exist when the gate is low (0.5 V). At 0.5 V, a signal applied to pins 3 and 4 (channel B) will pass. The unselected channel will have a gain of one or less.

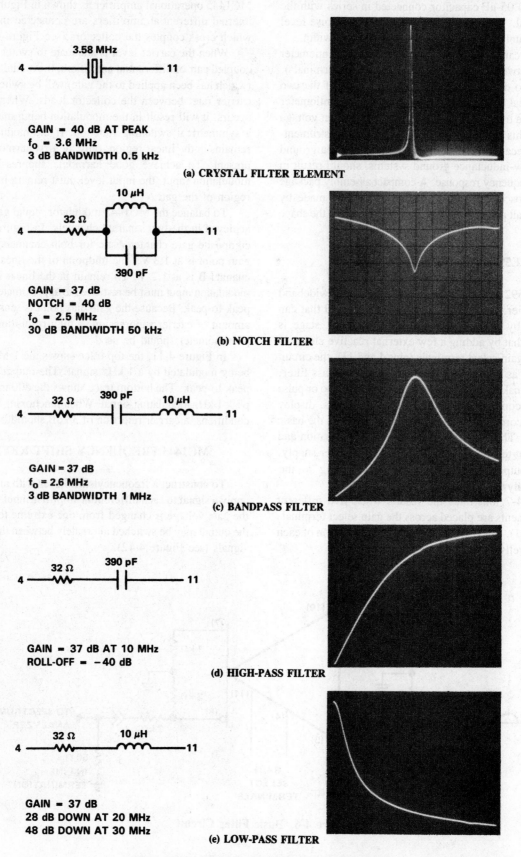

3.58 MHz

4 ———||——— 11

GAIN = 40 dB AT PEAK
$f_o$ = 3.6 MHz
3 dB BANDWIDTH 0.5 kHz

(a) CRYSTAL FILTER ELEMENT

10 µH

4 ——/\/\/\——•——•—— 11
32 Ω
390 pF

GAIN = 37 dB
NOTCH = 40 dB
$f_o$ = 2.5 MHz
30 dB BANDWIDTH 50 kHz

(b) NOTCH FILTER

32 Ω    390 pF    10 µH

4 ——/\/\/\——||——/\/\/\——— 11

GAIN = 37 dB
$f_o$ = 2.6 MHz
3 dB BANDWIDTH 1 MHz

(c) BANDPASS FILTER

32 Ω    390 pF

4 ——/\/\/\——||——— 11

GAIN = 37 dB AT 10 MHz
ROLL-OFF = –40 dB

(d) HIGH-PASS FILTER

32 Ω    10 µH

4 ——/\/\/\——/\/\/\——11

GAIN = 37 dB
28 dB DOWN AT 20 MHz
48 dB DOWN AT 30 MHz

(e) LOW-PASS FILTER

Figure 4-7. Reactive Component Application

4-4

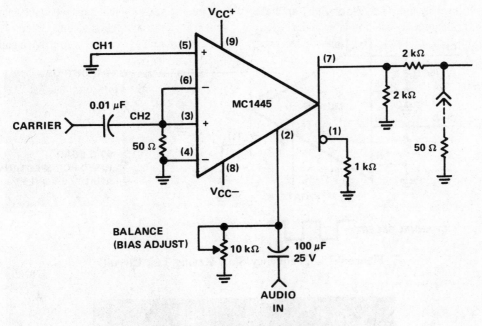

**Figure 4-8. Balanced Modulator**

In this manner, a binary-to-frequency conversion is obtained that is directly related to the binary sequence which is driving the gate input (pin 2). Figure 4-13 illustrates the waveforms of this basic frequency shift keying (FSK) application using the MC1445. The top trace illustrates a 20-kHz signal applied to channel A and a 4-kHz signal applied to channel B. The bottom trace illustrates a 1-kHz gating signal applied to the gate pin (2). The oscilloscope is triggered by this gate input signal.

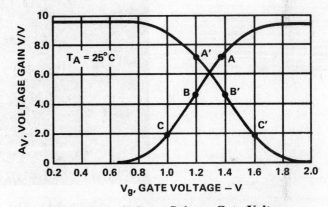

**Figure 4-10. Voltage Gain vs Gate Voltage**

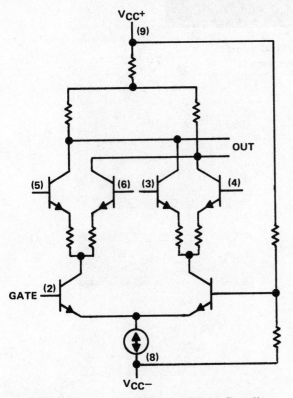

**Figure 4-9. Circuit Showing Cross-Coupling**

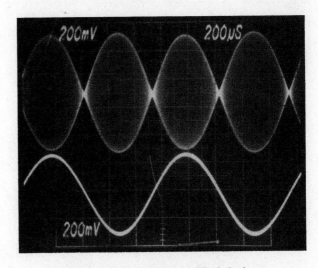

**Figure 4-11. Balanced Modulation**

4-5

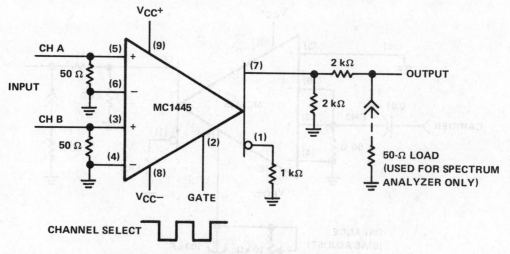

**Figure 4-12. Frequency Shift Keying Test Circuit**

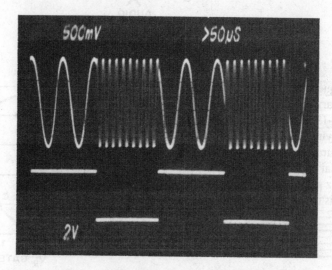

**Figure 4-13. FSK Output and Gate
Input Signal Waveforms**

# Section 5

# Voltage Regulators

## BASIC REGULATOR THEORY

The function of every voltage regulator is to convert a dc input voltage into a specific, stable, dc output voltage and maintain that voltage over a wide range of load current and input voltage conditions. To accomplish this, the typical voltage regulator (Figure 5-1) consists of:

1. A reference element that provides a known stable voltage level, ($V_{REF}$).
2. A sampling element to sample the output voltage level.
3. An error-amplifier element for comparing the output voltage sample to the reference and creating an error signal.
4. A power control element to provide conversion of the input voltage to the desired output level over varying load conditions as indicated by the error signal.

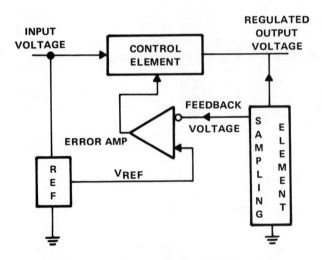

**Figure 5-1. Basic Regulator Block Diagram**

Although actual circuits may vary, the three basic regulator types are series, shunt, and switching. The four basic functions listed above exist in all three regulator types.

## VOLTAGE REGULATOR COMPONENTS

### REFERENCE ELEMENTS

The reference element forms the foundation of all voltage regulators since output voltage is directly controlled by the reference voltage. Variations in the reference voltage will be interpreted as output voltage errors by the error amplifier and cause the output voltage to change accordingly. To achieve the desired regulation, the reference must be stable

for all variations in supply voltages and junction temperatures. There are several common techniques which can be used to solve design problems using integrated circuit regulators. Many of these techniques are discussed in the section of the text that outlines error contributions.

### SAMPLING ELEMENT

The sampling element monitors the output voltage and converts it into a level equal to the reference voltage. A variation in the output voltage causes the feedback voltage to change to a value which is either greater or less than the reference voltage. This voltage difference is the error voltage which directs the regulator to make the appropriate response and thus correct the output voltage change.

### ERROR AMPLIFIER

The error amplifier of an integrated circuit voltage regulator monitors the feedback voltage for comparison with the reference. It also provides gain for the detected error level. The output of the error amplifier drives the control circuit to return the output to the preset level.

### CONTROL ELEMENT

All the previous elements discussed remain virtually unaltered regardless of the type regulator circuit. The control element, on the other hand, varies widely, depending upon the type of regulator being designed. It is the element that determines the classification of the voltage regulator; series, shunt, or switching. Figure 5-2 illustrates the three basic

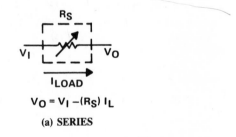

$$V_O = V_I - (R_S) I_L$$

**(a) SERIES**

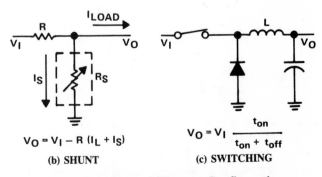

$$V_O = V_I - R (I_L + I_S)$$

**(b) SHUNT**

$$V_O = V_I \frac{t_{on}}{t_{on} + t_{off}}$$

**(c) SWITCHING**

**Figure 5-2. Control Element Configurations**

control element configurations, each of which is discussed in detail. These elements contribute an insignificant amount of error to the regulator's performance. This is because the sampling element monitors the output voltage beyond the control element and compensates for its error contributions. However, the control element directly affects parameters such as minimum input-to-output voltage differential, circuit efficiency, and power dissipation.

## REGULATOR CLASSIFICATIONS

### SERIES REGULATOR

The series regulator derives its name from its control element. The output voltage, $V_O$, is regulated by modulating an active series element, usually a transistor, that functions as a variable resistor. Changes in the input voltage, $V_I$, will result in a change in the equivalent resistance of the series element identified as $R_S$. The product of the resistance, $R_S$, and the load current, $I_L$ creates a changing input-to-output differential voltage, $V_I - V_O$, that compensates for the changing input voltage. The basic series regulator is illustrated in Figure 5-3, and the equations describing its performance are listed below.

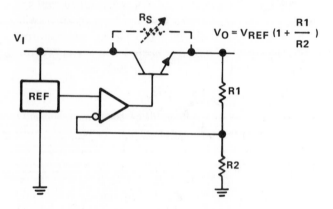

**Figure 5-3. Basic Series Regulator**

$$V_O = V_I - (V_I - V_O)$$
$$(V_I - V_O) = I_L R_S$$
$$V_O = V_I - I_L R_S$$

The change in $R_S$ for a changing input voltage is:

$$\Delta R_S = \frac{\Delta V_I}{I_L}$$

The change in $R_S$ for a changing load current:

$$\Delta R_S = \frac{\Delta I_L R_S}{I_L + \Delta I_L}$$

Series regulators provide a simple, inexpensive way to obtain a source of regulated voltage. In high-current applications, however, the voltage drop which is maintained across the control element will result in substantial power loss and a much lower efficiency regulator.

### SHUNT REGULATOR

The shunt regulator employs a shunt control element in which the current is controlled to compensate for varying input voltage or changing load conditions. The basic shunt regulator is illustrated in Figure 5-4.

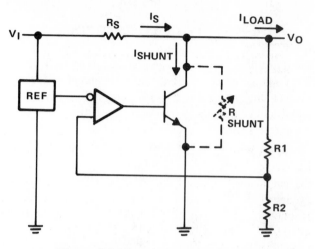

**Figure 5-4. Basic Shunt Regulator**

The output voltage, $V_O$ as with the series regulator, is held constant by varying the voltage drop across the series resistor, $R_S$, by varying the current $I_S$. $I_S$ may vary because of $I_L$ changes or it may vary because of current, $I_{(shunt)}$, through the shunt control element. For example, as $I_L$ increases, $I_{(shunt)}$ decreases to adjust the voltage drop across $R_S$. In this fashion $V_O$ is held constant.

$$V_O = V_I - I_S R_S$$
$$I_S = I_L + I_{(shunt)}$$
$$V_O = V_I - R_S[I_L + I_{(shunt)}]$$

The change in shunt current for a changing load current is:

$$\Delta I_{(shunt)} = -\Delta I_L$$

The change in shunt current for a changing input voltage is:

$$\Delta I_{(shunt)} = \frac{\Delta V_I}{R_S}$$

$$I_{(shunt)} = \frac{V_O}{R_{(shunt)}}$$

Even though it is usually less efficient than series or switching regulators, a shunt regulator may be the best choice for some applications. The shunt regulator is less sensitive to input voltage transients; does not reflect load current transients back to the source, and is inherently short-circuit proof.

### SWITCHING REGULATOR

The switching regulator employs an active switch as its control element. This switch is used to chop the input voltage at a varying duty cycle based on the load requirements. A basic switching regulator is illustrated in Figure 5-5.

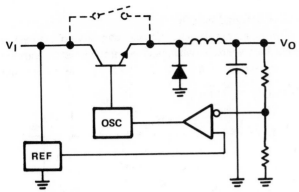

**Figure 5-5. Basic Switching Regulator (Step-Down Configuration)**

A filter, usually an LC filter, is then used to average the voltage present at its input and deliver that voltage to the output load. Because the pass transistor is either on (saturated) or off, the power dissipated in the control element is minimal. The switching regulator is therefore more efficient than the series or shunt type. For this reason, the switching regulator becomes particularly advantageous for applications involving large input-to-output differential voltages or high load-current requirements. In the past, switching voltage regulators were discrete designs. However, recent advancements in integrated circuit technology have resulted in several monolithic switching regulator circuits that contain all of the necessary elements to design step-up, step-down, or inverting voltage converters. The duty cycle may be varied by:

1. maintaining a constant on-time, varying the frequency
2. maintaining a constant off-time, varying the frequency
3. maintaining a constant frequency, varying the on/off times

## MAJOR ERROR CONTRIBUTORS

The ideal voltage regulator maintains constant output voltage despite varying input voltage, load current, and temperature conditions. Realistically, these influences affect the regulator's output voltage. In addition, the regulator's own internal inaccuracies affect the overall circuit performance. This section discusses the major error contributors, their effects, and suggests some possible solutions to the problems they create.

### REGULATOR REFERENCE TECHNIQUES

There are several reference techniques employed in integrated circuit voltage regulators. Each provides its particular level of performance and problems. The optimum reference depends on the regulator's requirements.

### Zener Diode Reference

The zener diode reference, as illustrated in Figure 5-6, is the simplest technique. The zener voltage itself, $V_Z$, forms the reference voltage, $V_{REF}$.

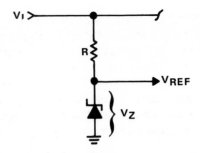

**Figure 5-6. Basic Zener Reference**

This technique is satisfactory for relatively stable supply-voltage and load-current applications. The changing zener current results in a change in the zener diode's reference voltage, $V_Z$. This zener reference model is illustrated in Figure 5-7.

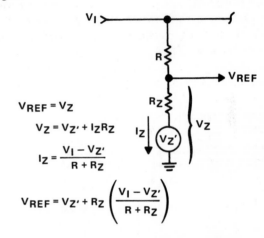

$$V_{REF} = V_Z$$
$$V_Z = V_{Z'} + I_Z R_Z$$
$$I_Z = \frac{V_I - V_{Z'}}{R + R_Z}$$
$$V_{REF} = V_{Z'} + R_Z \left( \frac{V_I - V_{Z'}}{R + R_Z} \right)$$

**Figure 5-7. Zener Reference Model**

### Constant-Current Zener Reference

The zener reference can be refined by the addition of a constant-current source as its supply. Driving the zener diode with a constant current minimizes the effect of zener impedance on the overall stability of the zener reference. An example of this technique is illustrated in Figure 5-8. The reference voltage of this configuration is relatively independent of changes in supply voltage and load current.

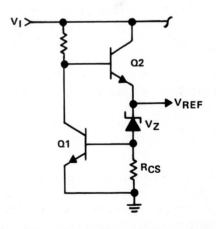

**Figure 5-8. Constant-Current Zener Reference**

$$V_{REF} = V_Z + V_{BE(Q1)}$$

$$I_Z = \frac{V_{BE(Q1)}}{R_{CS}}$$

In addition to superior supply voltage independence, the circuit illustrated in Figure 5-8 yields improved temperature stability. The reference voltage, $V_{REF}$, is the sum of the zener voltage ($V_Z$) and the base-emitter voltage of $Q1[V_{BE(Q1)}]$. A low temperature coefficient can be achieved by balancing the positive temperature coefficient of the zener with the negative temperature coefficient of the base-emitter junction of Q1.

### Band-Gap Reference

Another popular reference is the band-gap reference, which developed from the highly predictable emitter-base voltage of integrated transistors. Basically, the reference voltage is derived from the energy-band-gap voltage of the semiconductor material $[V_{go(silicon)} = 1.204\ V]$. The basic band-gap configuration is illustrated in Figure 5-9. The reference voltage, $V_{REF}$, in this case is:

$$V_{REF} = V_{BE(Q3)} + I_2 R_2$$

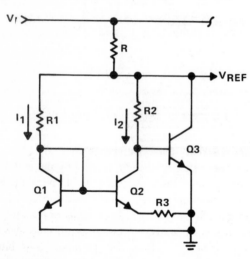

**Figure 5-9. Band-Gap Reference**

The resistor values of R1 and R2 are selected in such a way that the current through transistors Q1 and Q2 are significantly different ($I_1 = 10I_2$). The difference in current through transistors Q1 and Q2 also results in a difference in their respective base-emitter voltages. This voltage differential $[V_{BE(Q1)} - V_{BE(Q2)}]$ will appear across R3. Application of transistors with sufficiently high gain results in current $I_2$ passing through R3. In this instance, $I_2$ is equal to:

$$\frac{V_{BE(Q1)} - V_{BE(Q2)}}{R3}$$

$$\therefore\ V_{REF} = V_{BE(Q3)} + \left[\left(V_{BE(Q1)} - V_{BE(Q2)}\right)\frac{R2}{R3}\right]$$

By analyzing the effect of temperature on $V_{REF}$ it can be shown that the difference between two similar transistors' emitter-base voltages, when operated at different currents is:

$$V_{BE(Q1)} - V_{BE(Q2)} = \frac{kT}{q}\ \ln\frac{I_1}{I_2}$$

where

$$
\begin{aligned}
k &= \text{Boltzmann's constant} \\
T &= \text{absolute temperature — degrees K} \\
q &= \text{charge of an electron} \\
I &= \text{current}
\end{aligned}
$$

The base-emitter voltage of Q3 can also be expressed as:

$$V_{BE(Q3)} = V_{go}\left[1 - \frac{T}{T_O}\right] + V_{BEO}\left[\frac{T}{T_O}\right]$$

where

$$
\begin{aligned}
V_{go} &= \text{band-gap potential} \\
V_{BEO} &= \text{emitter-base voltage at } T_O
\end{aligned}
$$

$V_{REF}$ can then be expressed as:

$$V_{REF} = V_{go}\left[1 - \frac{T}{T_O}\right] + V_{BEO}\left[\frac{T}{T_O}\right]$$
$$+ \frac{R2}{R3}\ \frac{kT}{q}\ \ln\frac{I_1}{I_2}$$

Differentiating with respect to temperature yields

$$\frac{dV_{REF}}{dT} = -\frac{V_{go}}{T_O} + \frac{V_{BEO}}{T_O} + \frac{R2}{R3}\ \frac{k}{q}\ln\frac{I_1}{I_2}$$

If R2, R3, and $I_1$ are appropriately selected such that

$$\frac{R2}{R3}\ \ln\frac{I_1}{I_2} = [V_{go} - V_{BEO(Q3)}]\ C$$

where

$$C = \frac{q}{kT_O}$$

and

$$V_{go} = 1.2\ V$$

the resulting

$$\frac{dV_{REF}}{dT} = 0$$

The reference is temperature-compensated.

Band-gap reference voltage is particularly advantageous for low-voltage applications ($V_{REF} = 1.2$ V) and it yields a reference level that is stable even with variations in supply and temperature.

## SAMPLING ELEMENT

The sampling element used on most integrated circuit voltage regulators is an R1/R2 resistor divider network (Figure 5-10), which can be determined by the output-voltage-to-reference-voltage ratio.

$$\frac{V_O}{V_{REF}} = 1 + \frac{R1}{R2}$$

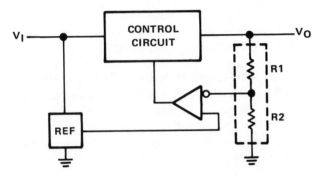

**Figure 5-10. R1/R2 Ladder Network Sampling Element**

Since the feedback voltage is determined by ratio and not absolute value, proportional variations in R1 and R2 have no effect on the accuracy of the integrated circuit voltage regulator. When proper attention is given to the layout of these resistors in an integrated circuit, their contribution to the error of the voltage regulator will be minimal. The initial accuracy is the only parameter affected.

## ERROR AMPLIFIER PERFORMANCE

If a stable reference and an accurate output sampling element exist, the error amplifier becomes the primary factor determining the performance of the voltage regulator. Typical amplifier performance parameters such as offset, common-mode and supply-rejection ratios, output impedance, and temperature coefficient affect the accuracy and regulation of the voltage regulator. These amplifier performance parameters will affect the accuracy of the regulator due to variations in supply, load, and ambient temperature conditions.

### Offset Voltage

Offset voltage is viewed by the amplifier as an error signal, as illustrated in Figure 5-11, and will cause the output to respond accordingly.

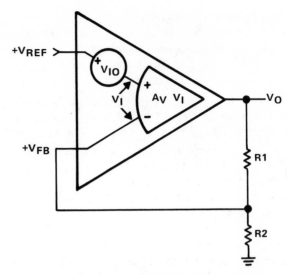

**Figure 5-11. Amplifier Model Showing Input Offset Voltage Effect**

$$V_O = A_V V_I$$

$$V_I = V_{REF} - V_{IO} - V_{FB}$$

$$V_{FB} = V_O \frac{R2}{R1 + R2}$$

$$V_O = \frac{V_{REF} - V_{IO}}{\frac{1}{A_V} + \left[ \frac{R2}{R1 + R2} \right]}$$

If $A_V$ is sufficiently large

$$V_O = (V_{REF} - V_{IO}) \left[ 1 + \frac{R1}{R2} \right]$$

$V_{IO}$ represents an initial error in the output of the integrated circuit voltage regulator. The simplest method of compensating for this error is to adjust the output voltage sampling element R1/R2.

### Offset Change with Temperature

The technique discussed above compensates for the amplifier's offset voltage and yields an accurate regulator, but only at a specific temperature. In most amplifiers, the offset voltage change with temperature is proportional to the initial offset level. Trimming the output voltage sampling element, does not reduce the offset voltage but merely counteracts it. At a different ambient temperature, the offset voltage changes and, thus, error is again introduced into the voltage regulator. Monolithic integrated circuit regulators use technology that essentially eliminates offset in integrated circuit amplifiers. With minimal offset voltage, drift caused by temperature variations will have little consequence.

## Supply Voltage Variations

The amplifier's power supply and common-mode rejection ratios are the primary contributors to regulator error which has been introduced by an unregulated input voltage. In an ideal amplifier, the output voltage is a function of the differential input voltage only. Realistically, the common-mode voltage of the input also influences the output voltage. The common-mode voltage is the average input voltage, referenced from the amplifier's virtual ground (see Figure 5-12 and the following equations).

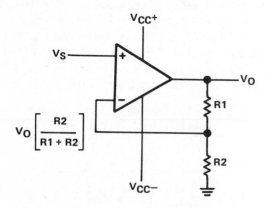

**Figure 5-12. Amplifier Model Showing Common-Mode Voltage**

$$\text{Virtual Ground} = \frac{V_{CC+} + V_{CC-}}{2}$$

$$V_{I(av)} = \frac{V_S + V_O\left[\dfrac{R2}{R1 + R2}\right]}{2}$$

$$V_{CM} = \frac{1}{2}\left[V_S + V_O\left(\frac{R2}{R1 + R2}\right) - \left(V_{CC+} + V_{CC-}\right)\right]$$

From this relation it can be seen that unequal variations in either power supply bus rail will result in a change in the common-mode voltage.

The common-mode voltage rejection ration (CMRR) is the ratio of the amplifier's differential voltage amplification to the common-mode voltage amplification.

$$CMRR = \frac{A_{VD}}{A_{VCM}}$$

$$A_{VCM} = \frac{A_{VD}}{CMRR}$$

That portion of output which is voltage contributed by the equivalent common-mode input voltage is:

$$V_O = V_{CM}A_{VCM} = \frac{A_{VD}V_{CM}}{CMRR}$$

The equivalent error introduced then is:

$$\text{COMMON-MODE ERROR} = \frac{V_{CM}}{CMRR}$$

The common-mode error represents an offset voltage to the amplifier. Neglecting the actual offset voltage, the output voltage of the error amplifier then becomes:

$$V_O = \left(V_{REF} + \frac{V_{CM}}{CMRR}\right)\left(1 + \frac{R1}{R2}\right)$$

Using constant-current sources in most integrated circuit amplifiers, however, yields a high power-supply (common-mode) rejection ratio. This power-supply rejection ratio is of such a large magnitude that the common-mode voltage effect on $V_O$ can usually be neglected.

## REGULATOR DESIGN CONSIDERATIONS

Various types of integrated circuit voltage regulators are available, each having its own particular characteristics, giving it advantages in various applications. The type of regulator used depends primarily upon the designer's needs and trade-offs in performance and cost.

### POSITIVE VERSUS NEGATIVE REGULATORS

This classification of voltage regulators is easily understood; a positive regulator is used to regulate a positive voltage, and a negative regulator is used to regulate a negative voltage. However, what is positive and negative may vary, depending upon the ground reference.

Figure 5-13 illustrates conventional positive and negative voltage regulator applications employing a continuous and common ground. For systems operating on a single supply, the positive and negative regulators may be interchanged by floating the ground reference to the load or input. This approach to design is recommended only where ground isolation serves as an advantage to overall system performance.

Figures 5-14 and 5-15 illustrate a positive regulator in a negative configuration and a negative regulator in a positive configuration, respectively.

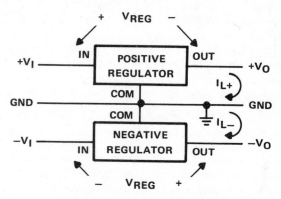

**Figure 5-13. Conventional Positive/ Negative Regulator**

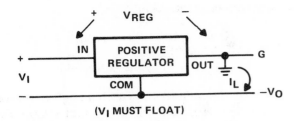

**Figure 5-14. Positive Regulator in Negative Configuration ($V_I$ Must Float)**

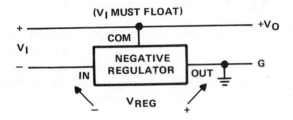

**Figure 5-15. Negative Regulator in Positive Configuration ($V_I$ Must Float)**

## FIXED VERSUS ADJUSTABLE REGULATORS

Many fixed three-terminal voltage regulators are available in various current ranges from most major integrated circuit manufacturers. These regulators offer the designer a simple, inexpensive method to establish a regulated voltage source. Their particular advantages are:

1. Ease of use
2. Few external components required
3. Reliable performance
4. Internal thermal protection
5. Short-circuit protection

There are disadvantages. The fixed three-terminal voltage regulators cannot be precisely adjusted because their output voltage sampling elements are internal. The initial accuracy of these devices may vary as much as $\pm 5\%$ from the nominal value; also the output voltages available are limited.

Current limits are based on the voltage regulator's applicable current range and are not adjustable. Listings of some fixed and variable voltage regulators are given at the end of this chapter. Extended range operation (increasing $I_{LOAD}$) is cumbersome and requires complex external circuitry.

The adjustable regulator may be well suited for those applications requiring higher initial accuracy. This depends on the complexity of the adjustable voltage regulator. Additionally, all adjustable regulators use external feedback, which allows the designer a precise and infinite voltage selection.

The output sense may also be referred to a remote point. This allows the designer to not only extend the range of the regulator (with minimal external circuitry), but also to compensate for losses in a distributed load or external pass components. Additional features found on many adjustable voltage regulators are: adjustable short-circuit current limiting, access to the voltage reference element, and shutdown circuitry.

## DUAL-TRACKING REGULATORS

The dual tracking regulator (Figure 5-16) provides regulation for two power supply buses, usually one positive and one negative. The dual-tracking feature assures a balanced supply system by monitoring the voltage on both power supply buses. If either of the voltages sags or goes out of regulation, the tracking regulator will cause the other voltage to vary accordingly (A 10% sag in the positive voltage will result in a 10% sag in the negative voltage.). These regulators are, for the most part, restricted to applications such as linear systems where balanced supplies offer a definite performance improvement.

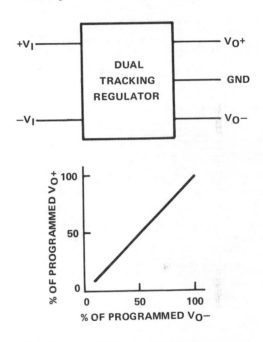

**Figure 5-16. Dual Tracking Regulator**

## SERIES REGULATORS

The series regulator is well suited for medium current applications with nominal voltage differential requirements. Modulation of a series pass control element to maintain a well regulated, prescribed, output voltage is a straightforward design technique. Safe-operating-area protection circuits such as overvoltage, fold-back current limiting, and short-circuit protection are additional functions that series regulators can supply. The primary disadvantage of the series regulator is its power consumption. The amount of power a series regulator (Figure 5-17) will consume depends on the load current being drawn from the regulator and is proportional to the input-to-output voltage differential. The amount of power consumed becomes considerable with increasing load or differential voltage requirements. This power loss limits the amount of power that can be delivered to the load because the amount of power that can be dissipated by the series regulator is limited.

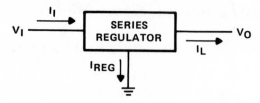

**Figure 5-17. Series Regulator**

The equations that describe these conditions are listed below. $P_{REG}$ is the power lost in the regulator, $I_I$ is the input current, $I_{REG}$ is the regulator current and $I_L$ is the load current. The differential voltage across the regulator is $(V_I - V_O)$.

$$P_{REG} = V_I I_I - V_O I_L$$

$$I_I = I_{REG} + I_L$$

Since $I_L$ is much greater than $I_{REG}$

$$I_I = I_L$$

$$P_{REG} = I_L (V_I - V_O)$$

**Floating Regulator**

The floating regulator (Figure 5-18) is a variation of the series regulator. The output voltage remains constant by changing the input-to-output voltage differential for varying input voltage. The floating regulator's differential voltage is modulated such that its output voltage when referenced to its common terminal $V_{O(reg)}$ is equal to its internal reference ($V_{REF}$). The voltage developed across the output-to-common terminal is equal to the voltage developed across $R1(V_{R1})$.

$$V_{O(reg)} = V_{REF} = V_{R1}$$

$$V_{R1} = V_O \left[ \frac{R1}{R1 + R2} \right]$$

$$V_O = V_{REF} \left[ 1 + \frac{R2}{R1} \right]$$

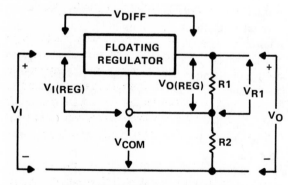

**Figure 5-18. Floating Regulator**

The common-terminal voltage is:

$$V_{COM} = V_O - V_{R1} = V_O - V_{REF}$$

The input voltage seen by the floating regulator is:

$$V_{I(reg)} = V_I - V_{COM}$$

$$V_{I(reg)} = V_I - V_O + V_{REF}$$

$$V_{I(reg)} = V_{DIFF} + V_{REF}$$

Since $V_{REF}$ is fixed, the only limitation on the input voltage is the allowable differential voltage. This makes the floating regulator especially suited for high-voltage applications ($V_I > 40$ V).

Practical values of output voltage are limited to practical ratios of output-to-reference voltages.

$$\frac{R2}{R1} = \frac{V_O}{V_{REF}} - 1$$

The floating regulator exhibits power consumption characteristics similar to that of the series regulator from which it is derived, but unlike the series regulator, it can also serve as a current regulator as shown in Figure 5-19.

$$V_O = V_{REF} \left[ 1 + \frac{R_L}{R_S} \right]$$

$$V_O = V_L + V_{O(reg)}$$

$$V_{O(reg)} = V_{REF}$$

$$V_L = V_{REF} \left[ 1 + \frac{R_L}{R_S} \right] - V_{REF}$$

$$V_L = V_{REF} \left[ \frac{R_L}{R_S} \right]$$

$$I_L = \frac{V_{LOAD}}{R_L}$$

$$I_{LOAD} = \frac{V_{REF}}{R_S}$$

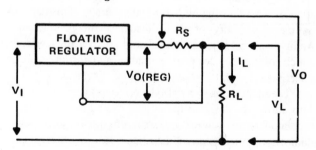

**Figure 5-19. Floating Regulator as a
Constant-Current Regulator**

## SHUNT REGULATOR

The shunt regulator, illustrated in Figure 5-20, is the simplest of all regulators. It employs a fixed resistor as its series pass element.

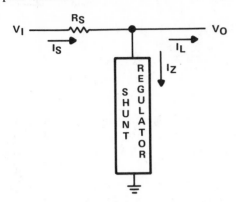

**Figure 5-20. Shunt Regulator**

Changes in input voltage or load current requirements are compensated by modulating the current which is shunted to ground through the regulator.

For changes in $V_I$:    $\Delta I_Z = \dfrac{\Delta V_I}{R_S}$

For changes in $I_L$:    $\Delta I_Z = -\Delta I_L$

The inherent short-circuit-proof feature of the shunt regulator makes it particularly attractive for some applications. The output voltage will be maintained until the load current required is equal to the current through the series element (see Figure 5-21).

$$I_L = I_S \ (I_Z = 0)$$

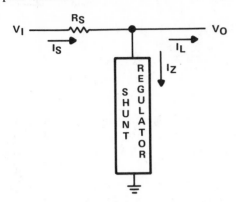

**Figure 5-21. Output Voltage vs Shunt Current of a Shunt Regulator**

Since the shunt regulator cannot supply any current, additional current required by the load will result in reducing the output voltage to zero.

$$V_O = V_I - I_L R_S$$

The short-circuit current of the shunt regulator then becomes:

$$V_O = 0$$

$$I_{SC} = \frac{V_I}{R_S}$$

## SWITCHING REGULATORS

The switching regulator lends itself primarily to the higher power applications or those applications where power supply and system efficiency are of the utmost concern. Unlike the series regulator, the switching regulator operates its control element in an on or off mode. Switching regulator control element modes are illustrated in Figure 5-22.

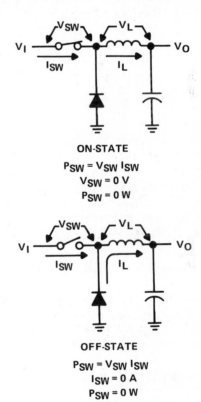

**ON-STATE**

$P_{SW} = V_{SW} I_{SW}$

$V_{SW} = 0\ V$

$P_{SW} = 0\ W$

**OFF-STATE**

$P_{SW} = V_{SW} I_{SW}$

$I_{SW} = 0\ A$

$P_{SW} = 0\ W$

**Figure 5-22. Switching Voltage Regulator Modes**

In this manner, the control element is subjected to a high current at a very low voltage or a high differential voltage at a very low current. In either case, power dissipation in the control element is minimal. Changes in the load current or input voltage are compensated for by varying the on-off ratio (duty cycle) of the switch without increasing the internal power dissipated in the switching regulator. See Figure 5-23(a).

For the output voltage to remain constant, the net charge in the capacitor must remain constant. This means the charge delivered to the capacitor must be dissipated in the load.

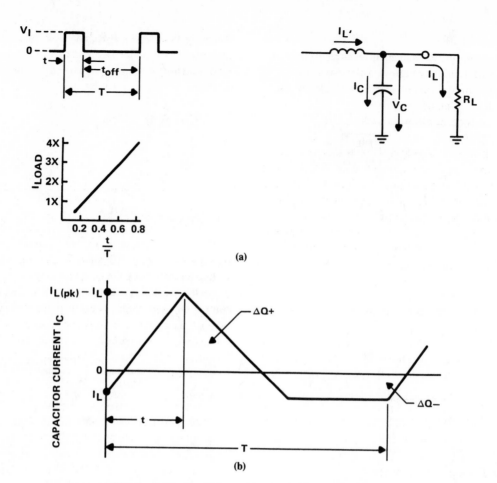

Figure 5-23. Variation of Pulse Width vs Load

$$I_C = I_L' - I_L$$

$$I_C = I_L \text{ for } I_L' = 0$$

$$I_C = I_{L(pk)} - I_L \text{ for } I_L = I_{L(pk)}$$

The capacitor current waveform then becomes that illustrated in Figure 4-23(b). The charge delivered to the capacitor and the charge dissipated by the load are equal to the areas under the capacitor current waveform.

$$\Delta Q+ = \frac{1}{2} \frac{(I_{L(pk)} - I_L)^2}{I_{L(pk)}} t\left(\frac{V_I}{V_C}\right)$$

$$\Delta Q- = I_L\left[ T - \frac{1}{2} t\left(\frac{V_I}{V_C}\right)\right.$$
$$\left. - \frac{1}{2} t\left(\frac{I_{L(pk)} - I_L}{I_{L(pk)}}\right)\left(\frac{V_I}{V_C}\right)\right]$$

By setting $\Delta Q+$ equal to $\Delta Q-$, the relationship of $I_L$ and $I_{L(pk)}$ for $\Delta Q = 0$ can be determined;

$$I_L = \frac{1}{2} I_{L(pk)}\left[\frac{V_I}{V_C} \frac{t}{T}\right]$$

As this demonstrates, the duty cycle t/T can be altered to compensate for input voltage changes or load variations.

The duty cycle t/T can be altered a number of different ways.

$t = t_{on}$ (inductor charge time)
$T = $ Total time ($t_{on} + t_{off} + t_I$) where $t_I$ is the time from $t_{off}$ until the start of the next charge cycle.

Knowing T then:

$$f = \frac{1}{T}$$

**Fixed On Time, Variable Frequency**

One technique of voltage regulation is to maintain a fixed or predetermined "on" time (t), the time the input voltage is being applied to the LC filter) and vary the duty cycle by varying the frequency (f). This method makes voltage conversion applications design easier (step-up, step-down, invert) since the energy stored in the inductor of the LC filter during the on-time (which is fixed) determines the amount of power deliverable to the load. Thus calculation of the inductor is fairly straightforward.

$$L = \frac{V}{I} t$$

where

L = value of inductance in microhenrys
V = differential voltage in volts
I = required inductor current defined by the load in amps
t = on-time in microseconds

The fixed-on-time approach is also advantageous from the standpoint that a consistent amount of energy is stored in the inductor during the fixed on-time period. this simplifies the design of the inductor by defining the operating parameters to which the inductor is subjected. The operating characteristic of a fixed-on-time switching voltage regulator is a varying frequency, which changes directly with changes in the load. This can be seen in Figure 5-24.

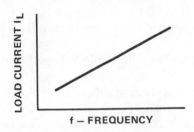

**Figure 5-24. Frequency vs Load Current for Fixed On-Time SVR**

## Fixed Off Time, Variable Frequency

In the fixed-off-time switching voltage regulator, the average dc voltage is varied by changing the on time (t) of the switch while maintaining a fixed off-time ($t_{OFF}$). The fixed-off-time switching voltage regulator behaves in a manner opposite that of the fixed-on-time regulator.

As the load current increases, the on time is made to increase, thus decreasing the operating frequency; this is illustrated in Figure 5-25. This approach provides the capability to design a switching voltage regulator that will operate at a well defined minimum frequency under full load conditions.

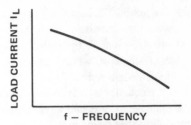

**Figure 5-25. Frequency vs Load Current for Fixed Off-Time SVR**

The fixed-off-time approach also allows a dc current to be established in the inductor under increased load conditions, thus reducing the ripple current while maintaining the same average current. The maximum current experienced in the inductor under transient load conditions is not as well defined as that found in the fixed-on-time regulator. Thus additional precautions should be taken to ensure that the inductor does not saturate.

## Fixed-Frequency, Variable Duty Cycle

The fixed-frequency switching regulator varies the duty cycle of the pulse train in order to change the average power. The fixed-frequency concept is particularly advantageous for systems employing transformer-coupled output stages. The fixed frequency permits efficient design of the associated magnetics. Transformer coupling also has advantages in single and multiple voltage-conversion applications. The fixed-frequency regulator will establish a dc current through the inductor (for increased load conditions) to maintain the required load current, with minimal ripple current. The single-ended and transformer-coupled configurations are illustrated in Figure 5-26.

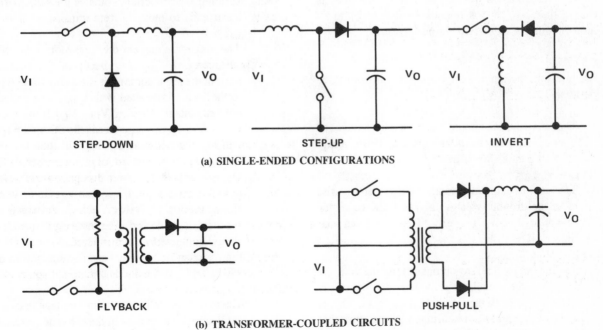

(a) SINGLE-ENDED CONFIGURATIONS

(b) TRANSFORMER-COUPLED CIRCUITS

**Figure 5-26. Switching Voltage Regulator Configurations**

These types of switching regulators can thus be operated with high efficiency to provide low-voltage, regulated outputs from a high-voltage, unregulated supply or vice versa. The switching frequency should be established at the optimum value for the switching components of the supply (transformer, switching transistor, inductor, and filter capacitor). High frequency operation is distinctly advantageous because the cost, weight, and volume of both L and C filter elements are reduced.

However, the frequency at which the effective series resistance of the filter capacitor equals its capacitive reactance is the maximum allowable frequency.

Operation above 20 kHz is desirable to eliminate the possibility of audible noise. Choosing an operating frequency that is too high will result in power switching transistor losses as well as "catch" diode losses. The higher cost of these high performance components must be balanced against the reduced cost, size, and weight of the L and C components when determining the optimum frequency for a specific application.

## REGULATOR SAFE OPERATING AREA

The safe operating area (SOA) is a term used to define the input and output voltage range, and load current range within which any device is designed to operate reliably. Exceeding these limits will result in a catastrophic failure or will render the device temporarily inoperative, depending upon the device and its performance characteristics. Integrated circuit voltage regulators with internal current limiting, thermal and short-circuit protection will merely shut down. External components, such as pass transistors on the other hand, may respond with catastrophic failure.

### REGULATOR SOA CONSIDERATIONS

Although particular design equations depend upon the type of integrated circuit voltage regulator used and its application, there are several boundaries that apply to all regulator circuits for safe, reliable performance.

### Input Voltage

The limits on the input voltage are derived from three considerations:

$V_{Imax}$

The absolute maximum rated input voltage as referenced to the regulator's ground. This is a safe operating area (SOA) destruct limit.

$(V_I - V_O)_{min}$

The input-to-output differential voltage also referred to as the dropout voltage, at which the regulator ceases to function properly. This is a functional limit.

$(V_I - V_O)_{max}$

The maximum input-to-output differential voltage. Usually, the regulator's power dissipation is exceeded prior to the $(V_I - V_O)_{max}$ limit. This is an SOA level that can be limited by the allowable Power Dissipation ($P_{Dmax}$).

### Load Current

$I_{Lmax}$

The maximum load current deliverable from the integrated circuit regulator. If internal current limiting is not provided, external protection should be provided. This is a functional limit that may be further limited by $P_{D\ max}$.

### Power Dissipation

$P_{Dmax}$

The maximum power that can be dissipated within the regulator. Power dissipation is the product of the input-to-output differential voltage and the load current, and is normally specified at or below a given case temperature. This rating is usually based on a 150 °C junction temperature limit. The power rating is an SOA limit unless the integrated circuit regulator provides an internal thermal protection.

### Output Voltage of an Adjustable-Voltage Regulator

$V_{Omin}$

The minimum output voltage a regulator is capable of regulating. This is usually a factor of the regulator's internal reference and is a functional limit.

$V_{Omax}$

The maximum output voltage a regulator is capable of regulating. This is largely dependent on the input voltage and is a functional limit.

### External Pass Transistor

For applications requiring additional load current, integrated circuit voltage regulator capabilities may be boosted with the addition of an external pass transistor. When employed, the external pass transistor, in addition to the voltage regulator, must be protected against operation outside its safe operating area. Operation outside the safe operating area is catastrophic to most discrete transistors.

$I_{Cmax}$

The maximum current the transistor is capable of sustaining. $I_{Cmax}$ now becomes the maximum current the regulator circuit is capable of delivering to the load. Associated with $I_{Cmax}$ is a collector-emitter voltage ($V_{CE} = V_I - V_O$). If the product $(V_I - V_{Omax})I_{Cmax}$ exceeds the SOA then $I_{Cmax}$ will have to be derated. This will then become a functional limit instead of a catastrophic limit. $I_{Cmax}$ is related to power dissipation and junction or case temperature. $I_{Cmax}$ must again be derated if the thermal or power ratings at which it is specified are exceeded. The resulting derated $I_{Cmax}$ should continue to be considered as a catastrophic limit. Actual $I_{Cmax}$ limits and derating information will appear on the individual transistor specification.

$V_{CEmax}$

The maximum collector-emitter voltage that can be applied to the transistor in the off-state. Exceeding this limit can be catastrophic.

$P_{Dmax}$

The maximum power that can be dissipated by the transistor. This is usually specified at a specific junction or case temperature. If the transistor is operated at higher temperatures, the maximum power must be derated in accordance with the operating rules specified in the transistor's applicable specification. Prolonged operation above the transistor's maximum power rating will result in degradation or destruction of the transistor.

## SAFE OPERATING PROTECTION CIRCUITS

Selection of the proper integrated circuit voltage regulators and external components will result in a reliable design in which all devices can operate well within their respective safe operating areas. Fault conditions (such as a short-circuit or excessive load) may cause components in the regulator circuit to exceed their safe operating area operation. Because of this situation, as well as protection for the load, certain protection circuits should be considered.

### Reverse Bias Protection

A potentially dangerous condition may occur when a voltage regulator becomes reverse biased. For example, if the input supply were crowbarred to protect either the supply itself or additional circuitry, the filter capacitor at the output of the regulator circuit would maintain the regulator's output voltage and the regulator circuit would be reverse biased. If the regulated voltage is large enough (greater than 7 V), the regulator circuit may be damaged. To protect against this, a diode can be used as illustrated in Figure 5-27.

**Figure 5-27. Reverse Bias Protection**

## CURRENT LIMITING TECHNIQUES

The type of current limiting used depends primarily on the safe operating area of the pass element used. The three basic current limiting techniques are series resistor, constant current, and fold-back current limiting.

### Series Resistor

This is the simplest method for short-circuit protection. The short-circuit current is determined by the current-limiting resistor $R_{CL}$, illustrated in Figure 5-28.

$$V_O = V_{O(reg)} - I_L R_{CL}$$

A short-circuit condition occurs when $V_O = 0$, thus:

$$I_{SC} = I_L @ (V_O = 0) = \frac{V_{O(reg)}}{R_{CL}}$$

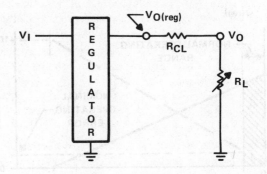

**Figure 5-28. Series Resistance Current Limiter**

The primary drawback of this technique is error introduced by the voltage dropped across $R_{CL}$ under varying load conditions. The % error, as illustrated by the following equations, depends on the $R_{CL}$ and $R_L$ values.

$$I_L = \frac{V_O}{R_L}$$

$$V_O = \frac{V_{O(reg)}}{1 + \frac{R_{CL}}{R_L}}$$

$$\% \text{ ERROR} = \frac{V_{O(reg)} - V_O}{V_{O(reg)}}$$

$$\% \text{ ERROR} = \frac{R_{CL}}{R_L + R_{CL}}$$

Maintaining $R_{CL}$ at a level which is an order of magnitude less than the nominal load impedance minimizes this effect.

$$R_{CL} = \frac{1}{10} R_L \qquad \% \text{ ERROR} = 9.1\%$$

This also yields a short-circuit current that is an order of magnitude greater than the normal operating load current.

$$I_{L(norm)} = \frac{V_{O(reg)}}{R_{CL} + R_{L(norm)}}$$

$$I_{SC} = \frac{V_{O(reg)}}{R_{CL}}$$

$$I_{SC} = 11 \, I_{L(norm)}$$

This technique is obviously inefficient since it requires using a regulator or pass element with current capabilities in excess (11X) of its normal operating capabilities.

The performance characteristics of a series resistance current limited regulator are illustrated in Figure 5-29.

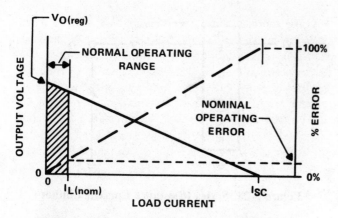

Figure 5-29. Performance Characteristics of a Series Resistance Current-Limited Regulator

## Constant-Current Limiting

Constant-current limiting is the most popular current-limiting technique in low-power, low-current regulator circuits. The basic configuration is illustrated in Figure 5-30.

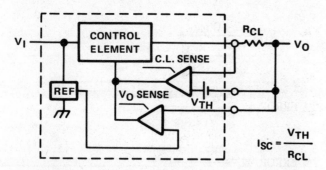

$$I_{SC} = \frac{V_{TH}}{R_{CL}}$$

Figure 5-30. Constant Current Limit Configuration

Note that this method requires access to the control element and remote voltage sense capabilities. By sensing the output voltage beyond the current limiting resistor, the circuit allows the regulator to compensate for the voltage changes across $R_{CL}$.

If an external pass transistor is used, its base current may be starved to accomplish constant-current limiting, as illustrated in Figure 5-31. Current limiting takes effect as the voltage drop across $R_{CL}$ approaches the potential required to turn on transistor Q1. As Q1 is biased on, the current

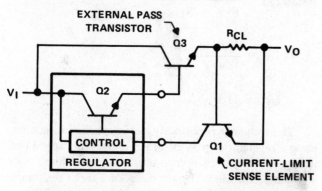

Figure 5-31. Constant Current Limiting for External Pass Transistor Applications

supplying the base of Q2 is diverted, thus decreasing the drive current to Q3, the regulator's pass transistor. The performance characteristics of a constant-current limited regulator are illustrated in Figure 5-32.

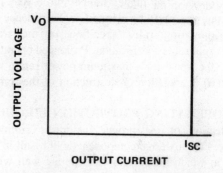

Figure 5-32. Constant Current Limiting

It should be noted that short-circuit conditions are the worst conditions that can be imposed on the pass transistor since it has to survive not only the short-circuit current, but it has to withstand the full input voltage across its collector and emitter terminals.

This normally requires the use of a pass transistor with power handling capabilities much greater than those required for normal operation i.e.:

$$V_I = 20 \text{ V} \qquad V_O = 12 \text{ V} \qquad I_O = 700 \text{ mA}$$

$$\text{NOMINAL } P_D = (20 \text{ V} - 12 \text{ V}) \times 0.7 \text{ A} = 5.6 \text{ W}$$

For $I_{SC} = 1 \text{ A}(150\% \, I_{OUT})$:

$$\text{SHORT-CIRCUIT } P_D = 20 \text{ V} \times 1 \text{ A} = 20 \text{ W}$$

This requirement may be reduced by the application of fold-back current limiting.

## Fold-Back Current Limiting

Fold-back current limiting is used primarily for high-current applications where the normal operating requirements of the regulator dictate the use of an external power transistor. The principle of fold-back current limiting provides limiting at a predetermined current ($I_K$). At this predetermined current, feedback reduces the load current as the load continues to increase ($R_L$ decreasing) and causes the output voltage to decay.

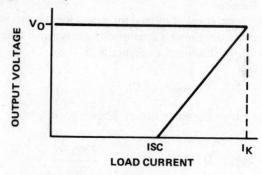

Figure 5-33. Fold-Back Current Limiting

The fold-back current-limiting circuit of Figure 5-34 behaves in a manner similar to the constant-current limit circuit illustrated in Figure 5-31. In Figure 5-33, the potential developed across the current limit sense resistor ($R_{CL}$) must not only develop the base-emitter voltage required to turn on Q1, but it must develop sufficient potential to overcome the voltage across resistor R1.

$$V_{BE(Q1)} = R_{CL}I_L - \frac{V_O + R_{CL}I_L}{R1 + R2} \times R1$$

$$\therefore I_K = \frac{V_{BE(Q1)}(R1 + R2) + V_OR1}{R_{CL}R2}$$

As the load current requirement increases above $I_K$, the output voltage ($V_O$) decays. The decreasing output voltage results in a proportional decrease in voltage across R1. Thus, less current is required through $R_{CL}$ to develop sufficient potential to maintain the forward-biased condition of Q1. This can be seen in the above expression for $I_K$. As $V_O$ decreases, $I_K$ decreases. Under short-circuit conditions ($V_O = 0$) $I_K$ becomes:

$$I_{SC} = I_K @ (V_O = 0) = \frac{V_{BE(Q1)}}{R_{CL}}\left[1 + \frac{R1}{R2}\right]$$

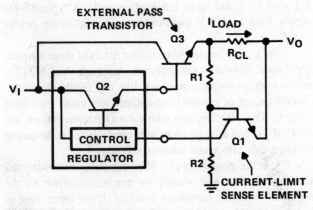

**Figure 5-34. Fold-Back Current Limit Configuration**

The approach illustrated in Figure 5-34 allows a more efficient design because the collector current of the pass transistor is less during short-circuit conditions than it is during normal operation. This means that during short-circuit conditions, when the voltage across the pass transistor is maximum, the collector-emitter current is reduced. As illustrated in Figure 5-35, fold-back current limiting fits closer to the typical performance characteristics of the transistor, thus allowing a better design match of the pass transistor to the regulator.

## THREE TERMINAL REGULATORS

Three-terminal IC regulators have been especially useful to the designer of small, regulated power supplies or on-card regulators. Three-terminal regulators are popular because they are small and require a minimum number of external components.

### STABILIZATION

Mounting and using three-terminal regulators usually presents no problem, however, there are several precautions that should be observed. Positive regulators, in general, use npn emitter follower output stages whereas negative regulators use npn common-emitter stages with the load connected to the collector. The emitter follower output stage configuration is not used in negative regulators because monolithic pnp series-pass transistors are more difficult to make. Due to their output stage configuration, positive regulators are more stable than negative regulators. Therefore, the practice of bypassing positive regulators may be omitted in some applications. It is good practice, however, to use bypass capacitors at all times.

For a positive regulator, a 0.33 $\mu$F bypass capacitor should be used on the input terminals. While not necessary for stability, an output capacitor of 0.1 $\mu$F may be used to improve the transient response of the regulator. These capacitors should be on or as near as possible to the regulator terminals. See Figure 5-36.

When using a negative regulator, bypass capacitors are a must on both the input and output. Recommended values are 2 $\mu$F on the input and 1 $\mu$F on the output. It is considered

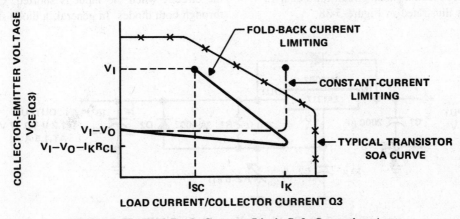

**Figure 5-35. Fold-Back Current Limit Safe Operating Area**

good practice to include a 0.1-$\mu$F capacitor on the output to improve the transient response (Figure 5-37). These capacitors may be mylar, ceramic, or tantalum, provided that they have good high frequency characteristics.

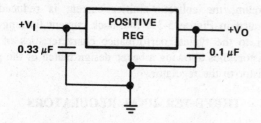

**Figure 5-36. Positive Regulator**

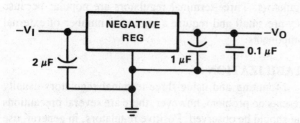

**Figure 5-37. Negative Regulator**

## FIXED DUAL REGULATORS

When building a dual power supply with both a positive and a negative regulator, extra precautions should be taken. If there is a common load between the two supplies, latch-up may occur. Latch-up occurs because a three-terminal regulator does not tolerate a reverse voltage of more than one diode drop. To prevent this latch-up problem, it is good design practice to place reversed-biased diodes across each output of a dual supply. While the diodes should not be necessary if the dual regulator outputs are referenced to ground, latch-up may occur at the instant power is turned on, especially if the input voltage to one regulator rises faster than the other. This latch-up condition usually affects the positive regulator rather than the negative regulator. These diodes prevent reverse voltage to the regulator and prevent parasitic action from taking place when the power is turned on. The diodes should have a current rating of at least half the output current. A recommended circuit for a dual 15 V regulated supply is illustrated in Figure 5-38.

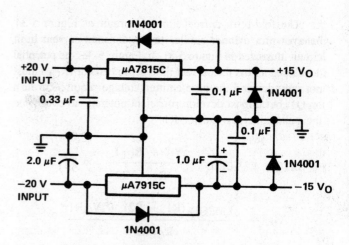

**Figure 5-38. Regulated Dual Supply**

In Figure 5-38, 1N4001 diodes are placed directly across the regulators, input to output. When a capacitor is connected to the regulator output, if the input is shorted to ground, the only path for discharging the capacitor normally is back through the regulator. This could be (and usually is) destructive to the regulator. The diodes across the regulator divert any discharge current, thus protecting the regulator.

## SERIES ADJUSTABLE REGULATORS

Figure 5-39 illustrates a typical circuit for an LM317 adjustable positive regulator with the output adjustable from 1.2 V to 17 V and up to 1.5 A of current. (A typical input supply uses a 25.2-V transformer and a full-wave bridge rectifier.)

Stabilization, as described earlier for fixed three-terminal regulators, is usually not required. Although the LM317 is stable with no output capacitors, like any feedback circuit, certain values of external capacitance can cause excessive ringing. This effect occurs with values between 500 pF and 5000 pF. Using a 10-$\mu$F aluminum electrolytic on the output swamps this effect and ensures stability.

C1 is the power supply filter capacitor following the rectifier section and should be connected close to the regulator input for maximum stability. If the input were to be shorted, D1 would divert the discharge current around the regulator, protecting it. Also, with both D1 and D2 in the circuit, when the input is shorted, C2 is discharged through both diodes. In general, a diode should be used in

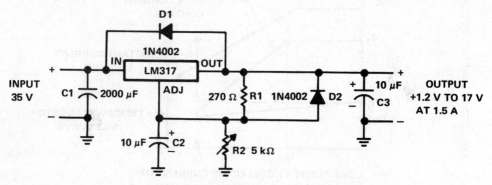

**Figure 5-39. Positive Adjustable Series Regulator**

the position occupied by D1 on all positive regulators to prevent reverse biasing. This becomes more important at higher output voltages since the energy stored in the capacitors is larger. Bypassing the adjustment terminal (C2) improves ripple rejection. Output capacitor C3 is added to improve the transient response of the regulator.

In both the negative (LM337) and the positive (LM317) series adjustable regulators there is an internal diode from the input to the output. If the total output capacitance is less than 25 $\mu$F, D1 may be omitted.

## THERMAL CONSIDERATIONS

Like any semiconductor circuit, lower operating temperature greatly improves reliability of a voltage regulator. It is good practice to make the input-to-output drop across a three-terminal regulator as low as possible while maintaining good regulation. Larger voltage drops mean more power dissipated in the regulator. Although most regulators are rated to withstand junction temperatures as high as 150 °C, heat sinking should be provided to maintain the lowest possible temperature.

## LAYOUT GUIDELINES

As implied in the previous sections, component layout and orientation plays an important, but often overlooked, role in the overall performance of the regulator. The importance of this role depends upon such things as power level, the type of regulator, the overall regulator circuit complexity, and the environment in which the regulator operates. The general layout rules, as well as remote voltage sensing, and component layout guidelines are discussed in the following text.

## LAYOUT DESIGN FACTORS

Most integrated circuit regulators use wide-band transistors to optimize their response. These regulators must be compensated to ensure stable closed-loop operation. This compensation can be counteracted by a layout which has excess external stray capacitance and line inductance. For this reason, circuit lead lengths should be held to a minimum. Lead lengths associated with external compensation or pass transistor elements are of primary concern. These

components especially, should be located as close as possible to the regulator control circuit. In addition to affecting a regulator's susceptibility to spurious oscillation, the layout of the regulator also affects its accuracy and performance.

### Input Ground Loop

Improper placement of the input capacitor can induce unwanted ripple on the output voltage. Care should be taken to ensure that currents in the input circuit do not flow in the ground line that is in common with the load return. This would cause an error voltage resulting from the peak currents of the filter capacitor flowing through the line resistance of the load return. See Figure 5-40 for an illustration of this effect.

### Output Ground Loop

Similar in nature to the problem discussed on the input, excessive lead length in the ground return line of the output results in additional error. Because the load current flows in the ground line, an error equivalent to the load current multiplied by the line resistance (R3′) will be introduced in the output voltage.

### Remote Voltage Sense

The voltage regulator should be located as close as possible to the load. This is true especially if the output voltage sense circuitry is internal to the regulator's control device. Excessive lead length will result in an error voltage developed across the line resistance (R4′).

$$V_O = V_{O(reg)} - (R_2' + R_3' + R_4') I_L + R_2' I_{reg}$$

$$\text{ERROR} = I_L(R_3' + R_4') - I_{Ireg} R_2'$$

If the voltage sense is available externally, the effect of the line resistance can be minimized. By referencing the low current external voltage sense input to the load, losses in the output line are compensated. Since the current in the sense line is very small, error introduced by its line resistance is negligible (Figure 5-41).

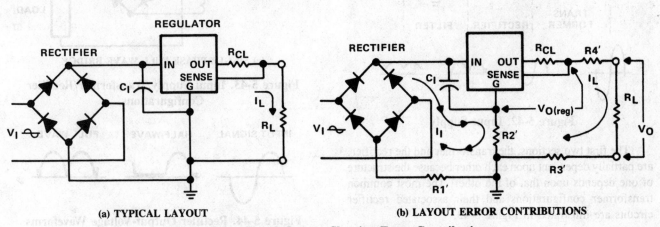

(a) TYPICAL LAYOUT

(b) LAYOUT ERROR CONTRIBUTIONS

**Figure 5-40. Circuit Layout Showing Error Contributions**

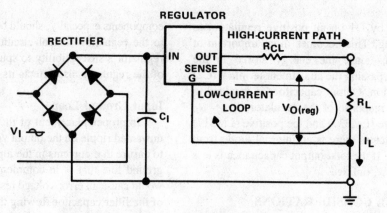

Figure 5-41. Proper Regulator Layout

## Thermal Profile Concerns

All semiconductor devices are affected by temperature; therefore, care should be taken to the placement of these devices so that their thermal properties are not additive. This is especially important where external pass transistors or reference elements are concerned.

## INPUT SUPPLY DESIGN

When the power source is an ac voltage, the transformer, rectifier, and input filter design are as important as the regulator design itself for optimum system performances. This section presents input supply and filter design information for designing a basic capacitor input supply.

## TRANSFORMER/RECTIFIER CONFIGURATION

The input supply consists of three basic sections: (1) input transformer, (2) rectifier, and (3) filter as illustrated in Figure 5-42.

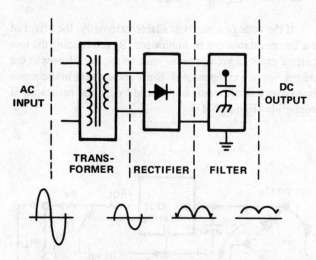

Figure 5-42. Input Supply

The first two sections, the transformer and the rectifier, are partially dependent upon each other because the structure of one depends upon that of the other. The most common transformer configurations and their associated rectifier circuits are illustrated in Figure 5-43.

The particular configuration used depends upon the application. The half-wave circuit [Figure 5-3(a)] is used in low-current applications. This is because the single rectifier diode experiences the total load current and its conversion efficiency is less than 50%. The full-wave configurations [Figures 5-43(b) and 5-43(c)] are used for higher current applications. The characteristic output voltage waveforms of these configurations are illustrated in Figure 5-44.

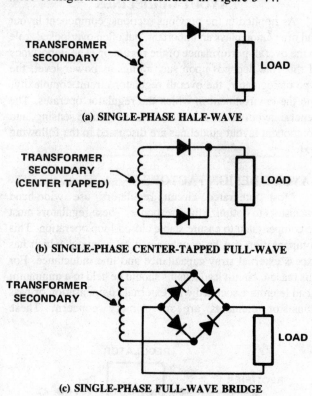

(a) SINGLE-PHASE HALF-WAVE

(b) SINGLE-PHASE CENTER-TAPPED FULL-WAVE

(c) SINGLE-PHASE FULL-WAVE BRIDGE

Figure 5-43. Input Supply Transformer/Rectifier Configurations

Figure 5-44. Rectifier Output-Voltage Waveforms

Before the input supply and its associated filter can be designed, the voltage, current, and ripple requirements of its load must be fully defined. The load, as far as the input supply is concerned, is the regulator circuit. Therefore, the input requirements of the regulator itself become the governing conditions.

Because the input requirements of the regulator control circuit govern the input supply and filter design, it is easiest to work backwards from the load to the transformer primary.

## CAPACITOR INPUT FILTER DESIGN

The most practical approach to a capacitor-input filter design remains the graphical approach presented by O.H. Schade[1] in 1943. The curves illustrated in Figures 5-45 through 5-48 contain all of the design information required for full-wave and half-wave rectifier circuits.

[1]O.H. Schade, "Analysis of Rectifier Operation", *Proc. IRE.*, **VOL. 31**, 343, 1943.

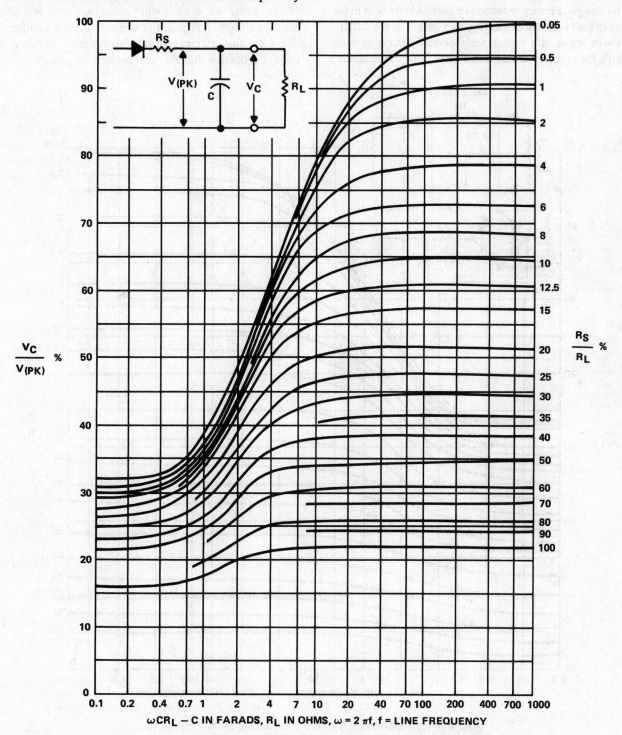

**Figure 5-45. Relation of Applied Alternating Peak Voltage to Direct Output Voltage in Half-Wave Capacitor-Input Circuits (From O.H. Schade, *Proc. IRE,* Vol. 31, p. 343, 1943)**

Figures 5-45 and 5-46 illustrate the ratio of the dc output voltage developed ($V_C$), to the applied peak input voltage ($V_{(PK)}$), as a function of $\omega CR_L$, for half-wave and full-wave rectified signals respectively. For a full-wave rectified application, the voltage reduction is less then 10% for $\omega CR_L > 10$ and $R_S/R_L < 0.5\%$. As illustrated, the voltage reduction decreases as $\omega CR_L$ increases or the $R_S/R_L$ ratio decreases. Minimizing the reduction rate, contrary to initial impressions, may prove to be detrimental to the optimum circuit design. Further reduction requires a reduction in the series to load resistance ratio ($R_S/R_L$) for any given $\omega CR_L$. This will result in a higher peak-to-average current ratio through the rectifier diodes (see Figure 5-47). In addition,

and probably of more concern, this increases the surge current experienced by the rectifier diodes during turn-on of the supply. It is important to realize that the surge current is limited only by the series resistance $R_S$.

$$I_{SURGE} = \frac{V_{SEC(PK)}}{R_S}$$

In order to control the surge current, additional resistance is often required in series with each rectifier. It is evident that a compromise must be made between the voltage reduction and the rectifier current ratings.

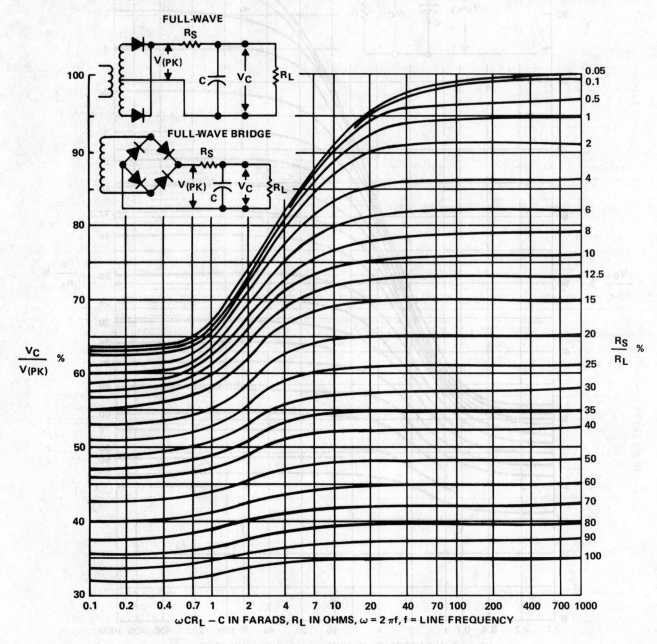

**Figure 5-46. Relation of Applied Alternating Peak Voltage to Direct Output Voltage in Full-Wave Capacitor-Input Circuits**
(From O.H. Schade, *Proc. IRE*, Vol. 31, p. 344, 1943)

The maximum instantaneous surge current is $V_{(pk)}/R_S$. The time constant ($\tau$) of capacitor C is:

$$\tau \cong R_S C$$

As a rule of thumb, the surge current will not damage the diode if:

$$I_{SURGE} < I_{F(SURGE)max} \text{ and } \tau < 8.3 \text{ ms}$$

Figure 5-48 illustrates the relationships between the ripple factor $r_f$, $\omega C R_L$, and $R_S/R_L$. The ripple factor is the ratio of the rms value of the ripple component of the output voltage, expressed as a percent of the nominal dc output voltage.

### SERIES REGULATORS

**Input Regulation**

The change in output voltage, often expressed as a percentage of output voltage, for a change in input voltage from one level to another.
NOTE: Sometimes this characteristic is normalized with respect to the input voltage change.

**Ripple Rejection**

The ratio of the peak-to-peak input ripple voltage, to the peak-to-peak output ripple voltage.
NOTE: This is the reciprocal of ripple sensitivity.

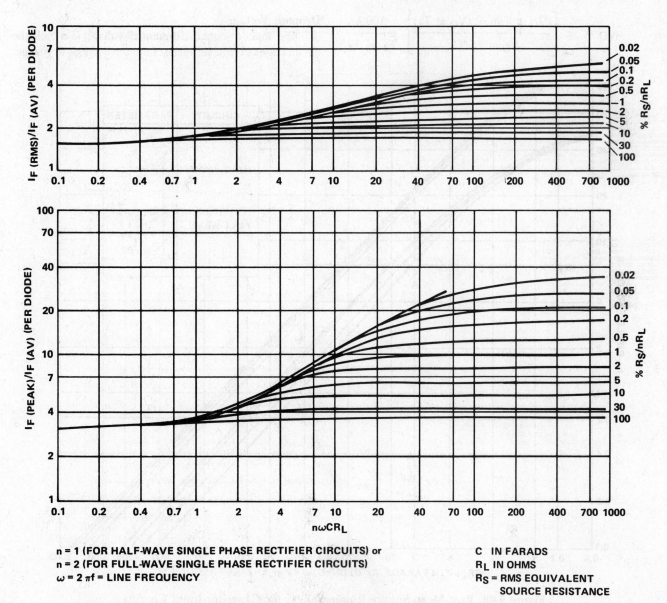

n = 1 (FOR HALF-WAVE SINGLE PHASE RECTIFIER CIRCUITS) or
n = 2 (FOR FULL-WAVE SINGLE PHASE RECTIFIER CIRCUITS)
$\omega = 2\pi f$ = LINE FREQUENCY

C  IN FARADS
$R_L$ IN OHMS
$R_S$ = RMS EQUIVALENT
      SOURCE RESISTANCE

**Figure 5-47. Relation of RMS and Peak to Average Diode Current in Capacitor Input Circuits
(From O.H. Schade, *Proc. IRE*, Vol. 31, p. 345, 1943)**

### Ripple Sensitivity

The ratio of the peak-to-peak output ripple voltage, sometimes expressed as a percentage of output voltage, to the peak-to-peak input ripple voltage.

NOTE: This is the reciprocal of ripple rejection.

### Output Regulation

The change in output voltage, often expressed as a percentage of output voltage, for a change in load current from one level to another.

### Temperature Coefficient of Output Voltage ($\alpha V_O$)

The ratio of the change in output voltage, usually expressed as a percentage of output voltage, to a change in temperature. This is the average value for the total temperature change.

$$\alpha_{VO} = \pm \left[ \frac{(V_O \text{ at } T_2) - (V_O \text{ at } T_1)}{V_O \text{ at } 25°C} \right] \frac{100\%}{T_2 - T_1}$$

### Output Voltage Change with Temperature

The percentage of change in the output voltage for a change in temperature. This is the net change over the total temperature range.

### Output Voltage Long-Term Drift

The change in output voltage over a long period of time.

### Output Noise Voltage

The rms output voltage, sometimes expressed as a percentage of the dc output voltage, with constant load and no input ripple.

### Current-Limit Sense-Voltage

A voltage that is a function of the load current and is normally used for control of the current-limiting circuitry.

### Dropout Voltage

The input-to-output differential voltage at which the circuit ceases to regulate against further reductions in voltage.

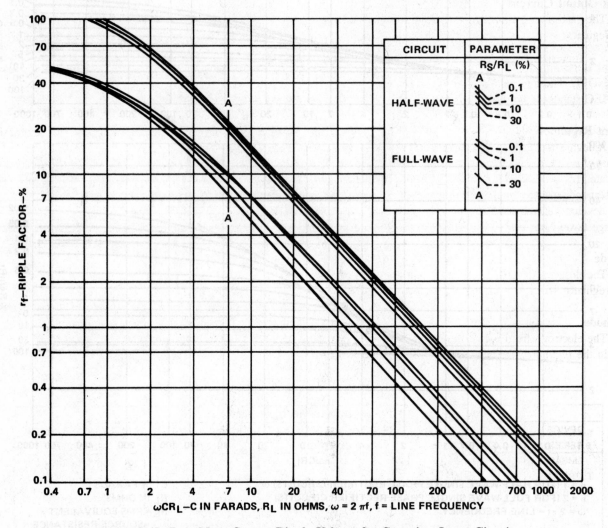

**Figure 5-48. Root-Mean-Square Ripple Voltage for Capacitor-Input Circuits**
(From O.H. Schade, *Proc. IRE*, Vol. 31, p. 346, 1943)

## Feedback Sense Voltage

The voltage that is a function of the output voltage, used for control of the regulator.

## Reference Voltage

The voltage that is compared with the feedback sense voltage to control the regulator.

## Bias Current

The difference between input and output currents. NOTE: This is sometimes referred to as quiescent current.

## Standby Current

The input current drawn by the regulator with no output load and no reference voltage load.

## Short-Circuit Output Current

The output current of the regulator with the output shorted.

## Peak Output Current

The maximum output current that can be obtained from the regulator.

## Shunt Regulators

NOTE: These terms and symbols are based on JEDEC and IEC standards for voltage regulator diodes.

## Shunt Regulator

A device having a voltage current characteristic similar to that of a voltage regulator diode. It is normally biased to operate in a region of low differential resistance (corresponding to the breakdown region of a regulator diode) and develops across its terminals an essentially constant voltage throughout a specified current range.

## Anode

The electrode to which the regulator current flows within the regulator when it is biased for regulation.

## Cathode

The electrode from which the regulator current flows within the regulator when it is biased for regulation.

## Reference Input Voltage ($V_{ref}$) (of an adjustable shunt regulator)

The voltage at the reference input terminal with respect to the anode terminal.

## Temperature Coefficient of Reference Voltage ($V_{ref}$)

The ratio of the change in reference voltage to the change in temperature. This is the average value for the total temperature change. To obtain a value in ppm/°C:

$$V_{ref} = \left[ \frac{(V_{ref} \text{ at } T_2) - (V_{ref} \text{ at } T_1)}{V_{ref} \text{ at } 25\,°C} \right] \left[ \frac{10^6}{T_2 - T_1} \right]$$

## Regulator Voltage ($V_Z$)

The dc voltage across the regulator when it is biased for regulation.

## Regular Current ($I_Z$)

The dc current through the regulator when it is biased for regulation.

## Regulator Current near Lower Knee of Regulation Range ($I_{ZK}$)

The regulator current near the lower limit of the region within which regulation occurs; this corresponds to the breakdown knee of a regulator diode.

## Regulator Current at Maximum Limit of Regulation Range ($I_{ZM}$)

The regulator current above which the differential resistance of the regulator significantly increases.

## Differential Regulator Resistance ($r_z$)

The quotient of a change in voltage across the regulator and the corresponding change in current through the regulator when it is biased for regulation.

## Noise Voltage ($V_{nz}$)

The rms voltage across the regulator with the regulator biased for regulation and with no input ripple.

## FIXED OUTPUT VOLTAGE REGULATORS

| POSITIVE OUTPUT REGULATORS | | | | |
|---|---|---|---|---|
| DEVICE SERIES | OUTPUT VOLTAGE TOLERANCE | MINIMUM DIFFERENTIAL VOLTAGE | OUTPUT CURRENT RATING | AVAILABLE VOLTAGE SELECTIONS |
| LM340 | ±5% | 2 V | 1.5 A | 8.5 V to 24 V |
| TL780-00C | ±2% | 2 V | 1.5 A | 3.5 V to 15 V |
| uA7800C | ±5% | 2 V to 3 V | 1.5 A | 10.5 V to 24 V |
| uA78L00C | ±10% | 2 V to 2.5 V | 100 mA | 8.2.6 V to 15 V |
| uA78L00AC | ±5% | 2 V | 100 mA | 8.2.6 V to 15 V |
| uA78M00C | ±5% | 2 V to 3 V | 500 mA | 9.5 V to 24 V |

| NEGATIVE OUTPUT REGULATORS | | | | |
|---|---|---|---|---|
| DEVICE SERIES | OUTPUT VOLTAGE TOLERANCE | MINIMUM DIFFERENTIAL VOLTAGE | OUTPUT CURRENT RATING | AVAILABLE VOLTAGE SELECTIONS |
| uA7900C | ±5% | 2 V to 3 V | 1.5 A | 8.5 V to 24 V |
| MC79L00AC | ±5% | 2 V | 100 mA | 3.5 V to 15 V |
| uA79M00C* | ±5% | 2 V to 3 V | 500 mA | 7.5 V to 24 V |

| AVAILABLE OUTPUT VOLTAGES FOR ABOVE REGULATOR SERIES | | | | | | | | | | | | | | |
|---|---|---|---|---|---|---|---|---|---|---|---|---|---|---|
| DEVICE SERIES | VOLTAGE SELECTIONS | | | | | | | | | | | | | |
| | 2.6 | 5 | 5.2 | 6 | 8 | 8.5 | 9 | 10 | 12 | 15 | 18 | 20 | 22 | 24 |
| LM340 | | X | | X | X | | | X | X | X | X | | | X |
| MC79L00AC | | X | | | | | | | X | X | | | | |
| TL780-00C | | X | | | | | | | X | X | | | | |
| uA7800C | | X | | X | X | X | | X | X | X | X | | X | X |
| uA78L00C | X | X | | 6.2 | X | | X | X | X | X | | | | |
| uA78L00AC | X | X | | 6.2 | X | | X | X | X | X | | | | |
| uA78M00C* | | X | | X | X | | | X | X | X | | X | X | X |
| uA7900C | | X | X | X | X | | | | X | X | X | | | X |
| uA79M00C* | | X | | X | X | | | | X | X | | X | | X |

*Also available in Military Temperature Range (M suffix)

## VARIABLE OUTPUT VOLTAGE REGULATORS

| POSITIVE OUTPUT SERIES REGULATORS | | | | |
|---|---|---|---|---|
| DEVICE NUMBER | DIFFERENTIAL VOLTAGE | | OUTPUT VOLTAGE | OUTPUT CURRENT |
| | MIN | MAX | MAX | RATING |
| LM317 | 1.2 V | 37 V | $V_I - 1.2$ V | 1.5 A |
| TL317 | 1.2 V | 32 V | $V_I - 1.2$ V | 100 mA |
| TL783 | 1.25 V | 125 V | 125 V | 700 mA |
| uA723C* | 3 V | 38 V | 37 V | 25 mA |

| NEGATIVE OUTPUT SERIES REGULATORS | | | | |
|---|---|---|---|---|
| DEVICE NUMBER | DIFFERENTIAL VOLTAGE | | OUTPUT VOLTAGE | OUTPUT CURRENT |
| | MIN | MAX | MAX | RATING |
| LM337 | 1.2 V | 37 V | $V_I + 1.2$ V | 1.5 A |

| POSITIVE SHUNT REGULATORS | | | | | |
|---|---|---|---|---|---|
| DEVICE NUMBER | SHUNT VOLTAGE | | SHUNT CURRENT | | TEMP. COEFF. |
| | MIN | MAX | MIN | MAX | MAX |
| TL430C | 3 V | 30 V | 2 mA | 100 mA | 200 ppm/°C |
| TL431C | 2.55 V | 36 V | 1 mA | 100 mA | 100 ppm/°C |
| TL431I** | 2.55 V | 36 V | 1 mA | 100 mA | 100 ppm/°C |

*Also available in Military Temperature Range (M suffix)
**I denotes Industrial Temperature Range

# Section 6

# Switching Power Supply Design

Modern electronic equipment usually requires one or more dc power sources. The usual method of supplying dc power is a power supply which converts ac power to dc power. The two types of dc power supplies in common use are classified by the type of regulator employed; linear regulator or switching regulator.

Linear power supplies consist of a power transformer, rectifier and filter circuits, and a linear regulator. Switching power supplies don't require line transformers; the ac input is rectified and filtered, chopped by a high frequency transistor switch/transformer combination, then rectified and filtered again.

Switching power supplies have been used for some time in the military and space industry due to their smaller size and higher efficiency. In 1975 switching power supplies were more cost effective than linear power supplies from approximately the 500 W power level. Now the breakeven point is down to approximately 5 W.

## BASIC OPERATION OF SWITCHING REGULATORS

Figure 6-1 is a block diagram of a typical switching power supply which consists of four basic circuits:
1. Input rectifier and filter.
2. High frequency inverter.
3. Output rectifier and filter.
4. Control circuit.

The ac line voltage is applied to an input rectifier and filter circuit. The dc voltage output from the rectifier and filter circuit is switched to a higher frequency (typically 25 kHz to 100 kHz) by the transistor switch in the high frequency inverter circuit. This circuit contains either a high frequency transformer or inductor, depending on the output voltage required.

Output from the high frequency inverter circuit is applied to the output rectifier and filter circuit. The circuit is monitored and controlled by the control circuit which attempts to keep the output at a constant level.

The control circuit consists of an oscillator driving a pulse-width modulator, an error amplifier, and a precision voltage reference. The error amplifier compares the input reference voltage with a sample of the voltage from the output rectifier and filter circuit. As the load increases the output voltage drops. The error amplifier senses this drop and causes the pulse-width modulator to remain on for a longer period of time, delivering wider control pulses to the transistor switch.

The width of the pulse determines how long the transistor switch allows current to flow through the high frequency transformer and, ultimately, how much voltage is available at the output. If the load decreases, narrower control pulses are delivered to the switching transistor until the output voltage remains at a constant value.

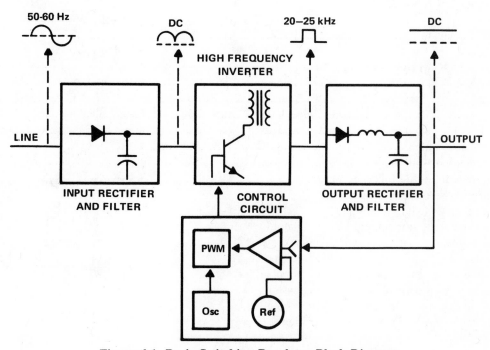

**Figure 6-1. Basic Switching Regulator Block Diagram**

## ADVANTAGES OF A SWITCHING REGULATOR

The primary advantages of switching regulators are higher efficiency and smaller size. Conventional linear series and shunt regulators operate in a continuous conduction mode, dissipating relatively large amounts of power. The efficiency of linear regulators is typically around 40% to 50%. When the input-to-output voltage differential is large, the resultant efficiency is much lower than 40%.

Switching regulators have typical efficiencies of 60% to 90%; much higher than either the linear series or shunt regulator. Switching regulators achieve their higher efficiency as a result of three factors:

1. The power-transistor switch is always turned completely on or off, except when it is switching between these two states, resulting in either low voltage or low current during most of its operation.
2. Good regulation can be achieved over a wide range of input voltage.
3. High efficiency can be maintained over wide ranges in load-current.

Switching regulators use the on-off duty cycle of the transistor switch to regulate the output voltage and current. By using a frequency much higher than the line frequency (typically 20 kHz to 500 kHz) the transformers, chokes, capacitors, and other filter elements can be made smaller, lighter, and less costly. The smaller elements used in switching regulators result in smaller power losses than the larger components used in linear regulators.

The highest cost elements of a switching power supply are the transistor switches. The remaining costs, in descending order, are due to the magnetic components, capacitors, and rectifiers.

## DISADVANTAGES OF A SWITCHING REGULATOR

Switching regulators can generate some electromagnetic and radio frequency interference (EMI/RFI) noise due to high switching currents and short rise and fall times. EMI/RFI noise, which is generated at higher frequencies (100 kHz to 500 kHz), is easily filtered. In those applications where a large series impedance appears between the supply and the regulator, the rapid changes in current also generate a certain amount of noise.

These problems may be overcome or significantly reduced by one or more of the following steps:

1. Reducing the series impedance.
2. Increasing the switching time.
3. Filtering the input and output of the regulator.

Switching regulators with a fixed frequency are easier to filter than regulators with a variable frequency because the noise is at only one frequency. Variable frequency regulators with a fixed "on" time increase or decrease the switching frequency in proportion to load changes, presenting a more difficult filtering problem.

## BASIC SWITCHING REGULATOR ARCHITECTURE

There are three basic switching regulator configurations from which the majority of present day circuits are derived:

1. Step-down, or "buck", regulator.
2. Step-up, or "boost", regulator.
3. Inverting, or "flyback" regulator (which is a variation of the "boost" regulator).

### The Step-Down Regulator

Figure 6-2 illustrates the basic step-down or "buck" regulator. The output voltage of this configuration is always less than the input voltage.

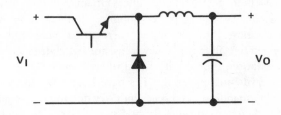

**Figure 6-2. Step-Down or "Buck" Switching Regulator Circuit**

In the buck circuit, a semiconductor switch is placed in series with the dc input from the input rectifier/filter circuit. The switch interrupts the dc input voltage providing a variable-width pulse to a simple averaging LC filter. When the switch is closed, the dc input voltage is applied across the filter and current flows through the inductor to the load. When the switch is open, the energy stored in the field of the inductor maintains the current through the load.

In the buck circuit, peak switching current is proportional to the load current. The output voltage is equal to the input voltage times the duty cycle.

$$V_O = V_I \times \text{Duty Cycle}$$

### The Step-Up Regulator

Another basic switching regulator configuration is the step-up or "boost" regulator (Figure 6-3). In this type of circuit, the output voltage is always greater than the input voltage.

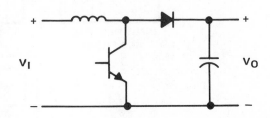

**Figure 6-3. Step-Up or "Boost" Switching Regulator Circuit**

The boost circuit first stores energy in the inductor and then delivers this stored energy along with the energy from the dc input voltage to the load. When the switch is closed, current flows through the inductor and the switch, charging the inductor but delivering no current to the load. When the switch is open, the voltage across the load equals the dc input voltage plus the charge stored in the inductor. The inductor discharges, delivering current to the load.

The peak switching current in the boost circuit is not related to the load current. The power output of a boost regulator can be determined by the following equation:

$$P_{OUT} = \frac{LI^2f}{2}$$

where:

$P_{OUT}$ = power output
$L$ = inductance
$I$ = peak current
$f$ = operating frequency

### The Inverting Regulator

The third switching regulator configuration is the inverting or "flyback" regulator. This circuit is a variation of the step-up or "boost" circuit discussed previously. The flyback circuit is illustrated in Figure 6-4.

Flyback regulators, which evolved from "boost" regulators, deliver only the energy stored by the inductor to the load. This type of circuit can step the input voltage up or down. When the switch is closed the inductor is charged, but no current is delivered to the load because the diode is reverse biased. When the switch is open the blocking diode is forward biased and the energy stored in the inductor is transferred through it to the load.

The flyback circuit delivers a fixed amount of power to the load regardless of load impedance. It is widely used in photo flash, capacitor-discharge ignition circuits, and battery chargers.

To determine the output voltage of an electronic equipment supply, the load ($R_L$) must be known. If the load is known, the output voltage may be calculated using the following equation:

$$V_O = \sqrt{P_O R_L} = I\sqrt{\frac{LfR_L}{2}}$$

where:

$V_O$ = voltage output
$P_O$ = power out
$R_L$ = load resistance
$I$ = inductor current
$f$ = operating frequency

The inductor current is proportional to the "on time" (duty cycle) of the switch and regulation is achieved by varying the duty cycle. However, the output also depends on the load resistance (which was not true with the step-down circuit).

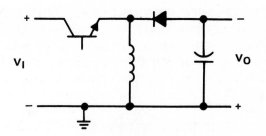

**Figure 6-4. Inverting or "Flyback" Switching Regulator Circuit**

Transient response to abrupt changes in the load is difficult to analyze. Practical solutions include limiting the minimum load and using the proper amount of filter capacitance to give the regulator time to respond to this change. Flyback type circuits are used at power levels of up to 100 W.

### FORWARD CONVERTERS

The forward converter family, which includes the push-pull and half-bridge circuits, evolved from the step-down or "buck" type of regulator. A typical forward converter circuit is illustrated in Figure 6-5.

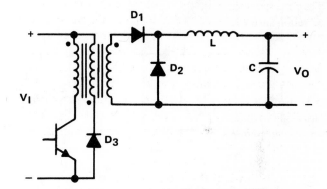

**Figure 6-5. Forward Converter Switching Regulator**

When the transistor switch is turned on the transformer delivers power to the load through diode D1 and the LC filter. When the switch is turned off diode D2 is forward biased and maintains current to the load.

Without the third winding, and diode D3, the converter would lose efficiency at higher frequencies. The function of this winding is to return energy stored in the transformer to the line and reset the transformer core after each cycle of operation.

This is a popular low power (up to about 200 W) converter and is almost immune to transformer saturation problems.

### Push-Pull Converter

The push-pull converter is probably one of the oldest switching regulator type circuits. It was first used in the 1930's with mechanical vibrators functioning as the switch. When transistors became available push-pull converters were used as free-running oscillators in the primary of many automobile communication converters.

Some recreational vehicles still use this free-running type of oscillator converter in dc-to-dc converters as well as in dc-to-ac inverters.

A typical push-pull converter circuit is shown in Figure 6-6.

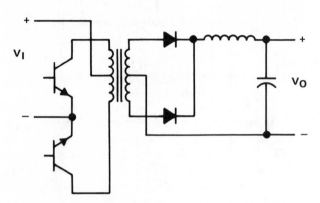

**Figure 6-6. Basic Push-Pull Converter Circuit**

### Half Bridge Converter

The most popular type of high power converter is the half bridge circuit illustrated in Figure 6-7.

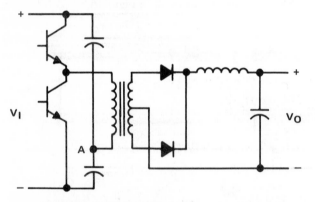

**Figure 6-7. Half Bridge Converter Circuit**

The half bridge converter has several advantages over the push-pull circuit. First, the midpoint between the capacitors (point A) can be charged to $V_I/2$. This allows the use of transistors with lower breakdown voltage. Second, because the primary is driven in both directions (push-pull), a full-wave rectifier and filter are used which allows the transformer core to be more effectively utilized.

### Full Bridge Converter

In contrast to the half bridge, the full bridge (or H-Bridge) converter uses four transistors as shown in Figure 6-8.

In a full bridge circuit the diagonally opposite transistors (Q1/Q2 or Q3/Q4) are turned on during alternate half cycles. The highest voltage any transistor is subjected to is $V_I$, rather than $2 \times V_I$ as is the case in the push-pull converter circuit. The full bridge circuit offers increased reliability because less voltage and current stress is placed on the transistors.

The disadvantage of this circuit is the space required by the four transistors and the cost of the two additional transistors.

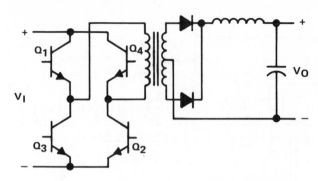

**Figure 6-8. Full Bridge Converter Circuit**

### TL593 FLOPPY DISK POWER SUPPLY

The TL593 incorporates, on a single monolithic chip, all the functions required for a pulse-width modulation control circuit. The TL593 is similar to the TL594, from which it was derived, except that the TL593 includes a current-limit amplifier instead of a second error amplifier.

The current-limit amplifier of the TL593 has an offset voltage of approximately 80 mV in series with the inverting input (pin 15). This makes it easier to design the current-limit portion of the power supply and also requires fewer components. With 80 mV on the inverting input, it is only necessary to apply an 80 mV control voltage to the non-inverting input (pin 16). This is easily accomplished by taking the voltage across a resistor in series with the load.

The floppy disk power supply schematic is shown in Figure 6-9. The power supply uses a pair of TIP34 pnp transistors in a push-pull configuration. The oscillation frequency is set at 25 kHz and $-5$ V at 500 mA by the .01 μF capacitor on pin 5 and the 5 kΩ resistor on pin 6.

The center connection of the two 5.6 kΩ resistors on pins 13 and 14 establishes a 2.5 V reference voltage on pin 2, which is the inverting input of the voltage control error amplifier. The voltage feedback to pin 1, the non-inverting input, comes from the center connection of the two 5.6 kΩ resistors located on the 5 V/2.5 A power supply output terminal. Because this voltage supplies the logic circuits, it requires closer regulation.

The 24 V winding, on the other hand, is not critical as it furnishes voltage for the stepping motor. The $-5$ V supply is regulated separately with a uA7905 three-terminal regulator.

In choosing components for this circuit, the same precautions taken in the construction of any switching power supply should be observed; be careful of layout, ground loops, and heatsinking of the power transistors. In the output section, where high frequency rectifiers are needed, either Schottky or fast recovery diodes should be used. For output capacitors, low equivalent series

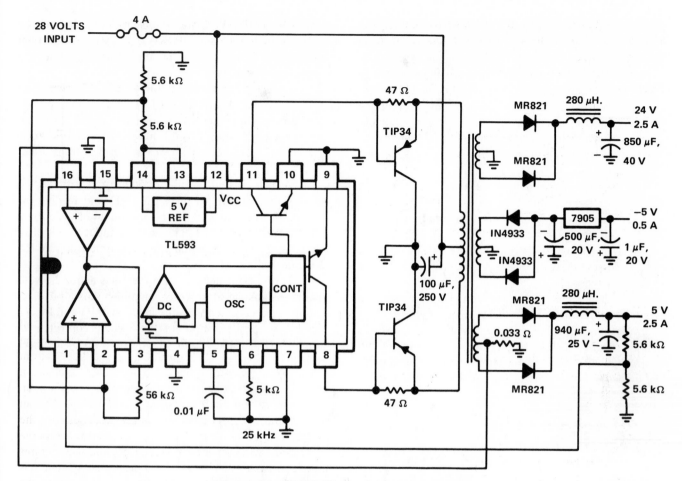

**Figure 6-9. TL593 Floppy Disk Power Supply**

resistance (ESR) types should be considered. The output ripple depends more on this resistance than on the capacitor value.

## TRANSFORMER CONSTRUCTION

The transformer for this circuit was wound on a toroid core. The core used was 3C8 ferrite material (F-42908-TC).

The winding layout is shown in Figure 6-10.

**Transformer Winding Data**

Primary A + B = 28 turns bifilar #20 HNP
Secondary C + D = 28 turns bifilar #20 HNP over A+B
Secondary E + F = 6 turns bifilar #20 HNP over C+D
Secondary G + H = 10 turns bifilar #26 HNP over E+F

NOTE: All windings to be center tapped.

**DC Resistance**

Winding 1 - 3 = 0.11 Ω
Winding 4 - 6 = 0.11 Ω
Winding 7 - 9 = 0.025 Ω
Winding 10 - 12 = 0.15 Ω

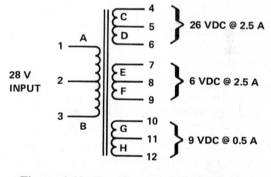

**Figure 6-10. Transformer Winding Layout**

## TL594 12-VOLT TO 5-VOLT STEP-DOWN REGULATOR

The TL594 switching voltage regulator operates as a step-down converter in a discontinuous mode. When the output current falls below a specified minimum value the inductor current becomes discontinuous. The advantages of a step-down converter in this mode of operation are:

1. The ripple voltage at the output can be kept low, even in high current designs.
2. The ratio of peak current in the switching device to output current is determined by the inductor value and is typically low. For a specific output

current requirement, the current rating for the switching transistor can be lower than for a transistor operating in a continuous mode.

3. Pulse-width modulation occurs with input voltage variations. Load variations are compensated for by modulation of the dc current level in the inductor, as well as by pulse-width modulation. This allows high efficiency to be maintained over the entire load range (from $I_O$ max to $I_O$ min).

The disadvantages of this type of converter are:

1. The size of the inductor used may result in a high inductance value.
2. Transient response is impaired by high inductance values.
3. Although peak current in the rectifier is reduced, losses due to reverse recovery current are increased.

The complete circuit for the TL594 Step-down Regulator is shown in Figure 6-11.

For this application the two switching transistors operate in phase with each other by grounding the output control, pin 13. The switching transistors supply input to the inductor, L, for part of the oscillator cycle. For the remaining part of the oscillator cycle the voltage across the inductor reverses and diode D1 starts conducting, maintaining current flow in the inductor while the transistors are off (see Figure 6-12).

The input supply through R1 to pin 12 is decoupled by capacitor C2. Capacitor C4 filters the output voltage. The timing components C3 and R6 set the oscillator frequency to 15 kHz. The 2.2 mH inductor can be made on an RM7 ferrite core with 94 turns of #28 transformer wire.

Output current limiting of 500 mA is provided by sensing the overcurrent level with R11 and feeding the resultant error voltage to the positive input of the current error amplifier on Pin 1. The negative input to this error amplifier is biased to 500 mV from reference divider R2, R3, and R4.

This resistor network also furnishes about 2.3 volts bias to the voltage control error amplifier. An output error voltage signal is taken from the junction of R1 and R8 and fed to the positive input of the voltage control error amplifier. The voltage control loop gain is set by feedback resistor R5.

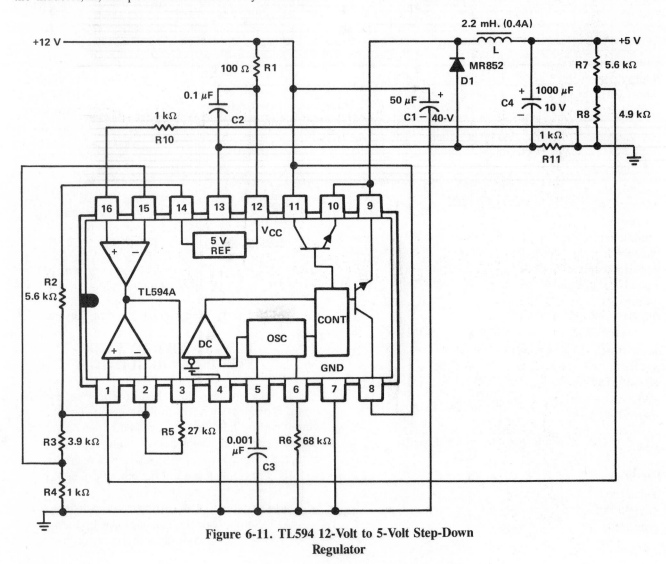

**Figure 6-11. TL594 12-Volt to 5-Volt Step-Down Regulator**

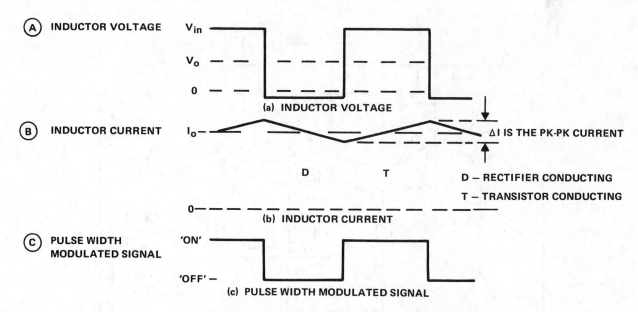

(a) INDUCTOR VOLTAGE

(b) INDUCTOR CURRENT

ΔI IS THE PK-PK CURRENT

D – RECTIFIER CONDUCTING

T – TRANSISTOR CONDUCTING

(c) PULSE WIDTH MODULATED SIGNAL

**Figure 6-12. 12-Volt to 5-Volt Series Switching Regulator Waveforms**

## SPECIFICATIONS

| | |
|---|---|
| Input Voltage | — 12 V nominal |
| | (10 V to 15 V) |
| Output Voltage | — 5 V ± 10% |
| Output Ripple | — 50 mV$_{pp}$ |
| Output Current | — 400 mA |
| Output Power | — 2 W at 5 V output |
| Short Circuit Protection | — 500 mA constant current |
| Efficiency | — typically 70% |

## THE TL594 CONTROL CIRCUIT

The TL594 is a fixed frequency pulse-width-modulation control for switching power supplies and voltage converters. The TL594 includes an adjustable oscillator, a pulse width modulator, and an error amplifier. Additional functions include over-current detection, independent dead-time control, a precision 5 V reference regulator, and output control logic which allows single-ended or push-pull operation of the two switching transistors. Figure 6-13 shows a block diagram of the TL594.

Modulation of the output pulses is accomplished by comparing the sawtooth waveform created by the internal oscillator on timing capacitor $C_T$ to either of two control signals. The output stage is enabled when the sawtooth voltage is greater than the voltage of the control signal. See Figure 6-14.

As the control signals increase the output pulse width decreases. The control signals are derived from two sources: the dead-time control and the error amplifiers. The dead-time comparator has a fixed offset of 10 mV which provides a preset dead time of about 5%. This is the minimum dead time that can be programmed with pin 4 grounded.

The pulse-width-modulation (PWM) comparator generates the control difference signal created by the input from either of the error amplifiers. One error amplifier is used to monitor the output voltage and provide a change in control signal voltage. The other error amplifier monitors the output current and its change in control voltage provides current limiting.

### Reference Regulator

The internal 5-volt reference at pin 14 provides a stable reference for the control logic, pulse steering flip-flop, oscillator, dead-time-control comparator and pulse-width-modulation circuitry. It is a band-gap circuit with short circuit protection and is internally programmed to an accuracy of ± 5%.

### Oscillator

The internal oscillator provides a positive sawtooth waveform to the dead-time and PWM comparators for comparison with the various control signals. The oscillator frequency is set by an external timing capacitor and resistor on pins 5 and 6. The oscillator frequency is determined by the equation:

$$f_{OSC} = \frac{1}{R_T C_T} \text{ (single-ended applications)}$$

The oscillator frequency is equal to the output frequency only for single-ended applications. The output frequency for push-pull applications is one-half the oscillator frequency as shown by the equation:

$$f_{OSC} = \frac{1}{2 R_T C_T} \text{ (push-pull applications)}$$

There is a frequency variation of ± 5% between devices due to internal component tolerances.

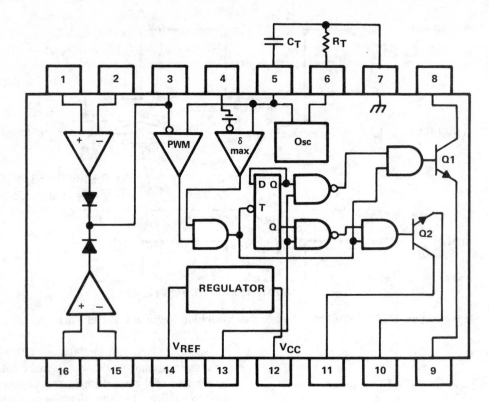

## PIN ASSIGNMENT

| PIN NO. | FUNCTION | PIN NO. | FUNCTION |
|---------|----------|---------|----------|
| 1. | ERROR AMP. 1, NONINVERTING INPUT | 9. | DRIVE TRANSISTOR 1, EMITTER |
| 2. | ERROR AMP. 1, INVERTING INPUT | 10. | DRIVE TRANSISTOR 2, EMITTER |
| 3. | COMPENSATION INPUT | 11. | DRIVE TRANSISTOR 2, COLLECTOR |
| 4. | DEAD TIME CONTROL INPUT | 12. | INPUT SUPPLY |
| 5. | OSCILLATOR TIMING CAPACITOR | 13. | OUTPUT MODE CONTROL |
| 6. | OSCILLATOR TIMING RESISTOR | 14. | STABILIZED REFERENCE VOLTAGE |
| 7. | GROUND | 15. | ERROR AMP 2, INVERTING INPUT |
| 8. | DRIVE TRANSISTOR 1, COLLECTOR | 16. | ERROR AMP 2, NONINVERTING INPUT |

**Figure 6-13. TL594 Block Diagram**

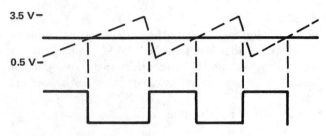

PWM CONTROL RANGE, PIN 3

RESULTANT OUTPUT PULSE WITH
PIN 3 VOLTAGE AS ABOVE PIN 13 WIRED FOR
SINGLE ENDED OPERATION

**Figure 6-14. Output Pulses vs. Sawtooth Control Voltage**

The oscillator charges the external timing capacitor, $C_T$, with a constant current which is determined by the external timing resistor, $R_T$. This circuit produces a linear ramp voltage waveform. When the voltage across the timing capacitor reaches 3.0 V, the circuit discharges and the charging cycle is initiated again.

### Dead Time and PWM Comparators

Both the dead time and PWM comparator functions use a single logic comparator with parallel input stages. The comparator output is a pulse-width-modulated signal, whose width is determined by comparison with the oscillator ramp waveform. The comparator outputs drive the output control logic.

A fixed 100 mV offset voltage input to the dead-time comparator allows a minimum dead time between output pulses to be maintained when the dead-time control input (pin 4) is grounded (Figure 6-15).

The full range of pulse width control (0% - 90%) is available when the dead time control voltage (pin 4) is between 3.0 V and 0 V. The relationship between control voltage and maximum output pulse width is essentially linear. A typical application for this may be in a push-pull converter circuit where overlap of the conduction times of power transistors must be avoided.

The PWM comparator input is coupled internally to the outputs of the two error amplifiers. This input is accessible on pin 3 for control loop compensation. The

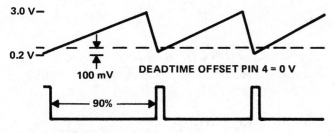

OSCILLATOR RAMP, PIN 5

**MAXIMUM OUTPUT PULSE WIDTH
SINGLE ENDED OPERATION, PIN 4 = 0 V**

**Figure 6-15. Deadtime Comparator Operation**

output pulse width varies from 90% of the period to zero as the voltage present at pin 3 varies from 0.5 V to 3.5 V (Figure 6-14).

### Error Amplifiers

Both error amplifiers are high gain amplifiers which operate as single-ended single-supply amplifiers, in that each output is active high only. This allows each amplifier to pull up independently for a decreasing output pulse width demand. With the outputs ORed together, the amplifier with the higher output level dominates. The open loop gain of these amplifiers is 60 dB. Both error amplifiers exhibit a response time of about 400 ns from their inputs to their outputs on pin 3. Figure 6-16 shows the amplifier transfer characteristics and a Bode plot of the gain curves.

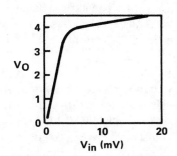

**AMPLIFIER TRANSFER CHARACTERISTICS**

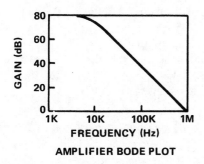

**AMPLIFIER BODE PLOT**

**Figure 6-16. Amplifier Performance Curves**

### Output Logic Control

The output control logic interfaces the pulse width modulator to the output stages. In the single-ended mode (both outputs conducting simultaneously) the pulse width modulated signal is gated through to both output stages when the output control (pin 13) is connected to ground.

For push-pull operation (each output stage conducting alternately) the output control (pin 13) is connected to the internal reference voltage (pin 14) enabling the pulse steering flip-flop. The flip-flop is toggled on the the trailing edge of the pulse width modulated signal gating it to each of the outputs alternately; therefore, the switching frequency of each output is one-half the oscillator frequency.

The output control (pin 13) must never be left open. It may be connected to the internal voltage reference (pin 14) or ground (pin 7).

### The Output Driver Stages

The two identical Darlington output drivers may be operated in parallel or push-pull mode. Both the collector and emitter terminals are available for various drive configurations. $V_{CE(sat)}$ of each output at 200 mA is typically 1.1 V in common-emitter configuration and 1.5 V in common-collector configuration. These drivers are protected against overload but do not have sufficient current-limiting to be operated as current source outputs.

### SOFT-START

Use of a soft-start protection circuit is recommended. This circuit prevents current surges during power-up and protects against false signals which might be created by the control circuit when power is applied.

Implementing a soft-start circuit is relatively simple using the dead-time control input (pin 4). Figure 6-17 shows an example.

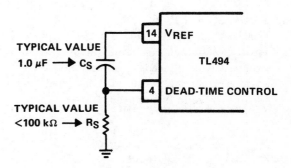

**Figure 6-17. Soft-Start Circuit**

Initially, capacitor $C_S$ forces the dead-time control input to follow the internal 5 V reference which disables both outputs (100% dead time). As the capacitor charges through $R_S$, the output pulse width increases until the control loop takes command.

### OVER-VOLTAGE PROTECTION

The dead-time control input (pin 4) also provides a convenient input for over-voltage protection, which may be sensed as an output voltage condition, or input voltage protection as shown in Figure 6-18.

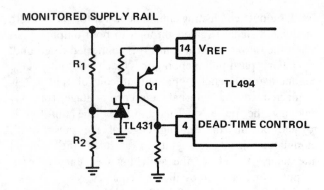

**Figure 6-18. Over-Voltage Protection Circuit**

A TL431 is used as the sensing element. When the monitored supply rail voltage increases to the point that 2.5 V is developed across R2, the TL431 conducts, Q1 becomes forward biased, and the dead-time control is pulled up to the reference voltage which disables the output transistors.

## DESIGNING A POWER SUPPLY
## 5 VOLT/10 AMP OUTPUT

### DESIGN OBJECTIVE
This design uses the TL594 integrated circuit based on the following parameters:

$$V_O = 5 \text{ V}$$
$$V_I = 32 \text{ V}$$
$$I_O = 10 \text{ A}$$
$$f = 20 \text{ kHz Switching Frequency}$$
$$V_R = 100 \text{ mV peak-to-peak } (V_{ripple})$$
$$\Delta I_L = 1.5 \text{ A Inductor Current Change}$$

### INPUT POWER SOURCE
The 32 V dc power source for this supply uses a 120 V input, 24 V output transformer rated at 75 VA. The 24 V secondary winding feeds a full-wave bridge rectifier followed by a current limit resistor (0.3 ohm) and two filter capacitors, as shown in Figure 6-19.

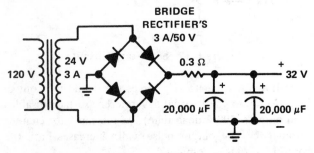

**Figure 6-19. Input Power Source**

The output current and voltage are determined by the following equations.

$$V \text{ rectifier} = V \text{ secondary} \times 2 = 24 \text{ V} \times 2 = 34 \text{ V}$$

$$I \text{ rectifier(avg)} \approx \left(\frac{V_O}{V_I}\right) \times I_O \approx \frac{5 \text{ V}}{32 \text{ V}} \times 10 \text{ A} \approx 1.6 \text{ A}$$

The 3 A/50 V full-wave bridge rectifier meets these calculated conditions. Figure 6-20 illustrates the switching and control section.

## CONTROL CIRCUITS
### Oscillator
The TL594 oscillator frequency is controlled by connecting an external timing circuit consisting of a capacitor and resistor to pins 5 and 6. The oscillator is set to operate at 20 kHz using the component values calculated by the following equations.

$$f = \frac{1}{R_T C_T}$$

where:

$$R_T = \text{Value of timing resistor}$$
$$C_T = \text{Value of timing capacitor}$$

Choose $C_T = 0.001 \text{ } \mu F$ and calculate RT.

$$R_T = \frac{1}{f \times C_T} = \frac{1}{20 \times 10^3 \times 0.001 \times 10^{-6}}$$
$$= 50 \text{ k}\Omega$$

### Error Amplifier
The error amplifier compares a sample of the 5 V output to a reference and adjusts the pulse-width modulator to maintain a constant output as shown in Figure 6-21.

The TL594's internal 5 V reference (pin 14) is divided to 2.5 V by R3 and R4. The output voltage error signal is also divided to 2.5 V by R8 and R9. If the output must be regulated to exactly 5.0 V, a 10 kΩ potentiometer may be used in place of R8 to provide an adjustment control.

To increase the stability of the error amplifier circuit, the output of the error amplifier is fed back to the inverting input through R7, reducing the gain to 100.

### Current Limit Amplifier
The power supply was designed for a 10 A load current and an $I_L$ swing of 1.5 A; therefore, the short circuit current should be

$$I_{SC} = I_O + \frac{I_L}{2} = 10.75 \text{ A}$$

The current limit portion of the circuit is shown in Figure 6-22.

Resistors R1 and R2 set a reference of about 1 V on the inverting input of the current limit amplifier. Resistor R11, in series with the load, applies 1 V to the non-

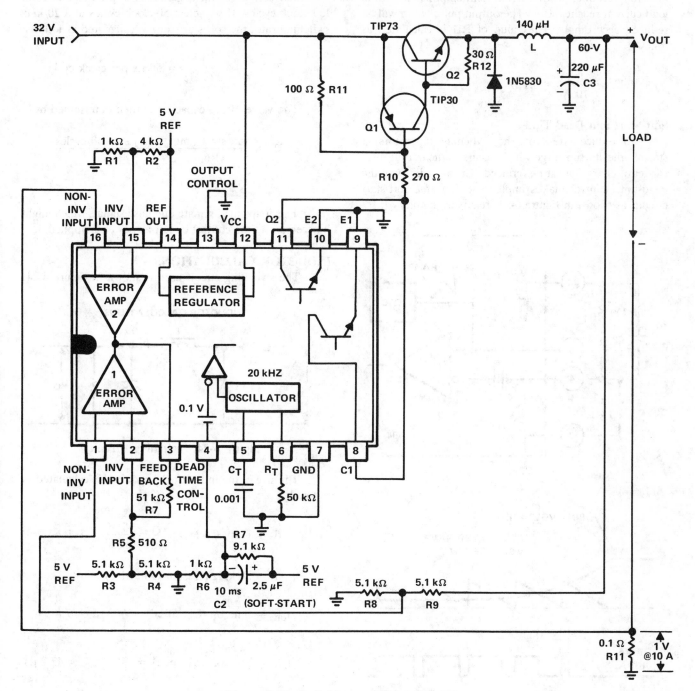

**Figure 6-20. Switching and Control Section**

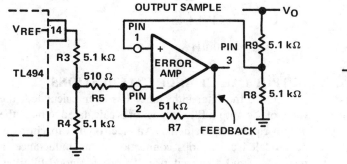

**Figure 6-21. Error Amplifier Section**

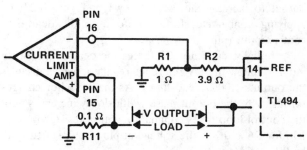

**Figure 6-22. Current Limit Circuit**

inverting terminal of the current limit amplifier when the load current reaches 10 A. The output pulse width will be reduced accordingly. The value of R11 is calculated as follows:

$$R11 = \frac{1\ V}{10\ A} = 0.1\ \Omega$$

### Soft-Start and Dead Time

To reduce stress on the switching transistors at startup, the startup surge which occurs as the output filter capacitor charges must be reduced. The availability of the dead-time control makes implementation of a soft-start circuit, as shown in Figure 6-23, relatively simple.

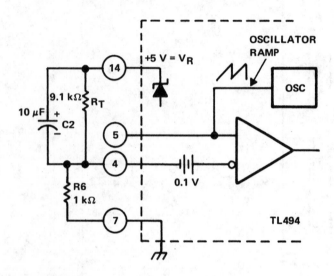

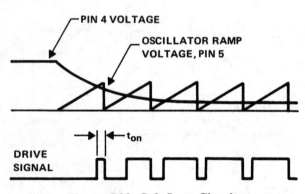

**Figure 6-23. Soft-Start Circuit**

The "soft-start" circuit allows the pulse width at the output to increase slowly, as shown in Figure 6-23, by applying a negative slope waveform to the dead-time control input (pin 4).

Initially, capacitor C2 forces the dead-time control input to follow the 5 V reference regulator, which disables the outputs (100% dead time). As the capacitor charges through R6, the output pulse width slowly increases until the control loop takes command. With a resistor ratio of 1:10 for R6 and R7, the voltage at pin 4 after startup will be 0.1 × 5 V or 0.5 V.

The soft-start time is generally in the range of 25 to 100 clock cycles. If we select 50 clock cycles at a 20 kHz switching rate, the soft start time is calculated as follows:

$$T = \frac{1}{f} = \frac{1}{20\ kHz} = 50\ \mu s \text{ per clock cycle}$$

The value of the capacitor is then determined by

$$C2 = \frac{\text{soft start time}}{R6} = \frac{50\ \mu s \times 50\ cycles}{1\ k\Omega}$$

$$= 2.5\ \mu F$$

This helps to eliminate any false signals which might be created by the control circuit as power is applied.

## INDUCTOR CALCULATIONS

The switching circuit used is shown in Figure 6-24.

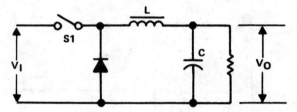

**Figure 6-24. Switching Circuit**

The size of the inductor (L) required is calculated as follows:

$$d = \text{Duty Cycle} = \frac{V_O}{V_I} = \frac{5\ V}{32\ V} = 0.156$$

$$f = 20\ kHz \text{ (Design Objective)}$$

$$t_{on} = \text{time on (S1 closed)} = \frac{1}{f} \times d = 7.8\ \mu s$$

$$t_{off} = \text{time off (S1 open)} = \frac{1}{f} - t_{on} = 42.2\ \mu s$$

$$L \approx \frac{(V_I - V_O) \times t_{on}}{\Delta IL} \approx \frac{(32\ V - 5\ V) \times 7.8\ \mu s}{1.5\ A}$$

$$\approx 140.4\ \mu H$$

$$L \approx 140\ \mu H$$

## OUTPUT CAPACITANCE CALCULATIONS

Once the filter inductance has been calculated, the value of the output filter capacitor is calculated to meet the output ripple requirements. An electrolytic capacitor can be modeled as a series connection of an inductance, a resistance, and a capacitance. To provide good filtering, the ripple frequency must be far below the frequencies at which the series inductance becomes important; so, the two components of interest are the capacitance and the effective series resistance (ESR). The maximum ESR is calculated according to the relation between the specified peak-to-peak ripple voltage and peak-to-peak ripple current.

$$\text{ESR(max)} = \frac{\Delta V_{O\ (ripple)}}{\Delta I_L} = \frac{0.1\ V}{1.5\ A} = 0.067\ \Omega$$

The minimum capacitance of C3 necessary to maintain the $V_O$ ripple voltage at less than the 100 mV design objective was calculated according to the following equation.

$$C3 = \frac{\Delta I_L}{8\ f\Delta V_O} = \frac{1.5\ A}{8 \times 20 \times 10^3 \times 0.1\ V} = 94\ \mu F$$

A 220 μF, 60 V capacitor is selected because it has a maximum ESR of 0.074 Ω and a maximum ripple current of 2.8 A.

## TRANSISTOR POWER SWITCH CALCULATIONS

The transistor power switch was constructed with a TIP30 pnp drive transistor and a TIP73 npn output transistor. These two power devices were connected in a pnp hybrid Darlington circuit configuration as shown in Figure 6-25.

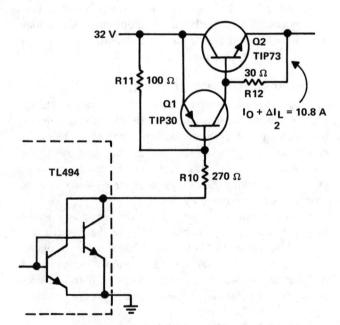

**Figure 6-25. Power Switch Section**

The hybrid Darlington must be saturated at a maximum output current of $I_O + \Delta I_L/2$ or 10.8 A. The Darlington $h_{FE}$ at 10.8 A must be high enough not to exceed the 250 mA maximum output collector current of the TL594. Based on published TIP30 and TIP73 $h_{FE}$

specifications, the required power switch minimum drive was calculated by the following equations to be 108 mA.

$$h_{FE}(Q1) \text{ at } I_C \text{ of } 1.2\ A = 10$$

$$h_{FE}(Q2) \text{ at } I_C \text{ of } 12.0\ A = 10$$

$$i_B \geq \frac{I_O + \frac{\Delta I_L}{2}}{h_{FE}(Q2) \times h_{FE}(Q1)} \geq 108\ mA$$

The value of R10 was calculated by the following equation.

$$R10 \leq \frac{V_I - (V_{BE}(Q1) + V_{CE}(TL594))}{i_B}$$

$$= \frac{32 - (1.3 + 0.7)}{0.108}$$

$$R10 \leq 277\ \Omega$$

Used on these calculations, the nearest standard resistor value of 270 Ω was selected for R10. Resistors R11 and R12 permit the discharge of carriers in the switching transistors when they are turned off.

The power supply described demonstrates the flexibility of the TL594 pulse-width-modulation control circuit. This power supply design demonstrates many of the power supply control methods provided by the TL594 as well as the versatility of the control circuit.

## TL497A SWITCHING VOLTAGE REGULATOR

The TL497A is a fixed-on-time, variable-frequency voltage regulator controller. The block diagram of the TL497A is shown in Figure 6-26.

The on-time is controlled by an external capacitor connected between the frequency control pin (pin 3) and ground. This capacitor, $C_T$, is charged by an internal constant-current generator to a predetermined threshold. The charging current and threshold vary proportionately with $V_{CC}$; thus, the on-time remains constant over the allowable input voltage range.

The output voltage is controlled by two series resistors in parallel with the supply output. The resistance ratios are calculated to supply 1.2 V to the comparator input (pin 1) at the desired output voltage. This feedback voltage is compared to the 1.2 V bandgap reference by the high-gain error amplifier. When the output voltage falls below the desired voltage, the error amplifier enables the oscillator circuit, which charges and discharges $C_T$.

The npn output transistor is driven "on" during the charging cycle of $C_T$. The internal transistor can switch currents up to 500 mA. It is current driven to allow operation from either the positive supply voltage or ground. An internal diode matched to the current

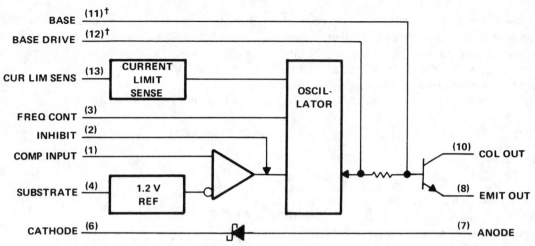

† The Base pin (# 11) and Base Drive pin (# 12) are used for device testing only. They are not normally used in circuit applications of the device.

**Figure 6-26. TL497A Block Diagram**

characteristics of the output transistor is included on the chip and may be used for blocking or commutating purposes.

The TL497A also contains current-limiting circuitry which senses the peak currents in the switching regulator and protects the inductor against saturation and the output transistor against overstress. The current limit is adjustable and is set by a single sense resistor between pins 13 and 14. The current-limit circuitry is activated when 0.5 V is developed across current-limit resistor $R_{CL}$.

The TL497A contains all the active elements required for constructing a single-ended dc-to-dc converter. The output transistor and the rectifier are uncommitted allowing maximum flexibility in the choice of circuit configuration.

The TL497A's primary feature is design simplicity. Using six external components; three resistors, two capacitors, and one inductor, the step-up, step-down, and inverting power supplies shown in Figure 6-27 may be constructed.

| STEP DOWN | STEP-UP | INVERTING |
|---|---|---|
| POS → POS | POS → POS | POS → NEG |
| $+V_I > +V_O$ | $+V_O > +V_I$ | $+V_I > -V_O$ |

## STEP-DOWN SWITCHING REGULATOR

The circuit in Figure 6-28(a) illustrates the basic configuration for a step-down switching regulator.

When switch S1 is closed, the current in the inductor and the voltage across the capacitor start to build up. The current increases while switch S1 is closed as shown by the inductor waveform in Figure 6-28(b). The peak current in the inductor is dependent on the time S1 is closed ($t_{on}$).

When S1 opens, the current through the inductor is $I_{pk}$. Since the current cannot change instantaneously, the voltage across the inductor inverts, and the blocking diode (D1) is forward biased providing a current path for the discharge of the inductor into the load and filter capacitor.

The inductor current discharges linearly as illustrated in Figure 6-28b.

For the output voltage to remain constant, the net charge delivered to the filter capacitor must be zero. The charge delivered to the capacitor from the inductor must be dissipated in the load. Since the charge developed in the inductor is fixed (constant on-time), the time required for the load to dissipate that charge will vary with the load requirements. It is important to use a filter capacitor with minimal ESR. Note, however, some ripple voltage is required for proper operation of the regulator.

Figure 6-29 shows a positive, step-down configuration both with and without an external pass transistor. Design equations for calculating the external components are included.

## STEP-UP SWITCHING REGULATOR

In the step-up regulator, the formulas change slightly. During the charging cycle (S1 closed) the inductor (L) is charged directly by the input potential. The peak current is not related to the load current as it was in the step-down regulator because during the inductor charge cycle the blocking diode D1 is reverse-biased and no charge is delivered to the load.

The circuit in Figure 6-30(a) delivers power to the load only during the discharge cycle of the inductor (S1 open). The diode (D1) is forward biased and the inductor discharges into the load capacitor. Figure 6-31 shows a positive, step-down configuration both with and without an external pass transistor. Design equations are included.

## INVERTING CONFIGURATION

The inverting regulator is similar to the step-up regulator. During the charging cycle of the inductor the load is isolated from the input. The only difference is in the potential across the inductor during its discharge. This can best be demonstrated by a review of the basic inverting regulator circuit (Figure 6-32).

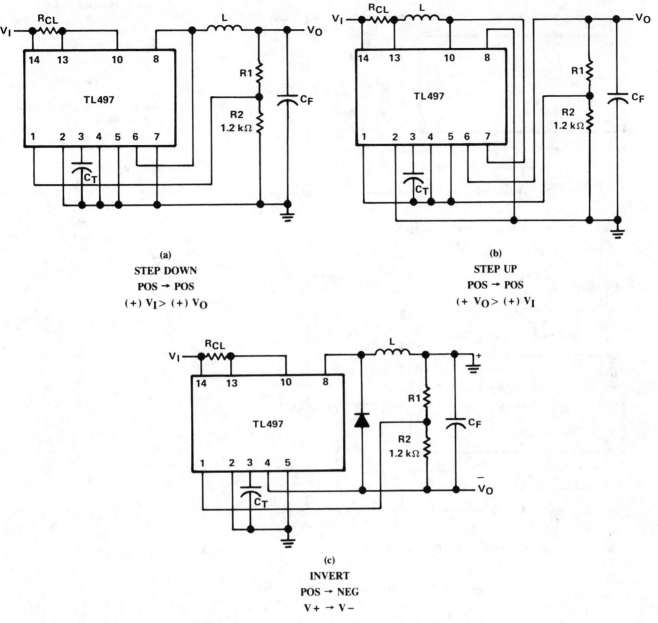

(a)

**STEP DOWN**
**POS → POS**
$(+) V_I > (+) V_O$

(b)

**STEP UP**
**POS → POS**
$(+ V_O > (+) V_I$

(c)

**INVERT**
**POS → NEG**
**V + → V −**

**Figure 6-27. Basic Power Supply Configurations**

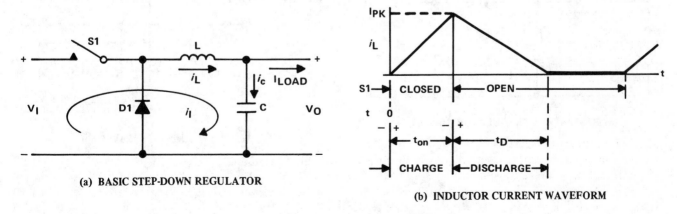

(a) BASIC STEP-DOWN REGULATOR

(b) INDUCTOR CURRENT WAVEFORM

**Figure 6-28. Step-Down Switching Regulator**

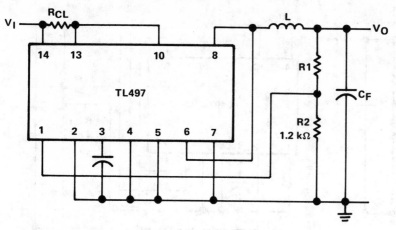

BASIC CONFIGURATION
$I_{PK} < 500$ mA)

## DESIGN EQUATIONS

- $I_{PK} = 2 \, I_{LOAD} \, max$
- $L \, (\mu H) = \dfrac{V_I - V_O}{I_{PK}} \, t_{on} \, (\mu s)$

Choose L (50 to 500 $\mu$H), calculate $t_{on}$ (20 to 150 $\mu$s)

- $C_T \, (pF) \approx 12 \, t_{on} \, (\mu s)$
- $R1 = (V_O - 1.2) \, k\Omega$
- $R_{CL} = \dfrac{0.5 \, V}{I_{PK}}$
- $C_F = \dfrac{(I_{PK} - I_{LOAD})^2}{(V_{ripple}) \, 2 \, I_{PK}} \times \dfrac{T_{on} \, V_I}{V_O}$

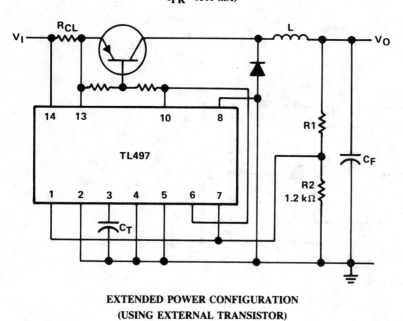

EXTENDED POWER CONFIGURATION
(USING EXTERNAL TRANSISTOR)

**Figure 6-29. Positive Regulator, Step-Down Configurations**

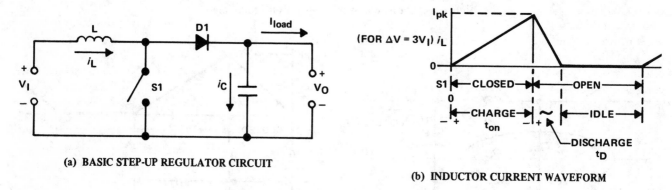

(a) BASIC STEP-UP REGULATOR CIRCUIT

(b) INDUCTOR CURRENT WAVEFORM

**Figure 6-30. Step-Up Switching Regulator**

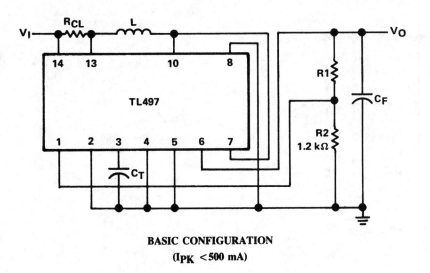

**BASIC CONFIGURATION**
**(I$_{PK}$ <500 mA)**

**DESIGN EQUATIONS**

- $I_{PK} = 2\, I_{LOAD}\, max\, 1 + \left[\dfrac{V_O}{V_I}\right]$

- $L\, (\mu H) = \dfrac{V_I}{I_{PK}}\, t_{on}\, (\mu s)$

Choose L (50 to 500 $\mu$H), calculate $t_{on}$ (25 to 150 $\mu$s)

- $C_T\, (pF) \approx 12\, t_{on}\, (\mu s)$

- $R1 = (V_O - 1.2)\, k\Omega$

- $R_{CL} = \dfrac{0.5\, V}{I_{PK}}$

- $C_F = \dfrac{(I_{PK} - I_{LOAD})^2}{(V_{ripple})\, 2\, I_{PK}} \times \dfrac{T_{on}\, V_I}{V_O}$

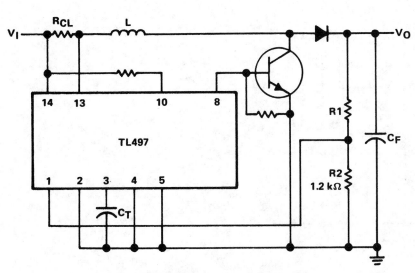

**EXTENDED POWER CONFIGURATION**
**(USING EXTERNAL TRANSISTOR)**

**Figure 6-31. Positive Regulator, Step-Up Configurations**

During the charging cycle (S1 closed) the inductor (L) is charged only by the input potential, similar to the step-up configuration. In the inverting configuration the input provides no contribution to the load current during the charging cycle. The maximum load current for discontinuous operation will be limited by the peak current, as observed in the step-up configuration. The inductor current waveform looks identical to the

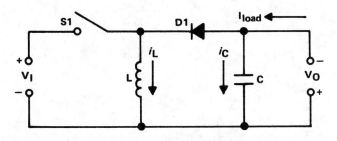

**Figure 6-32. Basic Inverting Regulator Circuit**

waveform demonstrated in the step-up configuration [see Figure 6-30(b)].

Figure 6-33 shows the inverting applications both with and without an external pass transistor. Design equations are also included.

Note that in the inverting configuration the internal diode is not used. An external diode must be used because pin 4 (substrate) must be the most negative point on the chip. The cathode of the internal diode is also the cathode of a diode connected to the substrate. When the cathodes are at the most negative voltage in the circuit, there will be conduction to the substrate resulting in unstable operation.

**DESIGN CONSIDERATIONS**

An oscilloscope is required when building a switching regulator. When checking the oscillator ramp on pin 3 the oscilloscope may be difficult to synchronize. This is a normal operating characteristic of this regulator and is

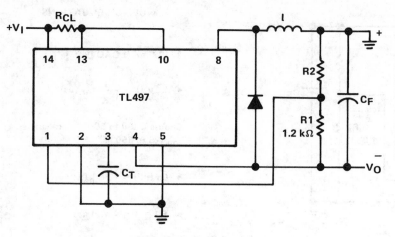

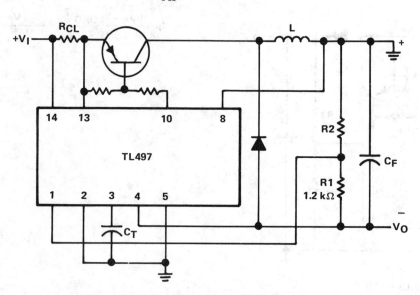

**BASIC CONFIGURATION**
**($I_{PK} < 500$ mA)**

**EXTENDED POWER CONFIGURATION**
**(USING EXTERNAL TRANSISTOR)**

**Figure 6-33. Inverting Applications**

### DESIGN EQUATIONS

- $I_{PK} = 2\, I_{LOAD}\, max \left[ 1 + \dfrac{V_O}{V_I} \right]$

- $L\,(\mu H) = \dfrac{V_I}{I_{PK}}\, t_{on}\,(\mu s)$

Choose L (50 to 500 $\mu$H), calculate $t_{on}$ (25 to 150 $\mu$s)

- $C_T\,(pF) \approx 12\, t_{on}\,(\mu s)$

- $R2 = (V_O - 1.2)\, k\Omega$

- $R_{CL} = \dfrac{0.5\ V}{I_{PK}}$

- $C_F = \dfrac{(I_{PK} - I_{LOAD})^2}{(V_{ripple})\, 2\, I_{PK}} \times \dfrac{t_{on}\, V_I}{V_O}$

caused by the asynchronous operation of the error amplifier to that of the oscillator. The oscilloscope may be synchronized by varying the input voltage or load current slightly from design nominals.

High frequency circuit layout techniques are imperative. Keep leads as short as possible and use a single ground point. Resistors R1 and R2 should be as close as possible to Pin 1 to eliminate noise pick-up in the feedback loop. The TL497A type of circuits do not need "hi-Q" inductors. They are, in fact, not desirable due to the broad frequency range of operation. If the "Q" is too high, ringing will occur. If this happens a shunt resistor (about 1 kΩ) may be placed across the coil to damp the oscillation.

While not necessary, it is highly desirable to use a toroidal inductor as opposed to a cylindrically wound coil. The toroidal type of winding helps to contain the flux

closer to the core and in turn minimize radiation from the supply. All high current loops should be kept to a minimum length using copper connections that are as large as possible.

### A STEP-DOWN SWITCHING REGULATOR DESIGN EXERCISE WITH TL497A

The schematic of a basic step-down regulator is shown in Figure 6-34.

This regulator will have the following design goals:

$V_I$ = 15 V
$V_O$ = 5 V
$I_O$ = 200 mA
$V_{ripple}$ = < 1.0% or 50 mV (1.0% × 5 V)

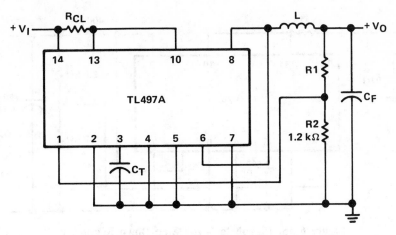

**Figure 6-34. Basic Step-Down Regulator**

Calculations:

$$I_{PK} = 2\, I_L \text{ max} = 400 \text{ mA}$$

For design margin, $I_{PK}$ will be designed for 500 mA which is also the limit of the internal pass transistor and diode.

$$\therefore I_{PK} = 500 \text{ mA}$$

The next step will be to select $t_{on}$. You may select a timing capacitor to match an inductor you may already have. You may also assume an on-time and calculate the inductor value. We will assume an on-time of 20 µs.

$$t_{on} = 20 \text{ µs}$$

$$L(\text{µH}) = \frac{V_I - V_O}{I_{PK}} \times t_{on} \text{ µs}$$

$$= \frac{15 - 5}{0.5} \times 20 = 400 \text{ µH}$$

$$L = 400 \text{ µH}$$

To set the TL497A for 5 V output:

$$R2 = 1.2 \text{ k}\Omega \text{ (fixed)}$$

$$R1 = (5 - 1.2) \text{ k}\Omega = 3.8 \text{ k}\Omega$$

To set current limiting:

$$R_{CL} = \frac{0.5}{I_L} = \frac{0.5}{500 \times 10^{-3}} = 1 \text{ }\Omega$$

$$R_{CL} = 1 \text{ }\Omega$$

For the on-time chosen, $C_T$ can be approximated:

$$C_T(\text{pF}) = 12\, t_{on} \text{ µs}$$

$$C_T = 240 \text{ pF}$$

or it may be selected from a table in the data sheet.

To determine filter capacitor ($C_F$) for desired ripple voltage:

$$C_F = \frac{(I_{PK} - I_L)^2}{(V_{ripple})\, 2\, I_{PK}} \times \frac{t_{on}\, V_I}{V_O}$$

$$C_F = \frac{(0.5 - 0.2)^2}{(0.05)\, 2 \times 0.5}$$

$$\times \frac{20 \times 10^{-6} \times 15}{5} = 108 \text{ µF}$$

We selected $C_F$ to be 120 µF, the next higher standard value.

Figure 6-35 illustrates the regulator with the calculated values applied to it.

A 150 µF filter capacitor may be used as a prefilter as well as a 0.01 µF disc capacitor to take care of any transients on the incoming $V_I$ rail.

For peak currents greater than 500 mA, it is necessary to use an external pass transistor and diode. Such a technique is illustrated in Figure 6-36 which is an automotive power supply. With a 12 V battery, this step-down regulator supplies 5 V at 2 A output current.

Figure 6-37 illustrates a basic step-up regulator. This design steps up the output voltage from 5 V to 15 V. The equations for determining the values of the external components are provided in Figure 6-31.

## DESIGN AND OPERATION OF AN INVERTING REGULATOR CONFIGURATION

Figure 6-38 illustrates a basic inverting regulator designed to have −5 V output with +5 V input using the design equations in Figure 6-33.

Conditions:

$$V_I = 5 \text{ V}$$
$$V_O = -5 \text{ V}$$
$$I_O = 100 \text{ mA}$$
$$V_{ripple} = 1.0\% \text{ or } 50 \text{ mV } (1\% \times 5 \text{ V})$$

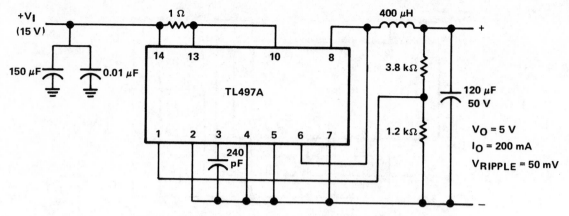

**Figure 6-35. 15-Volt to 5-Volt Step-Down Regulator**

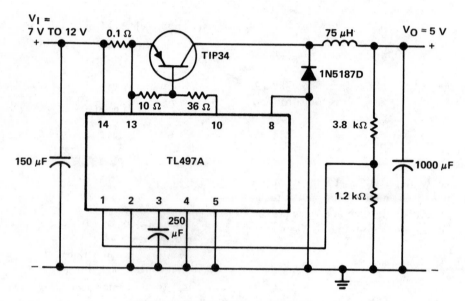

**Figure 6-36. Step-Down Regulator**

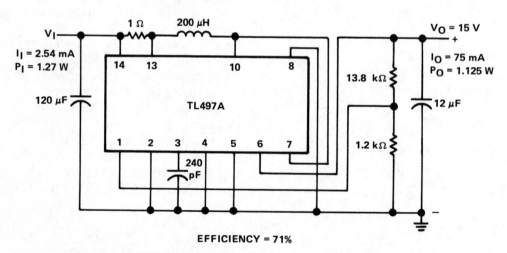

EFFICIENCY = 71%

**Figure 6-37. 5-Volt to 15-Volt Switching Regulator**

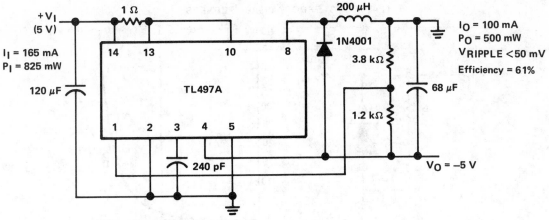

NOTE — Do not use internal diode (Pins 6, 7) on an inverting circuit.

**Figure 6-38. +5-Volt to −5-Volt Switching Regulator**

Calculations:

$$I_{PK} = 2 I_L(max) \left(1 + \frac{|V_O|}{V_I}\right)$$

$$I_{PK} = 400 \text{ mA (for design margin use 500 mA)}$$

Assume $t_{on} = 20 \text{ μs}$

$$C_{T(pF)} = 12 \ t_{on} \text{ μs}$$
$$C_T = 240 \text{ pF}$$

$$L = \frac{V_I}{I_{PK}} \ t_{on} = \frac{5}{0.5} \times 20 = 200 \text{ μH}$$

To set the output voltage:

$$R2 = 1.2 \text{ kΩ}$$

$$R1 = (5 - 1.2) \text{ kΩ} = 3.8 \text{ kΩ}$$

To set the current limiting:

$$R_{CL} = \frac{0.5}{I_{PK}} = \frac{0.5}{0.5} = 1 \text{ Ω}$$

$$RCL = 1 \text{ Ω}$$

$$C_F = \frac{(I_{PK} - I_L)^2}{(V_{ripple}) \ 2 \ I_{PK}} \times \frac{t_{on} \ V_I}{V_O}$$

To determine $C_F$ for desired ripple voltage:

$$C_F = \frac{(I_{PK} - I_L)^2}{(V_{ripple}) \ 2I_{PK}} \times \frac{t_{on} \ V_I}{|V_O|}$$

$$= \frac{(0.5 - 0.1)^2}{(0.05)2 \times 0.5} \times \frac{20 \times 10^{-6} \times 5}{|-5|}$$

$$C_F = 64 \text{ μF (nearest standard value = 68 μF)}$$

## ADJUSTABLE SHUNT REGULATOR
## TL430 - TL431

The TL430 and TL431 are three-terminal 'programmable' shunt regulators. The devices are basically the same except the TL431 contains a diode connected between the emitter and collector of the output transistor. The standard symbol and block diagram are shown in Figure 6-39.

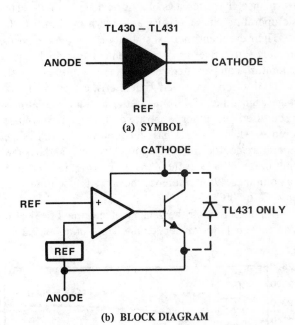

**Figure 6-39. TL430/TL431 Adjustable Shunt Regulators**

The circuit consists of a bipolar op amp driving an npn transistor. The reference on the TL430 is a band-gap reference (not temperature compensated). The TL431 has a true temperature compensated band-gap reference and is more stable and accurate than other shunt regulators. The TL431 also has a diode across the emitter-collector of the npn output transistor. If the cathode goes negative, the diode conducts around the transistor, emulating the

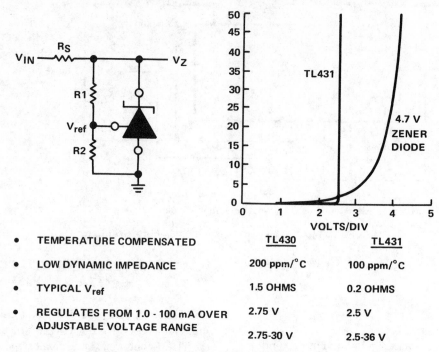

| | TL430 | TL431 |
|---|---|---|
| • TEMPERATURE COMPENSATED | | |
| • LOW DYNAMIC IMPEDANCE | 200 ppm/°C | 100 ppm/°C |
| • TYPICAL V$_{ref}$ | 1.5 OHMS | 0.2 OHMS |
| • REGULATES FROM 1.0 - 100 mA OVER ADJUSTABLE VOLTAGE RANGE | 2.75 V | 2.5 V |
| | 2.75-30 V | 2.5-36 V |

**Figure 6-40. Basic Operating Characteristics**

performance characteristics of a normal zener diode. The basic operating characteristics are shown in Figure 6-40.

Their excellent thermal stability make these devices extremely attractive as a replacement for high cost, temperature-compensated zeners. As seen in Figure 6-41, the TL431 offers improved characteristics, even at low voltages. Since the TL431 operates as a shunt regulator, it can be used as either a positive or negative voltage reference. The TL431 has an equivalent full-range temperature coefficient of 50 ppm/°C (typical) and has low output noise voltage. Note in the graph (Figure 6-41) that for a nominal 2.495 V reference the curve is essentially flat from 0°C to 70°C.

Depending upon the zener voltage, the TL431 also has an extremely low dynamic impedance of about 0.2 Ω,

compared to a standard zener diode's dynamic impedance of about 30 to 60 Ω.

A 2.5 V reference voltage is developed across R2 as shown in Figure 6-42. I$_{ref}$, the current input at the reference terminal, is about 10 μA. To maintain a steady reference, it is advisable to allow 1 mA of current flow through series resistors R1 and R2. This will assure a stable reference voltage independent of I$_{ref}$ variations. The TL431 is available in either the commercial temperature range of 0° - 70°C or the military temperature range of −55° to +125°C.

$$R = \frac{V_I - (V_{be} + V_O)}{I_R}$$

$$R = \frac{32 - (2 + 24)}{10 \text{ mA}} = 600 \text{ Ω}$$

$$V_O = \left(1 + \frac{R1}{R2}\right) V_{ref}$$

R1 = 21.4 kΩ
R2 = 2.5 kΩ

The circuit in Figure 6-43 uses a TL431 as a regulator to control the base drive to a TIP660 series pass transistor. For good reference stability, a current flow of about 1 mA (I$_2$) though the resistor divider is recommended. A 2.5 V reference voltage is developed across R2, and R1 will develop a voltage drop of 21.5 V. The Darlington power transistor is used because of the reduced base drive requirement of the TIP660 which has a V$_{be}$ (max) of about 2 V. The h$_{FE}$ at 2.5 A I$_C$ is about 1000, so it would only

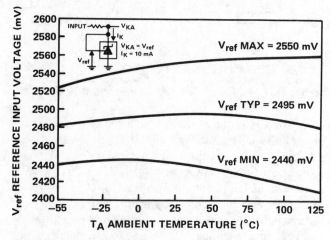

**Figure 6-41. Reference Input Voltage Versus Ambient Temperature**

require about 2.5 mA of base drive to produce 2.5 A of output current. In calculating the value of the current limit resistor, R3, we assume about 7.5 mA of current through the TL431. The value of R3, therefore, would be 600 Ω and the current about 10 mA, so a 1/2 W resistor will suffice. This is a simple method of designing a medium output current power-supply using only four components plus the series pass transistor.

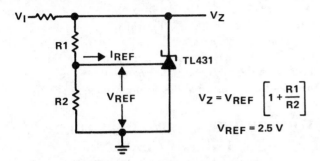

**Figure 6-42. Basic Operational Circuit**

$$V_Z = V_{REF}\left[1 + \frac{R1}{R2}\right]$$

$$V_{REF} = 2.5\ V$$

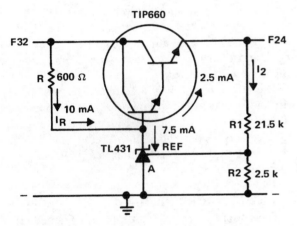

**Figure 6-43. Series Regulator Circuit**

## SHUNT REGULATOR APPLICATIONS CROWBAR

To protect solid-state electronic equipment from overvoltage due to a power-supply component failure, it is sometimes desirable to use a 'crowbar' circuit. When a preset voltage is exceeded, the SCR turns on, shorting the output and blowing the fuse on the input side of the crowbar circuit. The circuit in Figure 6-44 is set to trip when $V_O$ reaches 27 V. When that occurs, the reference voltage should be 2.5 V which turns on the TL431, thus biasing the SCR low. This turns the SCR on and immediately blows the safety fuse on the circuit input, thus protecting the equipment using this power supply.

$$V_L = \left(1 + \frac{R1}{R2}\right)V_{ref}$$

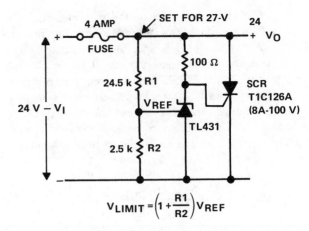

$$V_{LIMIT} = \left(1 + \frac{R1}{R2}\right)V_{REF}$$

**Figure 6-44. Shunt Regulator in Crowbar Circuit**

## CONTROLLING $V_O$ OF A FIXED OUTPUT VOLTAGE REGULATOR

Sometimes it is necessary to have a regulated output voltage different from that for which the regulator is designed. This may be accomplished with any three-terminal regulator, although it should be noted that the lowest obtainable voltage will be 2.5 V for the TL431 plus the voltage of the three-terminal regulator. In the circuit in Figure 6-45, the lowest possible regulated voltage would be 7.5 V (2.5 V for the TL431 + 5 V for the 7805). This particular circuit provides 9 V output using a uA7805 three-terminal regulator.

Note: Minimum $V_O$ = $V_{ref}$ + 5 V

$$V_O = \left(1 + \frac{R1}{R2}\right)V_{ref}$$

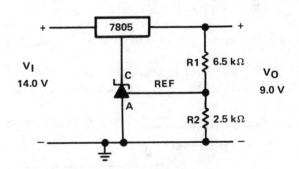

NOTE: MINIMUM $V_O$ = $V_{REF}$ + 5.0 V

$$V_O = \left(1 + \frac{R1}{R2}\right)V_{REF}$$

**Figure 6-45. Fixed Output Shunt Regulator**

## CURRENT LIMITER

Figure 6-46 is an example of a current limiter designed to limit the current from a 12 V supply to 1.5 A using a TIP31 npn transistor as the pass element. The value of R1 is calculated from the equation in Figure 6-46. The current through R1 is split almost equally in this circuit, with about 30 mA going to the TL431, and 30 mA for base drive to the TIP31. With a current load of 6 mA, and an R1 value of 128 Ω a 1/2 watt resistor is sufficient. When the voltage across the current limit resistor ($R_{CL}$) reaches 2.5 V (TL431 reference voltage), the base drive to the TIP31 is reduced and the output current is limited to 1.5 A.

$$R1 = \frac{V_I - (V_{be} + V_{RCL})}{I_1}$$

$$= \frac{12 - (1.8 + 2.5)}{0.06} = 128 \ \Omega$$

$$R_{CL} = \frac{V_{ref}}{I_L} = \frac{2.5 \ V}{1.5 \ A} = 1.7 \ \Omega$$

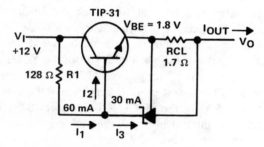

**Figure 6-46. Current Limiter**

## VOLTMETER SCALER

The circuit in Figure 6-47 is a voltmeter scaler (or multiplier) to extend the range of a 0 to 10 V voltmeter to 40 V. Most multiplier circuits extend the range with 0 V being the low reading on any given scale. This circuit actually divides the 40 V total range into 4 separate 10 V scales.

With the selector switch in position #1, the reference input of the TL431 is bypassed and the TL431

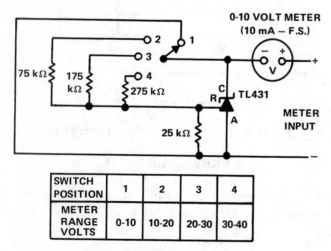

| SWITCH POSITION | 1 | 2 | 3 | 4 |
|---|---|---|---|---|
| METER RANGE VOLTS | 0-10 | 10-20 | 20-30 | 30-40 |

**Figure 6-47. Voltmeter Scaler**

does not influence circuit operation. The meter is effectively connected directly to the voltage being measured. This scale would be the normal meter range of 0 to 10 V.

When in position #2, a 75 kΩ and a 25 kΩ resistor are added in series across the anode and cathode of the TL431. The voltmeter will remain near zero until the input reaches 10 V. At this time, there is 2.5 V between the reference terminal and anode which causes the voltmeter to start reading at 10 V. It will continue reading on this scale until it reaches full scale, which is 20 V.

This sequence is repeated in 10 V steps until position #4 is reached. This circuit is very useful when expanded-scale voltmeter multiplication is required. The precision of the scaler depends upon the accuracy of the resistors.

# VOLTAGE-REGULATED, CURRENT-LIMITED BATTERY CHARGER FOR LEAD-ACID BATTERIES

There are a number of approaches to recharging lead-acid batteries. Many will return the battery to service, but fail to fully rejuvenate the battery. To keep a battery fully charged, and attain maximum battery life, proper charging techniques must be observed.

The status of a cell is determined by the specific gravity of the electrolyte solution. A specific gravity of 1.280 (obtained by hydrometer reading) indicates a fully charged cell. A reading of 1.250 or better is considered good. A fully discharged cell exhibits a specific gravity of 1.150 or less.

## BATTERY CHARGER DESIGN

The battery charger design shown in Figure 6-48 is based on a charging voltage of 2.4 V per cell, in accordance with most manufacturers' recommendations. The battery charger circuit pulses the battery under charge with 14.4 V (6 cells × 2.4 V per cell) at a rate of 120 Hz.

The design provides current limiting to protect the charger's internal components while limiting the charging rate to prevent damaging severely discharged lead-acid batteries. The maximum recommended charging current is normally about one-fourth the ampere-hour rating of the battery. For example, the maximum charging current for an average 44 ampere-hour battery is 11 A.

If the impedance of the load requires a charging current greater than the 11 A current limit, the circuit will go into current limiting. The amplitude of the charging pulses is controlled to maintain a maximum peak charging current of 11 A (8 A average).

The charger circuit is composed of four basic sections:

1. Rectifier
2. Voltage Regulator
3. Current Limiting
4. Series Pass Element

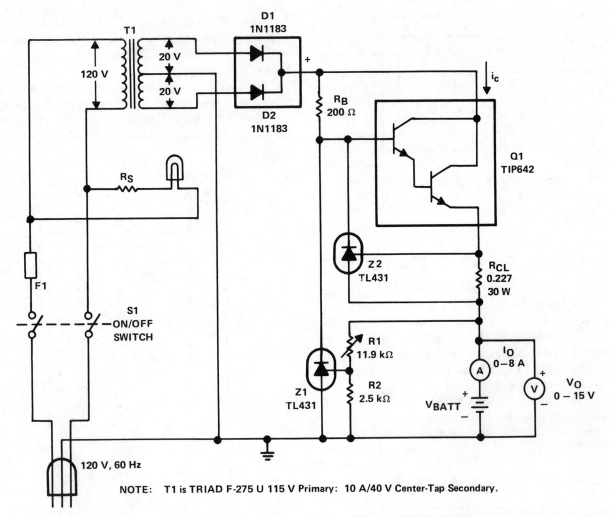

Figure 6-48. Current Limited and Voltage Regulated Battery Charger

## Rectifier Section

A full-wave rectifier configuration with a center-tapped transformer (Figure 6-49) achieves maximum performance with minimum component count. The breakdown voltage requirement for the diode is:

$$VR > Vsecondary(pk) - V_F(\text{rectifier drop})$$
$$\therefore VR > 20 \times 1.414 - 1 = 27.28 \text{ V}$$

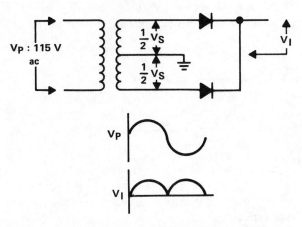

Figure 6-49. Full-Wave Rectifier Section of Circuit

This design is set to current limit at 11 A so a rectifier rating of 25 A is recommended to handle the maximum current drain plus any current surges. A pair of 1N1183 diodes was chosen (35 A/50 V rectifiers).

## Voltage Regulator Section

The components which make up the voltage regulator portion of the circuit are: Z1, Q1, R1, R2 and $R_B$ as shown in Figure 6-50.

Z1 is a TL431 programmable shunt regulator which serves as the control element, Q1 is the pass transistor, and R1 - R2 sense the output voltage providing feedback to Z1. R1 and R2 are chosen so that their node voltage is 2.5 V at the desired output voltage. This node voltage is applied to the TL431's error amplifier which compares it to the internal 2.5 V reference.

When the feedback voltage is less than the internal 2.5 V reference, the series impedance (anode-to-cathode) of the TL431 increases, decreasing the shunt current through the TL431. This increases the current available to the base of pass transistor Q1, increasing the output voltage.

When the feedback voltage is greater than the internal 2.5 V reference, the series impedance of the

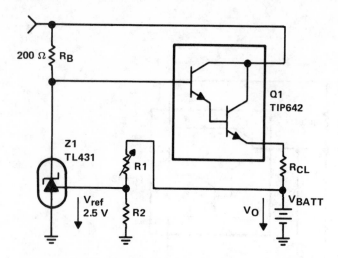

**Figure 6-50. Voltage Regulator Section of Circuit**

TL431 decreases, increasing the shunt current through the TL431. This decreases the current available to the base of Q1, decreasing the output voltage.

Because the feedback voltage is sensed at the output, the TL431 will compensate for any changes in the base-emitter drop of Q1 or the voltage dropped across $R_{CL}$ for various currents.

### Current Limiter Section

The components which make up the current-limit portion of this circuit are: Z2, Q1, and $R_{CL}$ as shown in Figure 6-51.

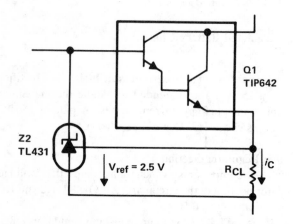

**Figure 6-51. Current Limiter Section of Circuit**

The value of the current-limit setting resistor, $R_{CL}$, is chosen so that 2.5 V will be developed across it at the desired limit current. The voltage across $R_{CL}$ is sensed by a TL431 programmable shunt regulator (Z2). When the output current is less than the current limit, $V_{ref}$ is less than 2.5 V and Z2 is a high impedance which does not affect the operation of Q1.

When the output current reaches maximum, $V_{ref}$ is 2.5 V and the impedance of Z2 decreases, decreasing the current available at the base of Q1 and controlling the maximum output current. Under this condition, shunt

regulator Z2 takes control of pass transistor Q1 and maintains a constant current, even into a short circuit.

### Series Pass Element

The series pass element used in this configuration is a conventional Darlington power transistor, whose control is derived from either Z1 or Z2 depending on the state of the battery being charged. See Figure 6-52.

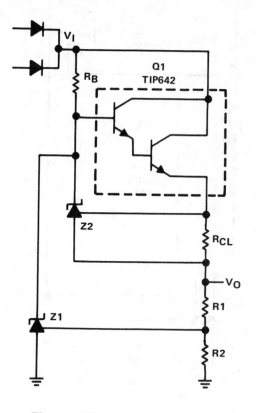

**Figure 6-52. Series Pass Element**

The performance characteristics of Q1 are important in determining the circuit design and in the choice of the transformer to be used. This relationship is shown in the following section on the design of the battery charger.

### Design Calculations

The values of R1 and R2 set the output voltage level at 2.4 V per cell or 14.4 V for 6 cells. For optimum performance of Z1, 1 mA should flow through the R1 and R2 combination.

$$R1 + R2 = \frac{14.4 \text{ V}}{1 \text{ mA}} = 14.4 \text{ k}\Omega$$

$$R2 = \frac{2.5 \text{ V}}{1 \text{ mA}} = 2.5 \text{ k}\Omega$$

$$R1 = 14.4 \text{ k}\Omega - 2.5 \text{ k}\Omega = 11.9 \text{ k}\Omega$$

For ease of final adjustment, a 20 k$\Omega$ potentiometer may be used for R1.

Current limiting starts when 2.5 V is developed across $R_{CL}$ at the desired current limit. For a 44 A hour battery, the maximum charge rate is 11 A.

$$R_{CL} = \frac{2.5\ V}{11\ A} = 0.227\ \Omega$$

The average current = $0.707 \times 11\ A = 7.777\ A$ or
$$\approx 8A$$

The average power dissipation = $I^2R = 8^2 \times 0.227$
$$= 14.5\ W$$

After the pass transistor has been selected, its base drive resistor, $R_B$, may be calculated. A TIP642 meets the requirements. From the data sheet:

$h_{FE}$ @ 11 A = 500 (min)
$V_{CE} \approx 2\ V$
$V_{BE} = 1.6\ V$
$P_{max} = 160\ W$ @ 40°C TC
$I_B = 22\ mA$ @ 11 A peak collector current

To calculate $R_B$, assume a worst case or short-circuit condition where:

$$R_B \approx \frac{V_I - V_{ref} - V_{BE(Q1)}}{I_{B(Q1)} + I_{SHUNT(Z2)}}$$

$$R_B \approx \frac{27.28 - 2.5 - 1.6}{0.022 + 0.12} = 163\ \Omega$$

While $R_B$ must be small enough so it does not limit the base current of Q1 at the desired $I_{CHG}$ of 8 A, however, it must be large enough to limit the current during short circuit conditions. This value should be less than the sum of the base drive current required by Q1 and $I_{SHUNT(max)}$ Z2.

$$R_B \approx \frac{(V_I - 14.4\ V - 2.5\ V - V_{BE(Q1)})}{I_{CHG}/h_{FE(Q1)}}$$

$$= \frac{27.28 - 14.4 - 2.5 - 1.6}{8/500}$$

$$R_B \approx \frac{8.78}{0.016} = 548.7\ \Omega$$

A value of $R_B$ within this range assures sufficient drive to Q1 for a charging rate of 8 A, yet allows total control of Q1 by Z2 during short-circuit conditions. $R_B$ was selected to be 200 $\Omega$.

### Power Dissipation and Heat Sinking

To determine the power dissipation in the 1N1183 rectifier and the TIP642 Darlington, the RMS currents and voltages must be calculated. The voltage and current paths are shown in Figure 6-53.

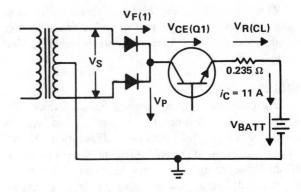

**Figure 6-53. Voltage and Current Path**

$$V_{CE(Q1)} = V_I - V_{BATT} - V_{RCL}$$
$$= 27.78 - 14.4 - 2.5 = 10.88\ V$$
$$V_{CE(Q1)} = 10.9\ V$$

The transistor power dissipation is:

$$P_{Q1} = I_{(RMS)} \times V_{CE(RMS)}$$
$$= (11\ A \times 0.707)(10.9\ V \times 0.707)$$
$$P_{Q1} = (7.78\ A)\ (7.7\ V)$$
$$P_{Q1} = 59.9\ W$$

The rectifier power dissipation is:

$$P_{(RECT)} = I_{(RMS)} \times V_F = (7.78\ A)\ (1.3\ V)$$
$$P_{(RECT)} = 10.1\ W\ total$$

If the pass transistor and rectifiers are mounted on separate heat sinks, the sinks must be capable of dissipating the heat transferred by each device and maintain a surface temperature which satisfies the temperature requirement for each device. Mounted separately, the respective heat sink requirements are as follows:

PASS TRANSISTOR          RECTIFIERS

$$R_{\theta CA} \leq \frac{150°C - 25°C}{59.9\ W} \qquad R_{\theta CA} < \frac{140°C - 25°C}{10.1\ W}$$

$$R_{\theta CA} \leq 2.08°C/W \qquad R_{\theta CA} < 11.4°C/W$$

Depending on the mass of the heat sink and the type of cabinet, forced air cooling may be required.

## VOLTAGE SUPPLY SUPERVISOR DEVICES

Voltage supply supervisor devices deliver a digital output signal (high or low) if supply voltage ($V_{CC}$) falls below a predefined value. The digital output signal remains in its high or low state for a certain period of time (t delay) after $V_{CC}$ returns to normal. These devices are used to sequentially initialize digital systems for proper operation at power-on or following a $V_{CC}$ interruption.

The versatility, few external components, and accurate threshold voltage of the TL7700 series make these devices easy to use in digital systems requiring $V_{CC}$ line supervision.

## GENERAL OPERATION

At power-on, digital systems must normally be forced into a definite initial state. In simple microcomputer and microprocessor applications an RC network connected to the RESET input pin will generally suffice. However, in more complex systems a discrete component design as illustrated in Figure 6-54 may be used.

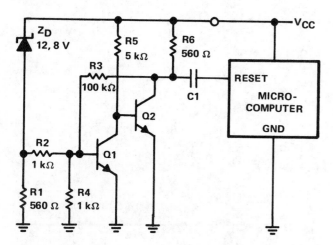

**Figure 6-54. Discrete Solution of a Voltage Supply Supervisor**

In this circuit, after $V_{CC}$ reaches a specific value, defined by $Z_D$, the input voltage divider, and $V_{BE}$, the collector of Q2 becomes high and coupling capacitor C1 provides enough power to the RESET input pin of the digital system to execute the reset function.

The major deficiency with this type of circuit is that after power-on and the system is operating, low $V_{CC}$ conditions and short drops in $V_{CC}$ may not be recognized. A small decrease of $V_{CC}$ below the recommended supply voltage can destroy the content of the memory and registers without activating the reset circuit. This may have catastrophic consequences.

Moreover, the circuit in Figure 6-54 contains an excessive number of components, one being $Z_D$, which has to be specially selected and is therefore relatively expensive.

Several features are provided in larger computers to prevent some of the problems just mentioned. In some cases the content of the memory is protected by a battery back-up. However, for most applications and in small microcomputer systems, these solutions are too expensive and generally not required. After any serious voltage drop, it is usually sufficient to force the microcomputer into a defined initial condition.

To implement this function, while preventing the problems previously mentioned, a chip with the following features is required:

1. Accurate detection of a serious voltage drop.
2. Generation of a continuous reset signal while the supply voltage is not in the operational range to prevent undefined operations.
3. Maintenance of the reset signal for a certain time after the supply voltage has returned to its nominal value to ensure a proper reset.

## TL7700 SERIES SUPERVISOR CHIPS

A functional block diagram of the chip is illustrated in Figure 6-55.

The most critical element of this chip is the reference voltage source, which consists of a very stable, temperature-compensated bandgap reference. An external capacitor (typically 0.1 µF) must be connected to the Reference (REF) voltage output to reduce the influence of fast transients in the supply voltage. The voltage at the SENSE INPUT pin is divided by resistors R1 and R2 and compared with the reference voltage. The divider is adjusted to achieve high accuracy at the probing operation during manufacture of the chip.

When the sensed input voltage is lower than the threshold voltage, the thyristor is triggered discharging the timing capacitor $C_T$. It is also possible to fire the thyristor with a TTL logic level (active low) at the $\overline{\text{RESIN}}$ input.

The thyristor is turned off again when the voltage at the SENSE INPUT (or $\overline{\text{RESIN}}$ input) increases beyond the threshold, or during short supply voltage drops when the discharge current of the capacitor becomes lower than the hold current of the thyristor.

Capacitor $C_T$ is recharged by a 100 µA current source; the charge time is calculated as follows:

$$t_d \text{ (internal time delay)} = C_T (1.3 \times 10^4)$$

A second comparator forces the output into the active state as long as the voltage at the capacitor is lower than the reference voltage. Figure 6-56 is a graph plotting $C_T$ versus $t_d$.

The SENSE INPUT pin is connected to $V_{CC}$ in typical applications. Figure 6-57 shows the timing of the Supply Voltage and $\overline{\text{RESET}}$ signals.

The minimum supply voltage for which operation is guaranteed is 3 V. Between POWER-ON (0 V) and 3 V, the state of the outputs is not defined. In practical applications this is not a limitation because the function of the reset inputs of the other devices is not guaranteed at such supply voltages.

Above 3 V capacitor $C_T$ is discharged and the outputs stay in the active state. When the input voltage

Note: SENSE INPUT pin connected to $V_{CC}$

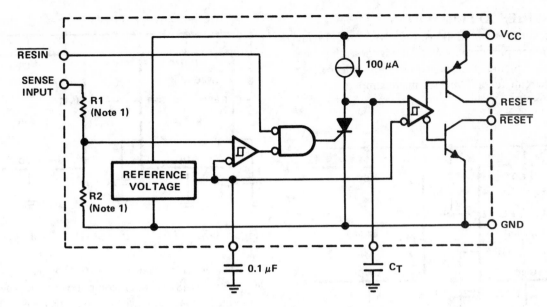

**Figure 6-55. TL7700 Series Function Block Diagram**

exceeds the threshold voltage, $V_S$, the thyristor is turned off and capacitor $C_T$ is charged. After a delay of $t_d$, the voltage passes the trigger level of the output comparator and the outputs become inactive. The microcomputer is then set to a defined initial state and starts operation.

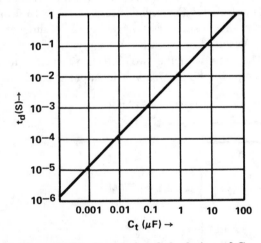

**Figure 6-56. Graph for Calculation of $C_T$**

## Operation During a Voltage Drop

The thyristor is triggered when the supply voltage drops below the minimum recommended value. After the supply returns to its required value the output stays in the active state for the duration of $t_d$.

The delay time, $t_d$, is determined by the requirements of the computer system to be controlled. Typically, in TTL systems, a reset time of 20 to 50 ns is sufficient. Microcomputers usually require a reset signal which lasts several machine cycles. The duration of the reset signal is dependent on the type of microcomputer, but is typically 10 to 200 µs. In most practical applications, $t_d$ is determined by the characteristics of the power supply.

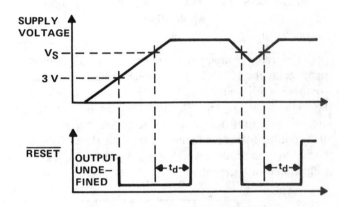

**Figure 6-57. Timing Diagram**

During and shortly after power-on make sure voltage fluctuations do not repetitively reset the system. Delay times of 10 to 20 ns will usually prevent this problem. Four versions of this device are available:

| | Threshold Voltage | $V_{CC}$ |
|---|---|---|
| TL7702A | 2.53 V | 3.0 — 18.0V |
| TL7705A | 4.55 V | 5.0 V |
| TL7712A | 10.8 V | 12.0 V |
| TL7715A | 13.5 V | 15.0 V |

The TL7702A may be used in applications where $V_{CC}$ voltages up to 18 V are used. The required trigger level (2.5 V) may be set with a resistor divider network at the SENSE INPUT pin. The TL7705A, TL7712A, and TL7715A have an internal resistor divider network and operate on 5 V, 12 V, and 15 V, respectively.

# TL7700 SERIES APPLICATIONS

Since, for most applications, the devices are already adjusted to the appropriate voltage levels these chips are easy to use. Figure 6-58 illustrates an undervoltage protection circuit for a TMS9940 microcomputer system with a 5 V power supply.

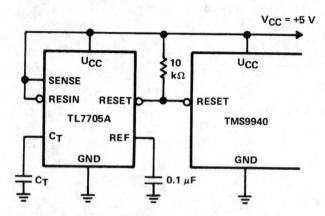

**Figure 6-58. TL7705A in 5-Volt Microcomputer Application**

External components are the 0.1 μF bypass capacitor at the REF terminal, which reduces transients from the supply voltage, and the $C_T$ capacitor, which sets the time delay $t_d$. The TL7705A devices do not have internal pull-up (or pull-down) resistors. An external 10 kΩ pull-up resistor is connected from the RESET pin to the 5 V $V_{CC}$ to produce a high level. A similar application is illustrated in Figure 6-59.

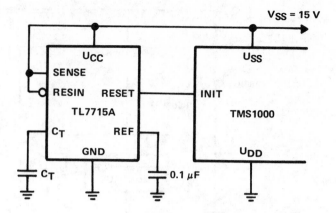

**Figure 6-59. TL7715A in TMS1XXXNLP Application**

This circuit utilizes a TL7715A as a protection device for a TMS1000 microcomputer system. The $C_T$ and reference bypass capacitors are also used in this application. Note, however, the absence of the pull-up resistor used in Figure 6-58. This circuit has a required internal pull-down resistor at the INIT INPUT pin on the TMS1000 microcomputer chip.

In large systems, where several supply voltages are required (e.g., TMS8080, TMS9900), it is necessary to supervise all supply voltages that may cause dangerous conditions if a power failure or transient occurs. The circuit illustrated in Figure 6-60 uses two TL7712A devices to check the positive and negative 12 V supplies. A TL7705A is used to check a 5 V supply.

The outputs of the two TL7712A's are fed to the RESIN input of the TL7705A. The output of this device, a

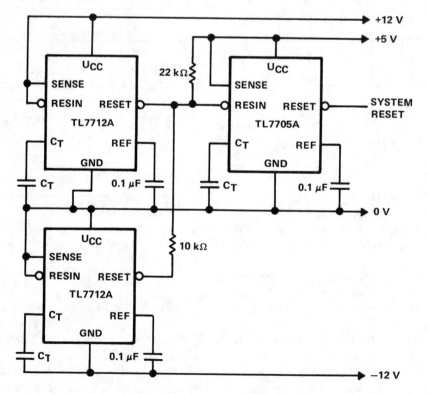

**Figure 6-60. Voltage Supervision of a Multiple Power Supply**

system reset signal, becomes active when any one of the three supply voltages fail.

The supply voltage supervisor devices were designed to detect very short voltage drops of 150 ns. In applications where this sensitivity is not required, the circuit may be delayed by adding an RC network ahead of the SENSE INPUT pin (Figure 6-61).

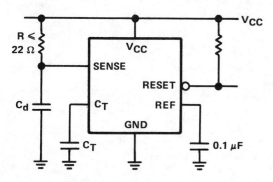

**Figure 6-61. Delayed Triggering**

To avoid influence on the threshold voltage of this input, the resistor should be less than 22 Ω. The capacitor $C_d$ is then calculated to the required delay time ($C_d = t/R$).

Another application for the TL7705A is in battery-buffered memory systems. After a line-voltage failure the content of the memory has to be protected against spikes on the write line. It is usually sufficient to switch the chip-select line into the inactive state; however, some memories also require that the write line be disabled. See Figure 6-62.

A switch, formed by transistor Q1 and diode D1, is inserted into the chip-select line of the memory. Under normal operation (line voltage present) the RESET output of the TL7705A is turned off (high), transistor Q2 is turned on, and transistor Q1 draws its base current through transistor Q2 and resistor R1.

When the chip-select line is switched from high to low transistor Q1 conducts and the CS input of the memory goes low. Because of the small dc load of resistor

R2 the saturation voltage of the transistor is very small (typically 40 mV).

When the chip-select line is switched high again transistor Q1 is turned off and diode D1 conducts, charging the circuit capacitance.

In case of a power failure the TL7705A is triggered and its RESET output becomes low, turning off transistor Q2 and the base current to transistor Q1. In this way the CS input of the memory is separated from the chip-select line. In some cases it is also recommended that memory be disabled during the system reset with the $\overline{RESIN}$ input. This protects the memory content against spikes on the write line during this time.

## uA723 PRECISION VOLTAGE REGULATOR

The uA723 monolithic integrated circuit voltage regulator is used extensively in power supply designs. The device consists of a temperature compensated reference amplifier, an error amplifier, a 150 mA series-pass transistor, and current-limiting circuitry. See Figures 6-63 and 6-64 for the functional diagram and schematic.

Additional external npn or pnp pass elements may be used when output currents exceeding 150 mA are required. Provisions are made for adjustable current limiting and remote shutdown. In addition, the device features low standby current drain, low temperature drift and high ripple rejection. The uA723 may be used with positive or negative supplies as a series, shunt, or floating regulator.

When using an external series pass device, the 3-dB bandwidth of the uA723 must also be taken into consideration. Adequate uA723 compensation may be provided by connecting a 100 to 500 pF capacitor from the compensation terminal to the inverting input. Extra capacitance may be required at both the input and output of any power supply due to the inductive effects of long lines. Adding output capacitance provides the additional benefit of reducing the output impedance at high frequencies.

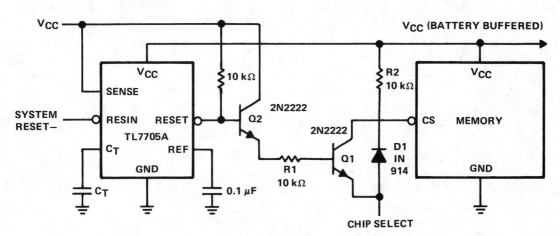

**Figure 6-62. Circuit Diagram for Memory Protection**

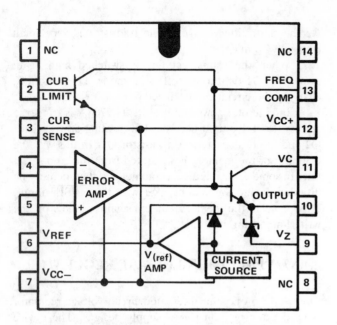

**Figure 6-63. uA723 Functional Block Diagram**

## TYPICAL APPLICATIONS

The required output voltage and current limits for the applications shown in Figure 6-65 can be calculated from the equations given in Table 6-1. In all cases the resulting resistor values are assumed to include a potentiometer as part of the total resistance. Table 6-2 affords a quick reference for many standard output voltage requirements.

### Table 6-1. Formulas for Output Voltages

Outputs from $+2$ to $+7$ V
[Figures 6-65 (a), (e), (f)]

$$V_O = V_{(ref)} \times \frac{R2}{R1 + R2}$$

Outputs from $+7$ to $+37$ V
[Figures 6-65 (b), (d), (e), (f)]

$$V_O = V_{(ref)} \times \frac{R1 + R2}{R2}$$

Outputs from $-6$ to $-250$ V
[Figure 6-65 (c)]

$$V_O = -\frac{V_{(ref)}}{2} \times \frac{R1 + R2}{R1}$$

$$R3 = R4$$

Current Limiting $\quad I_{(limit)} \approx \dfrac{0.65 \text{ V}}{R_{SC}}$

Foldback Current Limiting
[Figure 6-65 (f)]

$$I_{(knee)} \approx \frac{V_O R3 + (R3 + R4)0.65 \text{ V}}{R_{SC} \, R4}$$

$$I_{OS} \approx \frac{0.65 \text{ V}}{R_{SC}} \times \frac{R3 + R4}{R4}$$

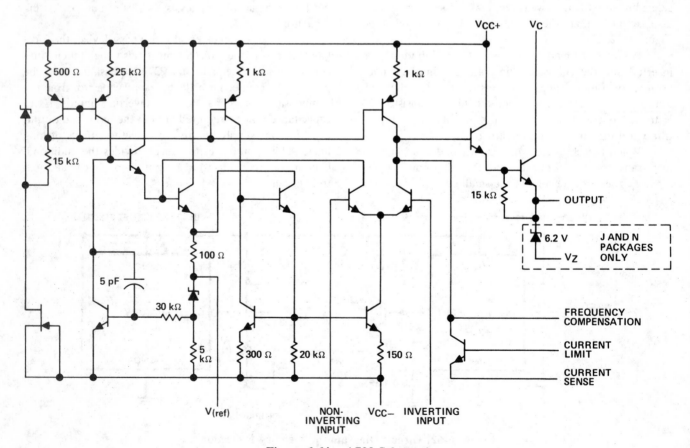

**Figure 6-64. uA723 Schematic**

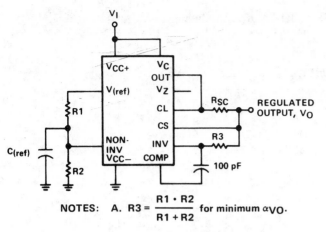

NOTES: A. $R3 = \dfrac{R1 \cdot R2}{R1 + R2}$ for minimum $\alpha_{VO}$.

B. R3 may be eliminated for minimum component count. Use direct connection (i.e., $R_3 = 0$).

**(a) BASE LOW-VOLTAGE REGULATOR**
($V_O$ = 2 to 7 Volts)

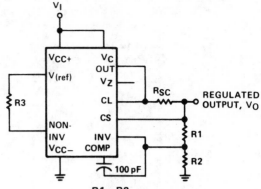

NOTES: A. $R3 = \dfrac{R1 \cdot R2}{R1 + R2}$ for minimum $\alpha_{VO}$.

B. R3 may be eliminated for minimum component count. Use direct connection (i.e., $R_3 = 0$).

**(b) BASIC HIGH-VOLTAGE REGULATOR**
($V_O$ = 7 to 37 VOLTS)

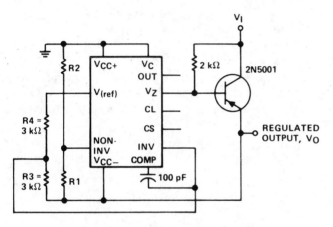

**(c) NEGATIVE-VOLTAGE REGULATOR**

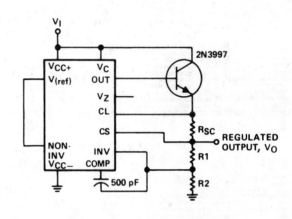

**(d) POSITIVE-VOLTAGE REGULATOR**
**(EXTERNAL N-P-N PASS TRANSISTOR)**

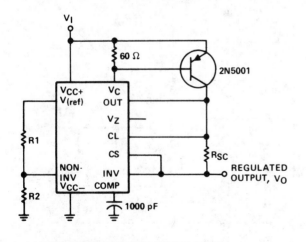

**(e) POSITIVE-VOLTAGE REGULATOR**
**(EXTERNAL P-N-P PASS TRANSISTOR)**

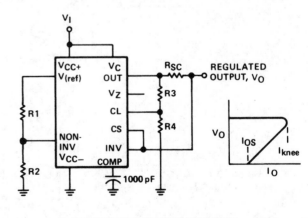

**(f) FOLDBACK CURRENT LIMITING**

**Figure 6-65. Typical Applications**

## Table 6-2. Resistor Values for Standard Output Voltages

| OUTPUT VOLTAGE (V) | APPLICABLE FIGURE (6-65) SEE NOTE 1 | FIXED OUTPUT ± 5% kΩ | | ADJUSTABLE OUTPUT ± 10% kΩ | | |
|---|---|---|---|---|---|---|
| | | R1 | R2 | R1 | P1 | R2 |
| +5.0 | a, e, f | 2.15 | 4.99 | 0.75 | 0.5 | 2.2 |
| +6.0 | a, e, f | 1.15 | 6.04 | 0.5 | 0.5 | 2.7 |
| +9.0 | b, d, e, f | 1.87 | 7.15 | 0.75 | 1.0 | 2.7 |
| +12.0 | b, d, e, f | 4.87 | 7.15 | 2.0 | 1.0 | 3.0 |
| +15.0 | b, d, e, f | 7.87 | 7.15 | 3.3 | 1.0 | 3.0 |
| −9.0 | c see | 3.48 | 5.36 | 1.2 | 0.5 | 2.0 |
| −12.0 | c note 2 | 3.57 | 8.45 | 1.2 | 0.5 | 3.3 |
| −15.0 | c | 3.57 | 11.5 | 1.2 | 0.5 | 4.3 |

NOTES: 1. To make the voltage adjustable, the R1/R2 divider shown in the figures must be replaced by the divider shown here.

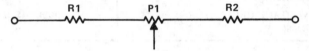

2. For negative output voltages less than 9 V, $V_{CC}+$ and $V_C$ must be connected to a level large enough to allow the voltage between $V_{CC}+$ and $V_{CC}-$ to be greater than 9 V.

## GENERAL PURPOSE POWER SUPPLY

The general purpose power supply shown in Figure 6-66 may be used for supply output voltages from 1 to 35 V.

The line transformer should be selected to give about 1.4 times the desired output voltage from the positive side of the filter capacitor, C1, to ground. R1 discharges the carriers in the base-emitter junction of the TIP31 when the drive is reduced. Its value is determined as follows:

$$R1 = \frac{\text{TIP31 Voltage (at point of conduction)}}{\text{Leakage Current of TIP31 and uA723 Output}}$$

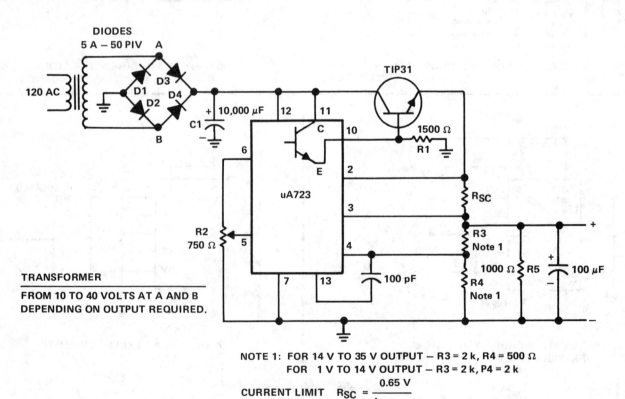

NOTE 1: FOR 14 V TO 35 V OUTPUT — R3 = 2 k, R4 = 500 Ω
FOR 1 V TO 14 V OUTPUT — R3 = 2 k, P4 = 2 k

CURRENT LIMIT $R_{SC} = \dfrac{0.65 \text{ V}}{I_{(limit)}}$

**Figure 6-66. General Purpose Power Supply**

where: TIP31 voltage at point of conduction is 0.35 V, leakage current (collector-base) of the TIP31 plus the collector-emitter leakage of the uA723 output transistor (worst case = 200 μA).

therefore: $R1 = \dfrac{0.35 \text{ V}}{0.0002 \text{ A}} = 1750 \ \Omega$ maximum

$$R1 = 1.5 \text{ k}\Omega \text{ (standard value)}$$

Potentiometer R2 sets the output voltage to the desired value by adjusting the reference input voltage. It is connected between pin 6 (7.15 V reference) and ground. The center arm of R2, connected to pin 5, will select any point between zero and the 7.15 V reference.

Resistors R3 and R4 are connected in series across the supply output. The junction of these two resistors is connected to the inverting input (pin 4) of the error amplifier establishing an output voltage reference. This voltage reference is compared to the selected voltage at the non-inverting input to the error amplifier (pin 5) to set the level of output voltage regulation. The values for R3 and R4 are listed in Note 1 of Figure 6-66.

$R_{SC}$ is the current limit set resistor. Its value is calculated as:

$$R_{SC} = \dfrac{0.65 \text{ V}}{I_L}$$

For example, if the maximum current output is to be 1 A, $R_{SC} = 0.65/1.0 = 0.65 \ \Omega$.

The 1 kΩ resistor, $R_S$, on the output is a light-load resistor designed to improve the no-load stability of the supply. The 100 μF electrolytic capacitor improves the overall output ripple voltage. A 100-pF capacitor from the compensation terminal (pin 13) to the inverting input

(pin 4) allows for gain variations in the uA723 error amplifiers and for parasitic capacitances.

The output voltage and current of this supply must be restricted to the specifications of the TIP31 series pass transistor. Since it is rated at two watts in free air at 25°C, sufficient heat sinking is necessary.

## 8-AMP REGULATED POWER SUPPLY FOR OPERATING MOBILE EQUIPMENT

It is often necessary to operate or test equipment used in automotive applications. This supply, as shown in Figure 6-67, provides up to 8 A at 13.8 V.

The uA723 is used as the control element, furnishing drive current to series-pass transistors which are connected in a Darlington configuration. Two 2N3055 npn transistors are used as the pass transistors, so proper heat sinking is necessary to dissipate the power.

This supply is powered by a transformer operating from 120 VAC on the primary and providing approximately 20 VAC on the secondary. Four 10-A diodes with a 100 PIV rating are used in a full-wave bridge rectifier. A 10,000 μF/36 VDC capacitor completes the filtering, providing 28 VDC.

The dc voltage is fed to the collectors of Darlington-connected 2N3055's. Base drive for the pass transistors is from pin 10 of the uA723 through a 200 Ω current limiting resistor, R1. The reference terminal (pin 6) is tied directly to the non-inverting input of the error amplifier (pin 5), providing 7.15 V for comparison.

The inverting input to the error amplifier (pin 4) is fed from the center arm of a 10 kΩ potentiometer connected across the output of the supply. This control is set for the desired output voltage of 13.8 V. Compensation of the error amplifier is accomplished with a 500-pF capacitor connected from pin 13 to pin 4.

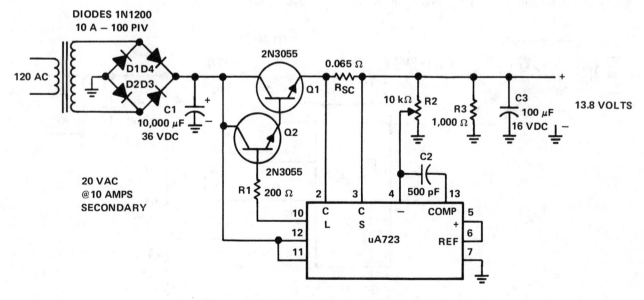

Figure 6-67. 8-Amp Regulated Power Supply

The 1 kΩ resistor on the output is a light load to provide stability when the supply has a no load condition. The 100 µF/16 VDC electrolytic capacitor completes the filter action and reduces the ripple voltage.

The current output of the supply is sampled through resistor $R_{SC}$ between the output transistor and the output terminal. The resistor value for a 10 A maximum current is calculated from the formula:

$$R_{SC} = \frac{0.65 \text{ V}}{I_{(load\ max)}} = \frac{0.65}{10} = 0.065\ \Omega$$

If the power supply should exceed 8 A or develop a short circuit, the uA723 regulator will bias the transistors to cutoff and the output voltage will drop to near zero until the short circuit condition is corrected. This circuit features a no-load-to-full-load (8 A) voltage regulation of no more than 0.2 VDC variation (better than 2% regulation).

## ± 15 VOLTS @ 1.0 AMP REGULATED POWER SUPPLIES

When working with operational amplifiers, a common requirement is plus and minus supplies in the 15 V range. A positive 15 V supply is shown in Figure 6-68 and a negative 15 V supply is shown in Figure 6-69.

### Positive Supply

The positive supply, shown in Figure 6-68, receives + 20 VDC from the rectifier/filter section. This is applied to pins 11 and 12 of the uA723 as well as to the collector of the 2N3055 series-pass transistor. The output voltage is sampled through R1 and R2 providing about 7 V with respect to ground at pin 4.

The reference terminal (pin 6) is tied directly to pin 5, the non-inverting input of the error amplifier. For fine trimming of the output voltage, a potentiometer may be installed between R1 and R2. A 100-pF capacitor from pin 13 to pin 4 furnishes gain compensation for the amplifier.

Base drive to the 2N3055 pass transistor is furnished by pin 10 of the uA723. Since the desired output of the supply is 1 A, maximum current limit is set to 1.5 A by resistor $R_{SC}$ whose value is calculated as:

$$R_{SC} = \frac{0.65 \text{ V}}{I_{(max\ limit)}} = \frac{0.65}{1.5} = 0.433\ \Omega$$

A 100-µF electrolytic capacitor is used for ripple voltage reduction at the output. A 1 kΩ output resistor provides stability for the power supply under no-load conditions. The 2N3055 pass transistor must be mounted on an adequate heat sink since the 3.5 W, 25°C rating of the device would be exceeded at 1 A load current.

### Negative Supply

The negative 15 V version of this power supply is shown in Figure 6-69.

The supply receives − 20 V from the rectifier/filter which is fed to the collector of the Darlington pnp pass transistor, a TIP105. A different uA723 configuration is required when designing a negative regulator.

The base drive to the TIP105 is supplied through resistor R5. The base of the TIP105 is driven from pin 9 ($V_Z$ terminal), which is the anode of a 6.2 V zener diode that connects to the emitter of the uA723 output control transistor.

The method for providing the positive feedback required for foldback action is shown in Figure 6-69. This technique introduces positive feedback by increased current flow through resistors R1 and R2 under short-circuit conditions. This forward biases the base-emitter junction of the 2N2907 sensing transistor, which reduces base drive to the TIP105.

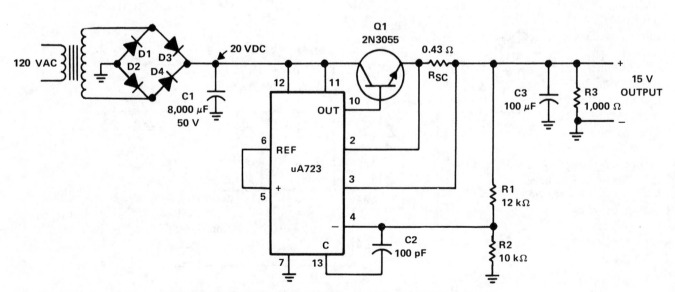

**Figure 6-68. +15-Volts at 1.0-Amp Regulated Power Supply**

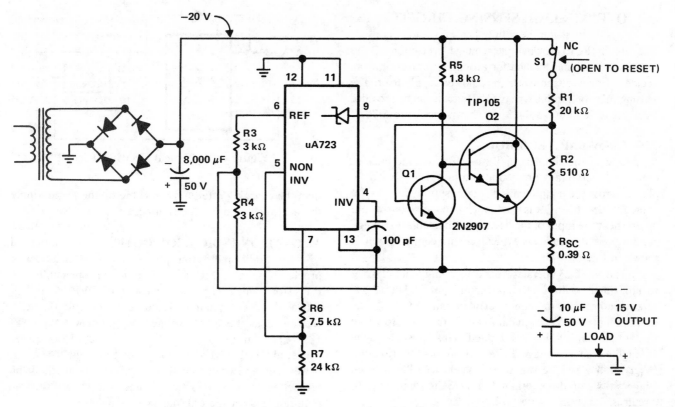

**Figure 6-69. – 15-Volts at 1.0-Amp Regulated Power Supply**

The final percentage of foldback depends on the relative contributions of the voltage drop across R2 and $R_{SC}$ to the base current of the 2N2907 sensing transistor. From the start of base-emitter conduction of the sense transistor to the full shut-off of the TIP105 pass transistor requires a 2 μA base current.

The latch condition, or 100% positive feedback, is generated by any change in the input voltage which increases the voltage drop across R2 turning on the sense transistor (2N2907). It can only be reset by breaking the positive feedback path with switch S1. This allows the series pass device to once more be driven in a normal fashion.

R3 and R4 are equal in value and divide the 7.15 V reference in half. The resulting 3.6 V reference is tied to the inverting input of the error amplifier. R6 and R7 are connected in series across the output of the power supply. The junction of R6 and R7 furnishes 3.6 V to the non-inverting input of the error amplifier. At this point the output is regulated at −15 V with respect to ground.

Resistors R1 and R2 are calculated as follows:

$$R1(k\Omega) = V_I - {}^*V_{SENSE(V)}$$
$$= 20 - 0.5$$
$$= 19.5 \text{ k}\Omega$$

$$R1 = 20 \text{ k}\Omega \text{ (standard value)}$$

$$R2(k\Omega) = {}^*V_{SENSE(V)} = 0.5 \text{ k or}$$
$$510 \text{ }\Omega \text{ (standard value)}$$

Resistor R5 $= (V_I - V_O - V_{BEQ2} - VR_{SC})$
$$\times \frac{(\text{min beta Q2})}{I_M (\text{max load current})}$$

$$R5 = (20 - 15 - 2.8 - 0.4)$$
$$\times \frac{1000}{1} = 1800 \text{ }\Omega$$

$$R5 = 1.8 \text{ k}\Omega$$

The current sense resistor $R_{SC}$ is calculated as follows:

$$R_{SC} = \frac{V_O}{I_M}\left(\frac{V_{SENSE}}{V_I - V_{SENSE}}\right) = \frac{15}{1}\left(\frac{0.5}{20 - 0.5}\right) = 0.384 \text{ }\Omega$$

$$R_{SC} = 0.39 \text{ }\Omega$$

Foldback limiting, as used in this circuit, is advantageous where excessive pass transistor power dissipation is a problem. The TIP105 can tolerate only 2 W dissipation in free air at 25°C ambient, so adequate heat sinking is necessary.

---

${}^*V_{SENSE}$ is defined as the base to emitter voltage needed to start turn-on of the 2N2907. From the data sheet this is about 0.5 V.

## OVERVOLTAGE SENSING CIRCUITS

The use of SCR crowbar overvoltage protection (OVP) circuits is a popular method for providing protection from accidental overvoltage stress for a power supply load. The sensing function for this type of OVP circuit can be provided by a single IC, the MC3423, as shown in Figure 6-70.

### THE CROWBAR TECHNIQUE

One of the simplest and most effective methods of obtaining overvoltage protection is to use a crowbar SCR placed across the equipment's dc power supply bus. As the name implies, the SCR is used much like a crowbar would be, to short the input of the dc supply when an overvoltage condition is detected. A typical circuit configuration is shown in Figure 6-71.

The MC3423 operates from a $V_{CC}$ minimum of 4.5 V to a maximum of 40 V. The input error amplifier has a 2.6 V reference between the non-inverting input and $V_{EE}$. The inverting input is $V_{sense1}$ (Pin 2) and is the point to which the output sense voltage is applied. This is usually done through a resistor voltage divider which sets the trip point ($V_{ref}$) at 2.6 V. The output of the device, Pin 8, then triggers the gate drive terminal of the SCR. A basic OVP circuit is shown in Figure 6-72.

When $V_{CC}$ rises above the trip point set by R1 and R2, an internal current source (Pin 4) begins charging capacitor C1 which is also connected to Pin 3. When triggered, Pin 8 supplies gate drive through the current limit resistor (RG) to the gate of the SCR. The minimum value of RG is given in Figure 6-73.

The value of capacitor C determines the minimum duration of the overvoltage condition necessary to trip the OVP. The value of C can be determined from Figure 6-74.

If the overvoltage condition disappears before C is charged, C discharges at a rate which is 10 times faster

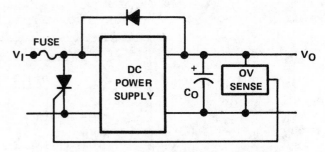

**Figure 6-71. Typical Crowbar Circuit**

than the charging rate, and resets the timing feature until the next overvoltage condition occurs.

### ACTIVATION INDICATION OUTPUT

An additional output for use as an OV indicator is provided on the MC3423. This is an open-collector transistor which saturates when the OVP circuit is activated. It will remain in a saturated state until the SCR crowbar pulls the supply voltage, $V_{CC}$, below 4.5 V.

This output may also be used to clock an edge-triggered flip-flop whose output inhibits or shuts down the power supply when the OVP trips. This method of protection reduces or eliminates the heat sinking requirements for the crowbar SCR.

### REMOTE ACTIVATION INPUT

Another feature of the MC3423 is its remote activation input, Pin 5, which has an internal pull-up current source. This input is CMOS/TTL compatible and, when held below 0.8 V, the MC3423 operates normally. However, if it is raised above 2 V, the OVP is activated regardless of whether an overvoltage condition is present. This feature may be used to accomplish an orderly and sequenced shutdown of system power supplies during a system fault condition.

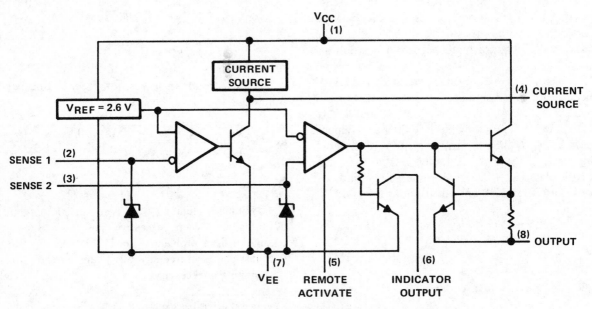

**Figure 6-70. MC3423 Overvoltage Crowbar Sensing Circuit Block Diagram**

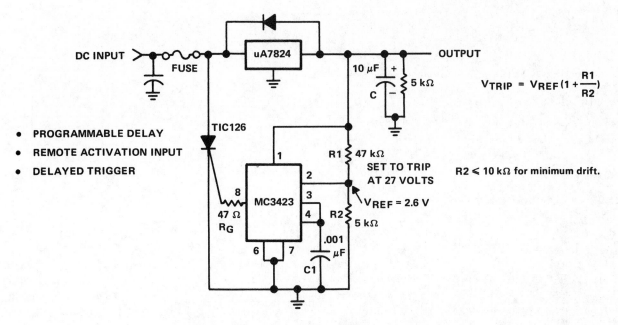

- PROGRAMMABLE DELAY
- REMOTE ACTIVATION INPUT
- DELAYED TRIGGER

$$V_{TRIP} = V_{REF}\left(1 + \frac{R1}{R2}\right)$$

R2 ≤ 10 kΩ for minimum drift.

**Figure 6-72. Overvoltage Protection Circuit**

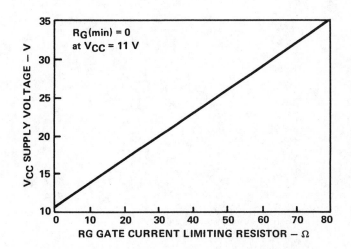

**Figure 6-73. Minimum RG vs Supply Voltage**

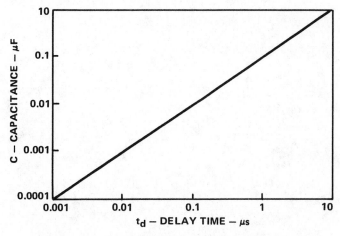

**Figure 6-74. Capacitance vs Minimum Overvoltage
Duration**

6-39

# Section 7

# Integrated Circuit Timers

Timing may be accomplished by a variety of methods; mechanical, thermal, chemical, electronic, or a combination of these. Regardless of the method, a timer depends upon a time base generated internally or applied from an external source. The spring-driven clock, for example, generates its own internal time base, whereas the electric clock uses the period of the ac line voltage as an external time base. The first consideration in the design of a solid state timer is the generation of a suitable time base.

## RC TIME-BASE GENERATOR

A simple time base circuit may be established by the use of a resistor, a capacitor, and sensing network as shown in Figure 7-1.

The time, t, for the capacitor C to charge to voltage $V_C$ in this circuit is:

$$t = \text{time in seconds}$$
$$\ln = \text{natural log}$$
$$R = \text{resistance in ohms}$$
$$C = \text{capacitance in farads}$$
$$V_C = \text{capacitor voltage in volts}$$
$$t = RC \ln \frac{V_{CC}}{V_{CC} - V_C}$$

For one RC time constant ($t = RC$) $V_C$ equals 63.21% of $V_{CC}$.

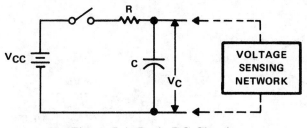

**Figure 7-1. Basic RC Circuit**

## A BASIC DELAY TIMER

A basic delay circuit may be implemented with an RC network, a discharge switch, a voltage reference, a threshold comparator and an output switch. The timer circuit and its typical waveforms are illustrated in Figure 7-2.

The circuit operates as follows: Initially the timer output ($V_O$) is high (near $V_{CC}$) and switch S is closed, shorting capacitor C to ground. When switch S is opened the timing period begins and $V_O$ is still high.

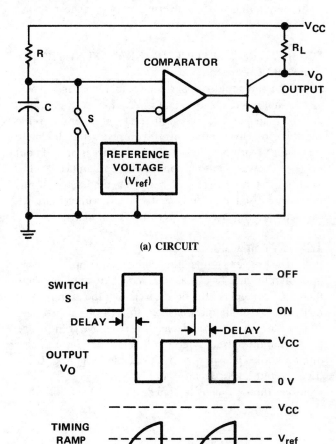

(a) CIRCUIT

(b) VOLTAGE WAVEFORMS

**Figure 7-2. Basic Delay Timer**

When switch S is opened capacitor C starts charging, through resistor R, toward the $V_{CC}$ rail. The voltage $V_C$ rises non-linearly, forming a timing ramp (Figure 7-2). $V_O$ is delayed from changing state until $V_C$ reaches the reference voltage, $V_{ref}$, which is some fraction of $V_{CC}$. When the timing ramp voltage reaches $V_{ref}$ the comparator output goes high, turning on the output transistor, thus switching the output low. The output will remain low until the switch S is closed or power is turned off.

The addition of another comparator, an RS type flip-flop and a discharge transistor to the structure shown in Figure 7-2 would allow a trigger pulse to start the timing function. Many other performance features including oscillation would be possible. NE555 type IC timers have all of these functions, except the timing resistor and capacitor, included on a single chip.

## NE/SE555 TIMERS

The NE555 was the first monolithic IC timer with multi-functional capabilities (introduced in 1972) and has been accepted as the standard for basic timing and oscillator functions. The NE555 (Figure 7-3) is a general-purpose bipolar IC capable of monostable and astable pulse generating modes covering a wide range of pulse durations and/or frequencies.

## DEFINITION OF BLOCK DIAGRAM FUNCTIONS
### Threshold Comparator

The threshold comparator compares its input with an internal reference level that is 2/3 $V_{CC}$. An input level greater than the reference will reset the timer's flip-flop resulting in a low output level and causing the discharge transistor to turn on. The internal reference is brought out on a pin allowing external control of the reference level to modify the timing period or reset the comparator. If this pin is not used it should be bypassed with a 0.01 μF capacitor to improve the timer's noise immunity.

### Trigger Comparator

The trigger comparator compares its input with an internal reference level that is 1/3 $V_{CC}$. An input level less than 1/3 $V_{CC}$ will set the flip-flop causing the output to go high and the discharge transistor to turn off. The trigger comparator functions on the leading (negative going) edge of the input pulse. Typically a minimum input pulse duration of 1.0 μs is required for reliable triggering. If the trigger input level remains lower than 1/3 $V_{CC}$ for longer than one timing cycle, the timer will retrigger itself after

the first output pulse. Propagation delay in the trigger comparator can delay turn off up to several microseconds after triggering. An output pulse duration of 10 μs or greater will prevent double triggering due to these effects.

### RS Flip-Flop

The RS flip-flop receives its reset input from the threshold comparator, its set input from the trigger comparator and an additional reset from an external source. The external reset input overrides all other inputs and can be used to initiate a new timing cycle. When this input is at a logic low level the timer output is low and the discharge transistor is on, resulting in a reset condition. The reset input is TTL compatible. When not used it is recommended that the reset pin be connected to the $V_{CC}$ rail to prevent false resetting.

### Discharge Transistor

The discharge transistor will be on when the device output is low. Its open-collector output is used to discharge the external timing capacitor during the reset phase of operation.

### Output Stage

The device output stage is driven by the flip-flop output. It is an active-pull-up, active-pull-down circuit with a 200 mA sink or source capability.

### 555 BASIC OPERATING MODES

There are two basic operating modes for 555 timer circuits: the monostable (one-shot) mode for timing functions, and the astable (free-running) mode for oscillator functions. There are many variations of the two basic modes, allowing numerous applications.

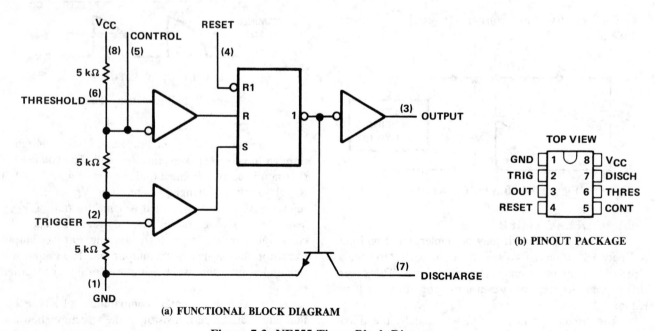

(a) FUNCTIONAL BLOCK DIAGRAM

(b) PINOUT PACKAGE

**Figure 7-3. NE555 Timer Block Diagram**

## Monostable Mode

Figure 7-4 illustrates the circuit and waveforms for the 555 connected in its most basic mode of operation — a triggered monostable.

With the trigger input terminal held higher than $1/3$ $V_{CC}$, the timer is in its standby state and the output is low. When a trigger pulse appears with a level less than $1/3$ $V_{CC}$, the timer triggers and its timing cycle starts. The output switches to a high level near $V_{CC}$ and concurrently $C_t$ begins to charge toward $V_{CC}$. When the $V_C$ voltage crosses $2/3$ $V_{CC}$, the timing period ends with the output falling to zero. The circuit is now ready for another input trigger pulse. The output pulse duration (T) is defined as $(1.1) \times R_t C_t$. In the monostable mode T is used to represent the on time which is the time base in this mode. With few restrictions, $R_t$ and $C_t$ can have a wide range of values. Assuming zero capacitor leakage current, there is no theoretical upper limit on T while the short pulse durations are limited by internal propagation delays to about 10 μs.

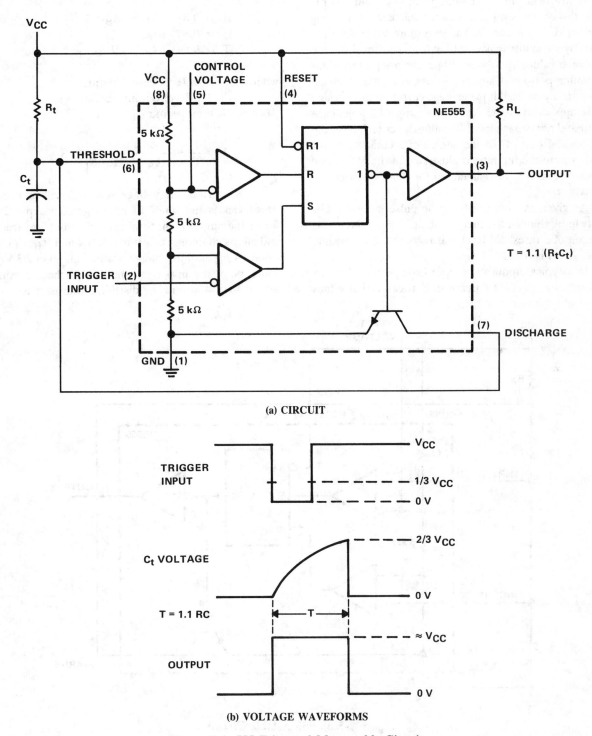

(a) CIRCUIT

$T = 1.1 (R_t C_t)$

(b) VOLTAGE WAVEFORMS

**Figure 7-4. 555 Triggered Monostable Circuit**

A reasonable lower limit for $R_t$, for 15 V operation, is about 1 kΩ for the NE555 and is limited only by power dissipation considerations. The upper $R_t$ limit, for a $V_{CC}$ of 15 V, is about 10 MΩ. Allowing for only 0.25 μA input leakage and 0.25 μA capacitor charging current the total current through $R_t$ at the threshold level would be 0.5 μA. $R_t$ max is equal to the voltage across $R_t$ at threshold, (which for a 15 V supply is 5 V), divided by 0.5 μA. This yields an $R_t$ max of 10 MΩ. However, lower values should be used if accurate timing is required.

A practical minimum value for $C_t$ is about 100 pF. Below this value stray capacitance becomes a limiting factor for timing accuracy. The maximum value for $C_t$ is limited by capacitor leakage. Low leakage capacitors are available in values up to about 10 μF and are preferred for long timing periods. Capacitor values as high as 1000 μF could possibly be used if the leakage current is low enough for the application. The real limitation on $C_t$ is leakage current and not capacitance. The ultimate criterion for the selection of $R_t$ and $C_t$ is the degree of accuracy desired. Staying within the limitations illustrated in the 555 device data sheet charts is recommended for relatively accurate designs.

As given in Figure 7-4(b), the pulse duration T is slightly more than an RC time constant (T = 1.1 RC). This is a result of a threshold level that is 66.7% of $V_{CC}$ while one RC level is 63.2% of $V_{CC}$.

In a typical application input leakage currents may also lead to some slight differences between actual values of "T" and calculated values. Operation at high speeds (very short pulse durations) will result in variations from the calculated values due to internal propagation delays.

## Astable Mode

Figure 7-5(a) illustrates the 555 connected as an astable timer. Like the monostable circuit, the astable circuit requires only a few external components.

Figure 7-5(b) shows the timing diagram. The timing calculations are as follows.

$$t_1 = 0.693 (R_A + R_B) C_t$$
$$t_2 = 0.693 R_B C_t$$
$$T = 0.693 (R_A + 2R_B) C_t$$

where: $t_1$ is high-level output period
$t_2$ is low-level output period
T is total period ($t_1 + t_2$)

$$f = \frac{1}{T} = \frac{1.44}{(R_A + 2R_B)C_t}$$

On startup, the voltage across $C_t$ will be near zero which causes the timer to be triggered via pin 2. This forces the output high, turning off the discharge transistor and allows charging of $C_t$ through $R_A$ and $R_B$. $C_t$ charges toward $V_{CC}$ until its voltage reaches a level of 2/3 $V_{CC}$, at which point the upper threshold is reached, causing the output to go low and the discharge transistor to turn on.

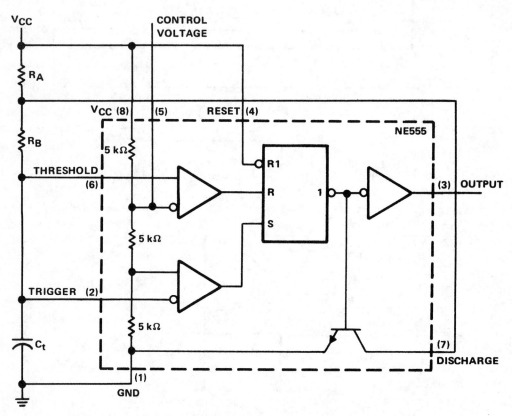

**Figure 7-5(a). 555 Astable Circuit**

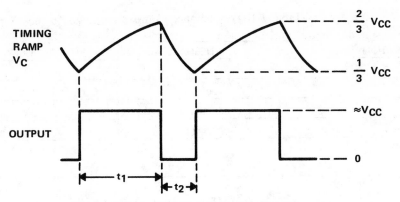

**Figure 7-5(b). NE555 Astable Timing Diagram**

Capacitor $C_t$ then discharges toward ground through $R_B$ until its voltage reaches 1/3 $V_{CC}$, the lower trigger point. This retriggers the timer, beginning a new cycle. The timer threshold input therefore oscillates between the 2/3 $V_{CC}$ and 1/3 $V_{CC}$ comparator threshold levels.

The frequency of operation is simply the reciprocal of T as stated above. The duty cycle for either the high or low output state is simply that period ($t_1$ or $t_2$) divided by the total period. For reliable operation, the upper frequency limit of the bipolar NE555 is about 100 kHz. Device upper frequency limitations are due to internal propagation delays. Low frequencies are not limited by the 555 devices but are limited by the leakage characteristics of $C_t$.

Specific duty cycles may be required in some applications. Duty cycle can be controlled (within limits) by adjusting the resistance ratios of $R_A$ and $R_B$ in Figure 7-5(a). As $R_B$ becomes large with respect to $R_A$, the duty cycle approaches 50% (square wave operation). Conversely, as $R_A$ becomes large with respect to $R_B$, the duty cycle increases toward 100%. $R_A$ must not be allowed to reach zero. Practical duty cycles range from 49.8% to 99% or in terms of resistor ratios $R_A$ may be 1/100 of $R_B$ or $R_B$ may be 1/100 of $R_A$.

### Accuracy

Although the 555 is a simple device, it performs accurately. In the monostable mode there is a typical initial error of only 1% due to process imperfections ($R_t$ and $C_t$ errors must be considered separately). For astable operation the error is somewhat greater, typically about 2%. Drift with temperature is typically 55 ppm/°C (or 0.005%/°C) for the monostable mode, and is about 150 ppm/°C for the astable mode.

### TLC555 TIMER

In 1984, TI introduced a LinCMOS version of the 555 timer, the TLC555. It features the performance characteristics of a bipolar 555 and, in addition, some important improvements. Table 7-1 is a performance comparison of major parametric differences in the NE555 and TLC555.

Due to its high-impedance inputs, the TLC555 is capable of producing accurate time delays and oscillations using less expensive, smaller timing capacitors than the NE555. A duty cycle of 50% in the astable mode is easily achieved using only one resistor and one capacitor as illustrated in Figure 7-6.

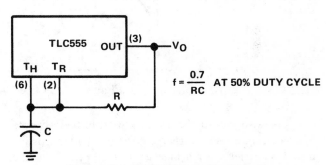

**Figure 7-6. TLC555 Astable Circuit**

While the complementary CMOS output is capable of sinking over 100 mA and sourcing over 10 mA, the TLC555 exhibits greatly reduced supply current spikes during output transitions (see Table 7-1). This minimizes the need for the large decoupling capacitors required by the bipolar 555. The TLC555 also provides very low power consumption (typically 1 mW at $V_{DD}$ = 5 V) for supply voltages ranging from 2 V to 18 V.

### TLC555 Astable Timing Equations

At astable operating frequencies above one megahertz, the propagation delays of the TLC555 must be accounted for in the equations for calculating the astable frequency (see Figure 7-7). The on-state resistance ($R_{Don}$) of the NMOS discharge transistor (typically 10 Ω) is also included to give greater accuracy. Besides the low to high and high to low progagation delays, ($t_{PLH}$ and $t_{PHL}$ respectively), two additional times, $T_C$ and $T_D$, must also be included along with the maximum charge and minimum discharge voltages, ($V_h$ and $V_1$ respectively).

As the capacitor is charging, it continues to charge up to $V_h$ after crossing the 2/3 $V_{DD}$ level for a time equal to the $t_{PHL}$ propagation delay. $T_D$ is the length of time it takes to discharge from $V_h$ to 2/3 $V_{DD}$.

**Table 7-1. Performance Comparison**

| SPECIFICATION | NE555 | TLC555 | UNITS |
|---|---|---|---|
| QUIESCENT CURRENT | 6.0 | 0.3 | mA |
| BIAS CURRENT | 500,000 | 10 | pA |
| MAXIMUM FREQUENCY | 100 | 2000 | kHz |
| CURRENT SPIKES | ≥200 | 3 | mA |

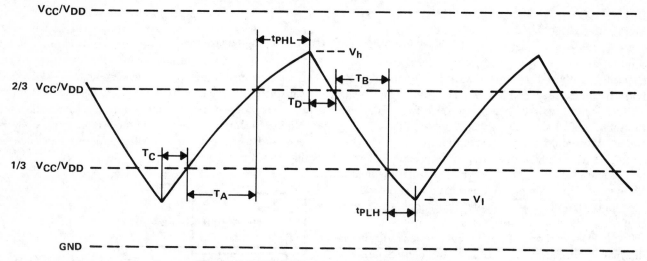

**Figure 7-7. TLC555 Astable Timing Diagram**

Likewise, during the discharge part of the cycle the capacitor continues to discharge down to $V_1$ after crossing the $1/3\ V_{DD}$ level for a time equal to $t_{PLH}$. $T_C$ is the length of time required to charge back up from $V_1$ to $1/3\ V_{DD}$.

$$R_T = R_A + R_B$$
$$R_T' = R_B + R_{Don}$$
$$T_A = 0.693\ R_T C_t$$
$$\therefore V_h = (2/3)V_{DD}\{1 - \mathrm{EXP}[-(0.693 + t_{pHL}/R_T C_T)]\} + (1/3)V_{DD}$$
$$\therefore V_1 = (2/3)V_{DD}\ \mathrm{EXP}[-(0.693 + t_{pLH}/R_T'C_T)]$$
$$\therefore T_C = -R_t C_t \ln\{1 - [(1/3)V_{DD} - V_1]/(V_{DD} - V_1)\}$$
$$\therefore T_D = (-R_T'C_t)\ \ln[(2/3)V_{DD}/V_h]$$
$$\therefore T_{period} = T_A + T_B + T_C + T_D + t_{PLH} + t_{PHL}$$
$$\therefore f_{astable} = 1/T_{period}$$

Notice that for $t_{PLH}$, $t_{PHL}$, and $R_{Don}$ equal to zero the above equations reduce to the standard equation as printed in the data book for the NE555:

$$\text{(NE555)}\ T_{period} = T_A + T_B = 0.693(R_A + 2R_B)(C_t)$$

It should also be noted that a 10% increase in astable frequency will also occur if a 0.1 μF capacitor is connected from the control voltage pin (pin 5) to ground.

**TLC556/NE556 DUAL UNIT**

The NE556 bipolar timer contains two NE555 timers in the same package, with common power-supply and ground pins. The LinCMOS version of the dual 555 timer is the TLC556. See Figure 7-8 for the pinout of these devices.

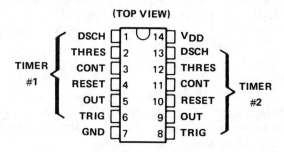

**Figure 7-8. 556 Dual Timer Pinout**

The TLC556 dual timer is identical to the NE556 electrically and functionally. It is fabricated using the LinCMOS process and has the same advantages noted for the TLC555.

**uA2240 PROGRAMMABLE TIMER/COUNTER**

The uA2240 programmable timer/counter is a special class of timer IC. This device includes a timing section made up of a timer similar to a 555 type, an eight-bit counter, a control flip-flop, and a voltage regulator. Timing periods from microseconds to days may be programmed with an accuracy of 0.5%. Two timing circuits cascaded could generate time delays of up to three years. The 2240 may be operated in either the monostable or astable mode with programmable timing in either mode. A functional diagram and pin-out are shown in Figure 7-9.

## DEFINITION OF uA2240 FUNCTIONS
### Voltage Regulator ($V_{REG}$)

The on-chip regulator provides voltage to the binary counter and control logic and through pin 15 to external circuits. If $V_{CC}$ (pin 16) is 15 V. $V_{REG}$ is typically 6.3 V. For a $V_{CC}$ of 5 V, $V_{REG}$ is typically 4.4 V. For a $V_{CC}$ supply of less than or equal to 4.5 V, pin 16 ($V_{CC}$) should be shorted to pin 15 ($V_{REG}$). The minimum supply voltage for this condition is 4 V. When supplying external circuitry via pin 15 (regulator output), the output current should be 10 mA or less.

### Control Logic

The control logic block provides trigger and reset signals to the binary counter and time-base generator flip-flops. Trigger and reset inputs are high impedance and TTL compatible, requiring only about 10 µA of input current. Therefore, they may be controlled by TTL, low level MOS or CMOS logic, and respond to positive input transitions. The reset input (pin 10) terminates the timing cycle by returning the counter flip-flops to zero and disabling the time-base oscillator. A logic-high reset stops

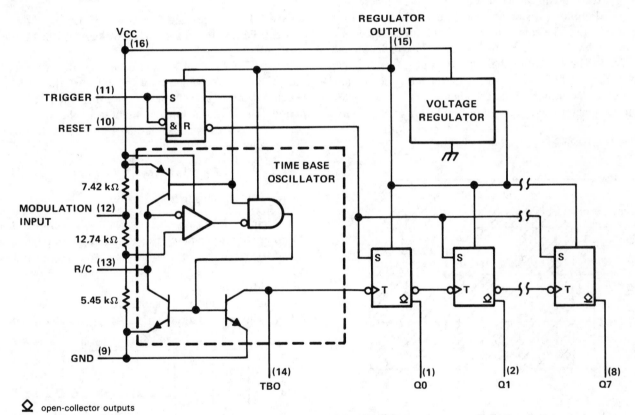

open-collector outputs

**(a) FUNCTIONAL BLOCK DIAGRAM**

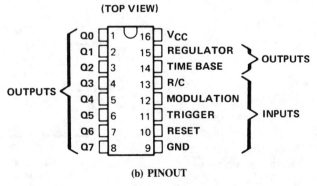

**(b) PINOUT**

**Figure 7-9. uA2240 Functional Block Diagram and Pinout**

the timer and sets all outputs high. When powered on, the uA2240 comes up in the reset state. A trigger input (pin 11) initiates the timing cycle by enabling the time-base oscillator and setting all outputs low. Once triggered, the circuit is immune to further trigger inputs until the timing cycle is completed or a reset signal is applied. However, the trigger takes precedence if both trigger and reset are applied simultaneously.

### Time-Base Oscillator

The heart of a uA2240 is its time-base oscillator that is made up of threshold comparators, a flip-flop, discharge and time-base output transistors, RC input, and a modulation and sync input.

### RC Input

A resistor and capacitor connected in series between $V_{CC}$ and ground provide an exponential ramp at the RC input (pin 13). The comparator thresholds are designed to detect at levels allowing a 63% charge time (1 RC time interval). Thus, the time-base output (TBO) pulse will have a period T = 1 RC. Figure 7-10 shows the recommended range of timing component values. The timing capacitor leakage currents must be low to allow it to charge to the comparator threshold levels with a large value (1 MΩ or greater) timing resistor.

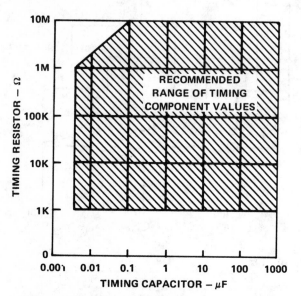

**Figure 7-10. Recommended Range of Timing Component Values**

### Modulation and Sync Input

The MOD input (pin 12) is nominally at 73% of the $V_{CC}$ level due to internal biasing. This level may be varied by connecting a resistor from pin 12 to ground or $V_{CC}$, or by applying an external voltage. This change, or modulation, of voltage on pin 12 changes the upper threshold for the time-base comparator resulting in a change, or modulation, of the time-base period T. Figure 7-11 illustrates the effects of an externally applied modulation voltage on the time-base period.

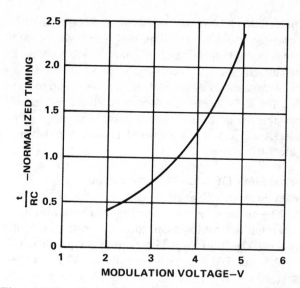

**Figure 7-11. Normalized Change in Time Base Period as a Function of Modulation Voltage at Pin 12**

The MOD input may also be used to synchronize the time-base oscillator with an external clock. Synchronization is achieved by setting the time-base period (T) to be an integer multiple of the sync pulse period ($T_S$). This is accomplished by choosing R and C timing components so that:

$$T = RC = T_S \times M$$

where: M is an integer from 1 to 10.

Figure 7-12 gives the typical pull-in range for harmonic synchronization versus the ratio of time-base period to sync pulse period ($T/T_S$).

### Threshold Comparators

The two levels of threshold are set at 27% and 73% of $V_{CC}$. Charging and discharging of the timing capacitor

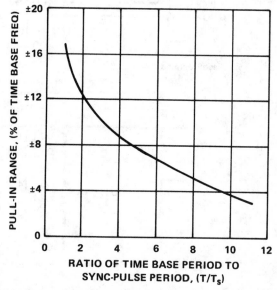

**Figure 7-12. Typical Pull-In Range for Harmonic Synchronization**

occurs between these two levels. When charging from the 27% level toward $V_{CC}$ to the second threshold at 73%, the percentage interval to be changed is $73 - 27$ or 46%. The actual percentage of the range from 27% to the $V_{CC}$ rail is 73% so the charge range to be covered is 0.46/0.73 or 63%, exactly one RC time constant. The resulting time base $T = RC$.

### Oscillator Flip-Flop

Comparator outputs feed the oscillator flip-flop which controls the discharge and time-base output (TBO) transistors. Once triggered (see Figure 7-13) the oscillator continues to run until reset. Output pulses from the TBO are internally connected to the counter input for automatic triggering. The TBO output is an open-collector transistor and requires a pull-up resistor (typically 20 k$\Omega$) to be connected to the $V_{REG}$ output (pin 15). Grounding the TBO output (pin 14) will disable the counter section.

NOTE: When using a high supply voltage ($V_{CC} > 7$ V) and a small timing capacitor ($C < 0.1 \mu F$) the pulse width of the TBO output may be too narrow to trigger the counter section. Connecting a 300 pF capacitor from pin 14 to ground will widen the TBO output pulse width and allow a proper trigger time. This capacitor is also recommended to improve noise immunity.

### Binary Counter

The uA2240 has an on-chip 8-bit binary counter with outputs that are buffered open-collector type stages. Each output is capable of sinking 2 mA at 0.4 V $V_{OL}$. At turn on, or in the reset condition, all counter outputs are high, or in the off state. Following a trigger input (Figure 7-14) the outputs will change states according to the sequence shown. The outputs may be used individually, or can be

connected together in a wired-OR configuration for special programming.

Combining counter outputs in a wired-OR configuration results in the addition of the time delays associated with each output connected together. As an example pin 5 alone results in a timing cycle ($T_O$) that is equal to 16T. Similarly connecting $Q_0$ (pin 1), $Q_4$ (pin 5), and $Q_7$ (pin 8) together will yield $T_O = (1 + 16 + 128)T = 145$ T. A proper selection of counter output terminals will allow programming of $T_O$ from 1 T to 255 T.

### uA2240 BASIC OPERATING MODES
### Monostable Operating Mode

Figure 7-15 illustrates the 2240 used in the monostable mode.

In the circuit, Figure 7-15(a), $R_t$ and $C_t$ set the time base, T, for the desired time period, $T_O$. Programming of various output times may be accomplished by connecting the desired counter output pins together. The timer output appears across $R_L$. The output pulse width, $T_O$, is equal to the number of timing pulses, n, multiplied by $R_t C_t$ or $T_O = n R_t C_t$.

As shown in the timing diagram, Figure 7-15(b), the output is high (at $V_{CC}$) prior to triggering. When a trigger pulse is received, the output falls low and the timing cycle is initiated. The time-base oscillator will now run until the counter reaches the count programmed by the selector switches or jumpers. When this count is reached, the output rises from the low level to $V_{CC}$. This rise in level is fed to the reset input, which stops the oscillator and resets the counter. The timer is now in its standby state, awaiting the next trigger pulse.

R1 is a load resistor for the time-base output. The 270 pF capacitor on the time-base pin is a noise bypass to

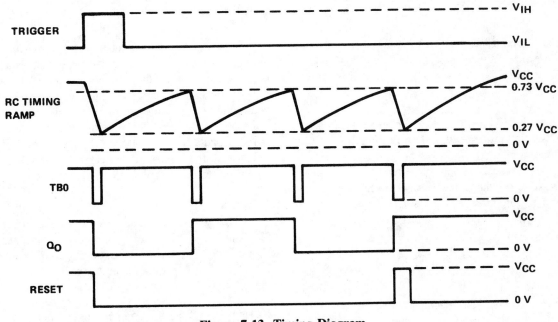

**Figure 7-13. Timing Diagram**

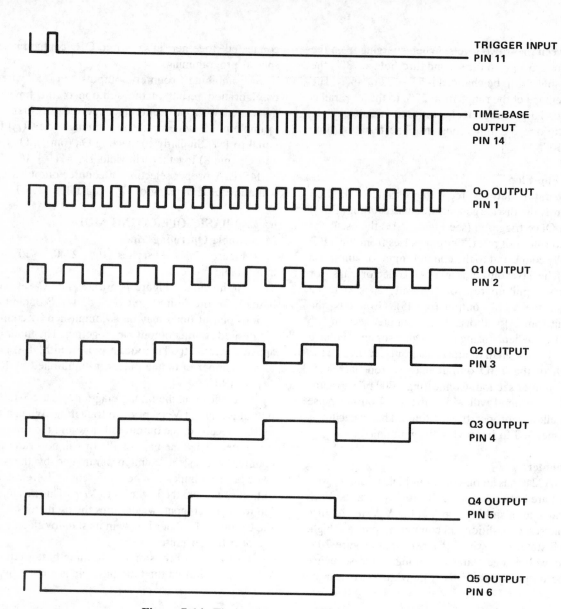

**Figure 7-14. Timing Diagrams of Output Waveforms**

ensure noise immunity within the time-base oscillator. The $R_t$ and $C_t$ value ranges appear in Figure 7-15. The maximum oscillator frequency should be limited to about 100 kHz.

### Astable Operating Mode

The astable mode circuit is shown in Figure 7-16(a). This circuit is similar to the monostable circuit with the exception that the reset is not connected to the output. This allows the oscillator to continue oscillating once started by a trigger pulse. With a single counter output connected to $R_L$ and the output bus, the frequency of oscillation will be:

$$f_o = \frac{1}{2nR_tC_t}$$

where: n is the counter tap selected (1, 2, 4, 8, etc)

The factor 2 is required because the basic timing taps are multiples of 1/2 cycle.

This circuit will not self-start on power-up. A pulse applied to the trigger input will start the synchronous oscillations. The oscillator may be stopped by applying a reset pulse, which causes the output to go high. It will remain in this state until triggered again. If automatic power-up oscillation is desired, connect the trigger input to pin 15 (regulator output). The timing component ranges shown in the monostable circuit, Figure 7-15, are applicable to the astable mode circuit.

### Accuracy

The 2240 timer is somewhat more complex than the 555 family. Timing accuracy is good, typically 0.5% at a $V_{CC}$ of 5 V. The maximum operating frequency is about 130 kHz. The trigger and reset inputs have a threshold sensitivity of 1.4 V.

### GENERAL DESIGN CONSIDERATIONS

Several precautions should be taken with respect to the $V_{CC}$ supply. The most important is good power supply

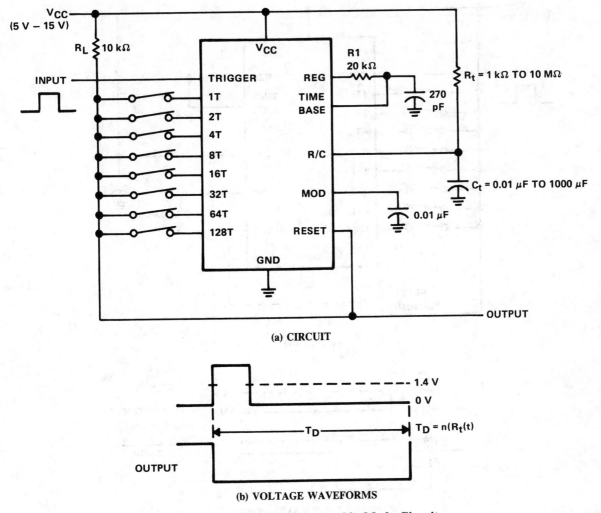

**(a) CIRCUIT**

**(b) VOLTAGE WAVEFORMS**

**Figure 7-15. uA2240 Monostable Mode Circuit**

filtering and bypassing. Ripple on the supply line can cause loss of timing accuracy. A capacitor from $V_{CC}$ to ground, ideally directly across the device, is necessary. The capacitance value will depend on the specific application. Values of from 0.01 μF to 10 μF are not uncommon. The capacitor should be as close to the device as physically possible.

If timing accuracy is to be maintained, stable external components are necessary. Most of the initial timing error is due to the inaccuracies of the external components. The timing resistors should be the metal film type if accuracy and repeatability are important design criteria. If the timing is critical, an adjustable timing resistor is necessary. A good quality multi-turn pot might be used in series with a metal film resistor to make up the R portion of the RC network.

The timing capacitor should also be high quality, with very low leakage. Do not use ceramic disc capacitors in the timing network under any circumstance. Several acceptable capacitor types are silver mica, mylar, polystyrene, and tantulum. If timing accuracy is critical over temperature, timing components with a small positive temperature coefficient should be chosen. The

most important characteristic of the capacitor is low leakage. Obviously any leakage will subtract from the charge count causing the actual time to be longer than the calculated value.

One final precaution should be observed. Make certain that the power dissipation of the package is not exceeded. With extremely large timing capacitor values, a maximum duty cycle which allows some cooling time for the discharge transistor may be necessary.

## MISSING PULSE DETECTOR

Figure 7-17 illustrates an NE555 timer utilized as a missing pulse detector. This circuit will detect a missing pulse or abnormally long spacing between consecutive pulses in a train of pulses. The timer is connected in the monostable mode. In addition, a 2N2907 is connected with the collector grounded and the emitter tied to pins 6 and 7. This outboard switch is in parallel with the internal discharge transistor. The transistor base is connected to the trigger input of the NE555.

For this application, the time delay should be set slightly longer than the timing of the input pulses. The timing interval of the monostable circuit is continuously

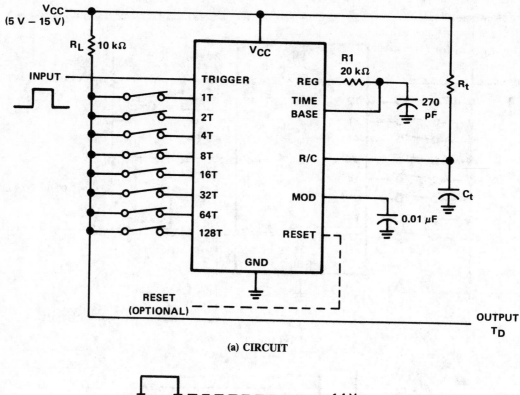

(a) CIRCUIT

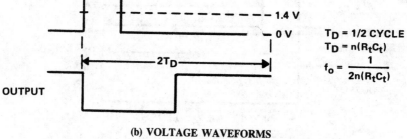

$$T_D = 1/2 \text{ CYCLE}$$
$$T_D = n(R_t C_t)$$
$$f_o = \frac{1}{2n(R_t C_t)}$$

(b) VOLTAGE WAVEFORMS

Figure 7-16. uA2240 Astable Mode Circuit

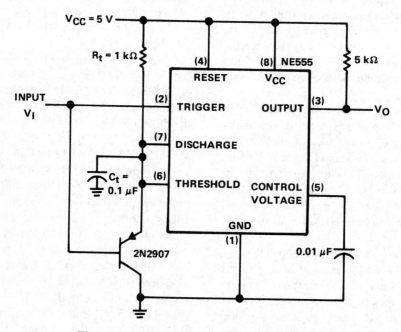

Figure 7-17. Missing Pulse Detector Circuit

retriggered by the input pulse train ($V_I$). The pulse spacing is less than the timing interval, which prevents $V_C$ from rising high enough to end the timing cycle. A longer pulse spacing, a missing pulse, or a terminated pulse train will permit the timing interval to be completed. This will generate an output pulse ($V_O$) as illustrated in Figure 7-18. The output remains high on pin 3 until a missing pulse is detected at which time the output goes low.

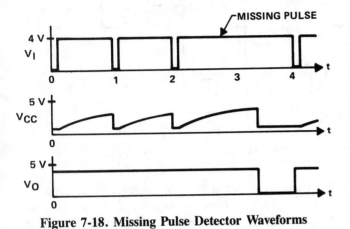

**Figure 7-18. Missing Pulse Detector Waveforms**

The NE555 monostable circuit should be running slightly slower (lower in frequency) than the frequency to be analyzed. Also, the input cannot be more than twice this free-running frequency or it would retrigger before the timeout and the output would remain in the low state continuously. The example in Figure 7-17 operates in the monostable mode at about 8 kHz so pulse trains of 8 to 16 kHz may be observed.

## NE555 ONE-SHOT TIMER

Figure 7-19 shows an NE555 connected in its most basic mode of operation, a triggered monostable one-shot. This simple circuit consists of only the two timing components $R_t$ and $C_t$, the NE555, and bypass capacitor C2. While not essential for operation, C2 is recommended for noise immunity.

During standby, the trigger input terminal is held higher than 1/3 $V_{CC}$ and the output is low. When a trigger pulse appears with a level less than 1/3 $V_{CC}$, the timer is triggered and the timing cycle starts. The output rises to a high level near $V_{CC}$, and at the same time $C_t$ begins to charge toward $V_{CC}$. When the $C_t$ voltage crosses 2/3 $V_{CC}$, the timing period ends with the output falling to zero, and the circuit is ready for another input trigger. This action is illustrated in Figure 7-20.

Due to the internal latching mechanism, the timer will always time out when triggered, regardless of any subsequent noise (such as bounce) on the trigger input. For this reason the circuit can also be used as a bounceless switch by using a shorter RC time constant. A 100 kΩ resistor for $R_t$ and a 1 μF capacitor for $C_t$ would give a clean 0.1 s output pulse when used as a bounceless switch.

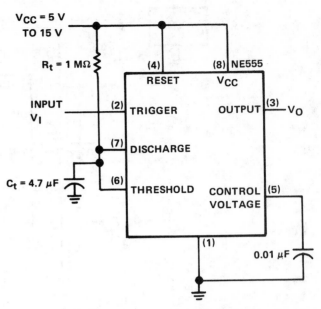

**Figure 7-19. NE555 One-Shot Timer**

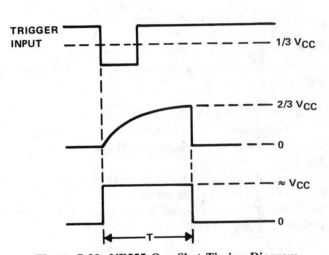

**Figure 7-20. NE555 One-Shot Timing Diagram**

## OSCILLOSCOPE CALIBRATOR

The oscilloscope is one of the most useful electronic instruments. It is capable of displaying both low and high frequency signals on its screen, in a form which lends itself to circuit analysis. Calibrated amplifiers and time base generators are usually incorporated.

The calibrator shown in Figure 7-21 can be used to check the accuracy of the time-base generator as well as to calibrate the input level of the amplifiers.

The calibrator consists of an NE555 connected in the astable mode. The oscillator is set to exactly 1 kHz by adjusting potentiometer P1 while the output at pin 3 is being monitored against a known frequency standard or frequency counter. The output level likewise is monitored from potentiometer P2's center arm to ground with a standard instrument. P2 is adjusted for 1 V peak-to-peak at the calibrator output terminal. The circuit may be supplied with at least 8 V and is regulated to 5 V to supply the NE555.

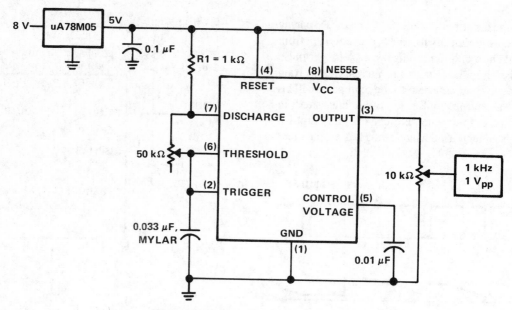

**Figure 7-21. Oscilloscope Calibrator**

During operation, the calibrator output terminal will produce a 1 kHz square wave signal at 1 V peak-to-peak with about 50% duty cycle. For long term oscillator frequency stability, C1 should be a low leakage mylar capacitor.

## DARKROOM ENLARGER TIMER

An enlarger timer is essential for consistent quality and repeatability. The timer controls the exposure time of the paper in the enlarger.

The NE555 circuit illustrated in Figure 7-22 is a basic one-shot timer with a relay connected between the output and ground. It is triggered with the normally open momentary contact switch which when operated, grounds the trigger input (pin 2). This causes a high output to energize K1 which closes the normally open contacts in the lamp circuit. They remain closed during the timing interval, then open at time out. Timing is controlled by a 5 MΩ potentiometer, $R_t$. All timer driven relay circuits should use a reverse clamping diode, such as D1, across the coil. The purpose of diode D2 is to prevent a timer output latch up condition in the presence of reverse spikes across the relay.

With the RC time constant shown, the full scale time is about 1 minute. A scale for shaft position of the 5 MΩ potentiometer can be made and calibrated in seconds. Longer or shorter full scale times may be achieved by changing the values of the RC timing components.

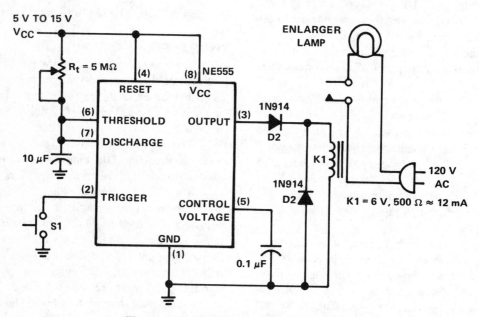

**Figure 7-22. Darkroom Enlarger Timer**

## TOUCH SWITCH

An interesting type of circuit that uses an IC timer is shown in Figure 7-23. This circuit is a "touch switch", a device in which switching action is accomplished without conventional mechanical movement of a lever or push button. A circuit such as this would also be useful in a burglar alarm.

The circuit is basically an NE555 monostable, the only major difference being its method of triggering. The trigger input is biased to a high value by the 22 MΩ resistor. When the contact plates are touched, the skin resistance of the operator will lower the overall impedance from pin 2 to ground. This action will reduce the voltage at the trigger input to below the 1/3 $V_{CC}$ trigger threshold and the timer will start. The output pulse width will be T = 1.1 R1C1, in this circuit about 5 seconds. A relay connected from pin 3 to ground instead of the LED and resistor could be used to perform a switching function. Diodes should be used with the relay as shown in Figure 7-22.

The contact strips or plates may be copper, brass, or any conducting material arranged for convenient finger contact.

## BASIC SQUARE WAVE OSCILLATOR

A basic square wave oscillator is shown in Figure 7-24. The NE555 is connected in the astable mode and uses only three timing components ($R_A$, $R_B$, and $C_t$). A 0.01 µF bypass capacitor is used on pin 5 for noise immunity.

Operating restrictions of the astable mode are few. The upper frequency limit is about 100 kHz for reliable operation, due to internal storage times. Theoretically there is no lower frequency limit, only that imposed by $R_t$

and $C_t$ limitations. There are many variations of this astable circuit, but it is shown here in its simplest form.

Oscillators such as this are useful in test equipment or as a signal generator for testing other circuits.

The frequency for the circuit in Figure 7-24 may be calculated as follows.

$$f = \frac{1.44}{(R_A + 2R_B)C_t}$$

$$= \frac{1.44}{(4.7K + 2M)(0.0047 \ \mu F)}$$

$$= \frac{1.44}{9.42209 \times 10^{-3}}$$

$$f = 152.8 \ Hz$$

## LINEAR RAMP GENERATOR

A very useful modification to the standard monostable configuration is to make the timing ramp a linear waveform, rather than an exponential one. The linear charging ramp is most useful where linear control of voltage is required. Some possible applications are a long period voltage controlled timer, a voltage to pulse width converter, or a linear pulse width modulator.

One of the simplest methods to achieve a linear ramp monostable is to replace the timing resistor, $R_t$, with a constant current source as illustrated in Figure 7-25. Q1 is the current source transistor, supplying constant current to the timing capacitor $C_t$. When the timer is triggered, the clamp on $C_t$ is removed and $C_t$ charges linearly toward $V_{CC}$ by virtue of the constant current supplied by Q1. The threshold at pin 6 is 2/3 $V_{CC}$; here, it is termed $V_C$. When

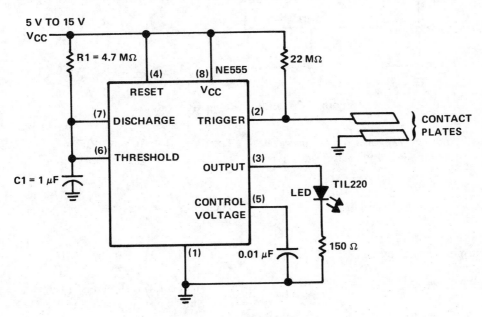

**Figure 7-23. Touch Switch**

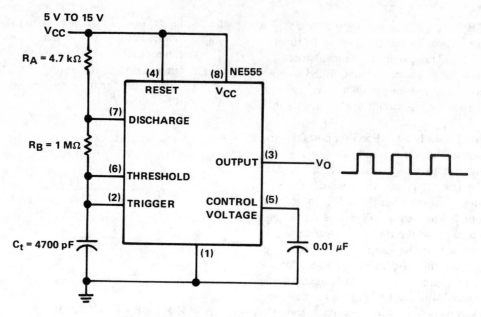

**Figure 7-24. Basic Square Wave Oscillator**

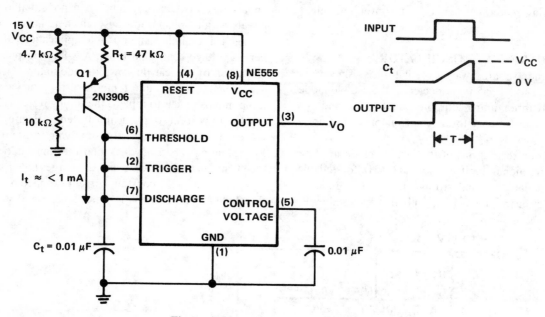

**Figure 7-25. Linear Ramp Generator**

the voltage across $C_t$ reaches $V_C$ volts, the timing cycle ends. The timing expression for output pulse width T is:

$$T = \frac{V_C C_t}{I_t}$$

where: $V_C$ is the voltage at pin 5
$I_t$ is the current supplied by Q1

$I_t$ can be approximated for 15 V $V_{CC}$ as:

$$\frac{\text{Voltage across } R_t}{I_t} = \frac{4.2 \text{ V}}{R_t \; 47 \text{ k}\Omega}$$

Then T is: $T \approx 0.24 \; V_C R_t C_t$
$\approx 0.24 \; (10)(4.7 \text{ k}\Omega)(0.01 \; \mu F)$
$\approx 1 \text{ ms}$

The ramp frequency $f_0$ is then:

$$f_0 = \frac{1}{2T} = \frac{1}{0.002} = 0.5 \text{ Hz}$$

In general, $I_t$ should be 1 mA or less, and $C_t$ can be any value compatible with the NE555.

## FIXED-FREQUENCY VARIABLE-DUTY-CYCLE OSCILLATOR

In a basic astable timer configuration timing periods $t_1$ and $t_2$, as shown in Figure 7-26, are not controlled independently. This makes it difficult to maintain a constant period (T) if either $t_1$ or $t_2$ is varied. Figure 7-26 illustrates this relationship.

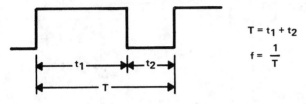

$$T = t_1 + t_2$$
$$f = \frac{1}{T}$$

**Figure 7-26. Astable Mode Output Timing**

A number of methods have been developed to maintain a constant period T for this versatile timer. One method, as illustrated in Figure 7-27, employs a circuit that adds two diodes to the basic astable mode circuit.

In this circuit the charge ($R_{AB}$) and discharge ($R_{BC}$) resistances are determined by the position of the common wiper arm (B) of the potentiometer, making it possible to adjust the duty-cycle by adjusting $t_1$ and $t_2$ proportionately without changing the period T.

At startup, the voltage across $C_t$ is less than the trigger level voltage (1/3 $V_{DD}$), causing the timer to be triggered via pin 2. The output of the timer (pin 3) goes

high, turning off the discharge transistor (pin 7) and allowing $C_t$ to charge through diode D1 and resistance $R_{AB}$.

When capacitor $C_t$ charges to the upper threshold voltage (2/3 $V_{DD}$), the flip-flop is reset and the output (pin 3) goes low. Capacitor $C_t$ then discharges through diode D2, resistance $R_{BC}$. When the voltage at pin 2 reaches 1/3 $V_{DD}$, the lower threshold or trigger level, the timer triggers again and the cycle is repeated.

In this circuit the oscillator frequency remains fixed and the duty cycle is adjustable from < 0.5% to > 99.5%.

## ALTERNATING LED FLASHER

It is often desirable to have two LEDs turn on and off alternately. Advertising signs frequently use this type of operation. Alternating LED action is easily accomplished using the circuit shown in Figure 7-28 with the TLC555 operating in the astable mode.

The timing components are R1, R2, and $C_t$. C1 is a bypass capacitor used to reduce the effects of noise. At startup, the voltage across $C_t$ is less than the trigger level voltage (1/3 VDD), causing the timer to be triggered via pin 2. The output of the timer (pin 3) goes high, turning LED1 off, LED2 on, the discharge transistor (pin 7) off, and allowing $C_t$ to charge through resistors R1 and R2.

When capacitor $C_t$ charges to the upper threshold voltage (2/3 $V_{DD}$), the flip-flop is reset and the output (pin 3) goes low. LED1 is turned on, LED2 is turned off, and capacitor $C_t$ discharges through resistor R2 and the

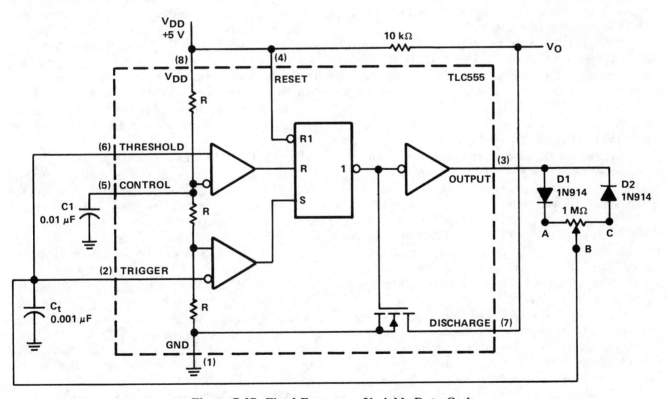

**Figure 7-27. Fixed-Frequency Variable-Duty Cycle Astable Oscillator**

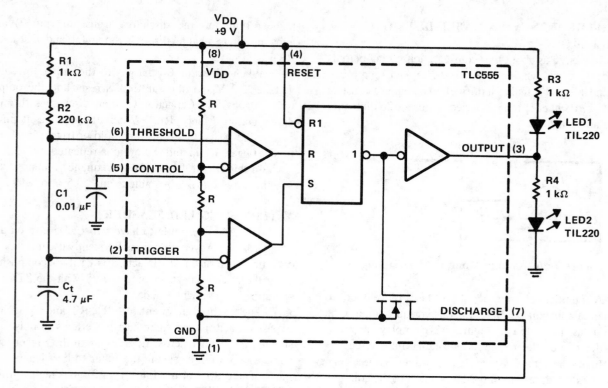

**Figure 7-28. Alternating LED Flasher**

discharge transistor. When the voltage at pin 2 reaches 1/3 $V_{DD}$, the lower threshold or trigger level, the timer triggers again and the cycle is repeated.

The totem-pole output at pin 3 is a square wave with a duty cycle of about 50%. The output alternately turns on each LED at slightly less than one blink per second.

If the unit is battery operated, the TLC555 uses minimum current to produce this function. With a 9-V battery the circuit draws 5 mA (no load) and 15 mA when turning on an LED. Most of the ON current is LED current.

## POSITIVE-TRIGGERED MONOSTABLE

The standard 555 ordinarily requires a negative-going trigger pulse to initialize operation; however, a positive-going triggger pulse may be used to start the timing cycle with the circuit shown in Figure 7-29.

In this design the trigger input (pin 2) is biased to 6 V (1/2 $V_{DD}$) by divider R1 and R2. The control input (pin 5) is biased to 8 V (2/3 $V_{DD}$) by the internal divider circuit. With no trigger voltage applied, point 'A' is at 4 V (1/3 $V_{DD}$). To turn the timer on, the voltage at point 'A' has to be greater than the 6 V present on pin 2.

A positive 5 V trigger pulse ($V_I$) applied to the control input (pin 5) is ac coupled through capacitor C1, adding the trigger voltage to the 8 V already on pin 5 which results in 13 V with respect to ground. The pulse width of the input trigger ($V_I$) is not critical; the main criterion is that the width of the input trigger pulse (following C1) should be less than the desired output pulse

width. The output pulse width is determined by the values of $R_t$ and $C_t$.

When the voltage at point 'A' is increased to 6.5 V, which is greater than the 6 V on pin 2, the timer cycle is initialized. The output of the timer (pin 3) goes high, turning off the discharge transistor (pin 7) and allowing $C_t$ to charge through resistor $R_t$. When capacitor $C_t$ charges to the upper threshold voltage of 8 V (2/3 $V_{DD}$), the flip-flop is reset and the output (pin 3) goes low. Capacitor $C_t$ then discharges through the discharge transistor.

The timer is not triggered again until another trigger pulse is applied to the control input (pin 5).

## VOLTAGE-CONTROLLED OSCILLATOR

There are many different types of voltage controlled oscillator (VCO) circuits that can use an IC timer. VCO circuits are valuable for instrumentation, electronic music applications, and function generators. The output is a rectangular pulse stream whose frequency is related to the external control voltage. A VCO circuit using the TLC555 is shown in Figure 7.30.

At startup, the voltage at the trigger input (pin 2) is less than the trigger level voltage (1/3 $V_{DD}$), causing the timer to be triggered via pin 2. The output of the timer (pin 3) goes high, allowing capacitor $C_t$ to charge very rapidly through diode D1 and resistor R1. The charge time of $C_t$ is extremely short and may essentially be neglected.

When capacitor $C_t$ charges to the upper threshold voltage (2/3 $V_{DD}$), the flip-flop is reset, the output (pin 3)

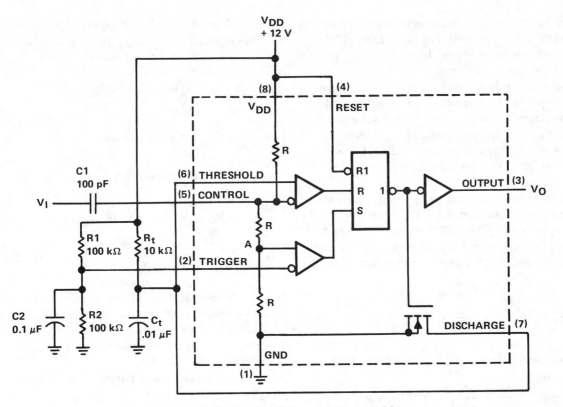

**Figure 7-29. Positive-Triggered Monostable**

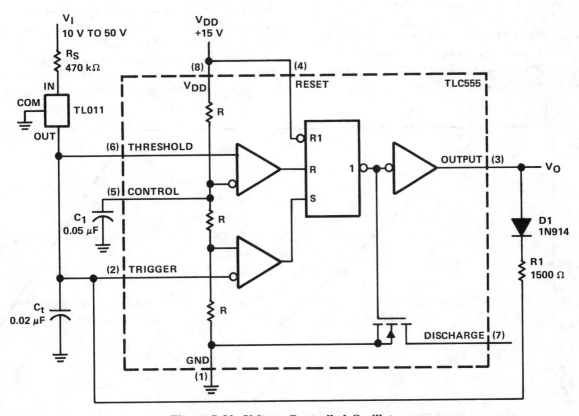

**Figure 7-30. Voltage-Controlled Oscillator**

goes low, and capacitor $C_t$ discharges through the current mirror, TL011. When the voltage at pin 2 reaches $1/3$ $V_{DD}$, the lower threshold or trigger level, the timer triggers again and the cycle is repeated.

The input voltage ($V_I$) determines the constant current output of the current mirror, which is used as a voltage to current converter and sets the discharge rate of capacitor $C_t$. The discharge time of $C_t$ determines the frequency of the oscillator. As the input voltage is varied from 10 V to 50 V, the output frequency varies at a linear rate.

As an example, assume an application calls for an output midrange frequency of 500 Hz. Since $T = 1/f$, the time between output pulses will be 2 ms. The charge time, which will be less than 1 μs, may be neglected. The discharge current of $C_t$ for a specific input control voltage is:

$$I_{DISCHARGE} = \frac{V_I}{R_S} = \frac{10\ V}{470\ k\Omega} = 20\ \mu A \text{ at 10 V input}$$

$$I_{DISCHARGE} \text{ at midrange} = 50\ \mu A \text{ at 25 V input}$$

$$I_{DISCHARGE} = \frac{V_I}{R_S} = \frac{50\ V}{470\ k\Omega} = 100\ \mu A \text{ at 50 V input}$$

With an input voltage of 10 V to 50 V, the TL011 current will vary linearly from 20 μA to 100 μA. Figure 7-31 shows the voltage to frequency conversion obtained with two different values for capacitor $C_t$. With $C_t = 0.001$ μF, a frequency range of 3.3 kHz to 10 kHz is obtained. When a value of 0.02 μF is used, a frequency range of 187 Hz to 1 kHz is obtained.

Since the capacitor, $C_t$, discharges from 10 V to 5 V ($2/3$ $V_{DD}$ to $1/3$ $V_{DD}$), the capacitor value may be calculated for 500 Hz as follows:

$$C = \frac{IT}{V_C} = \frac{(50\ \mu A)\ (0.002)}{5}$$

$$I = \text{midrange discharge current}$$

$$T = \frac{1}{f} = \text{midrange output pulse}$$

$$V_C = 5\ V \text{ (charge-discharge)}$$

$$C = \frac{(50 \times 10^{-6})\ (0.002)}{5} = 0.02\ \mu F$$

Note that the current mirror is sinking current during both the charge and discharge of $C_t$. However, the small discharge current is easily overcome during the charge cycle by the lower impedance, high-current charge path from the output pin.

For linear ramp applications, the output is obtained across $C_t$.

## CAPACITANCE-TO-VOLTAGE METER

This circuit performs a function that is somewhat different than a frequency-to-voltage converter. The circuit can be more easily analyzed by examining the individual sections as shown in Figure 7-32.

Timer U1 operates as a free-running oscillator at 60 Hz, providing trigger pulses to timer U2 which operates in the monostable mode. Resistor R1 is fixed and

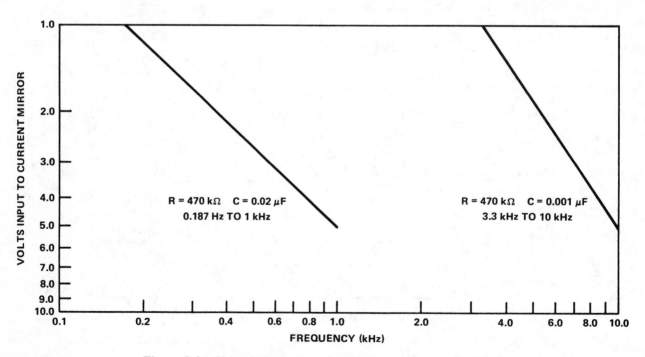

**Figure 7-31. Voltage-Controlled Oscillator Frequency vs Voltage**

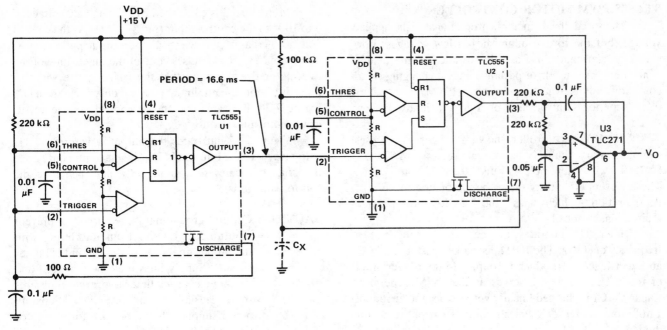

**Figure 7-32. Capacitance-to-Voltage Meter Chart**

capacitor Cx is the capacitor being measured. While the output of U2 is 60 Hz, the duty cycle depends on the value of Cx. U3 is a combination low-pass filter and unity-gain follower whose dc voltage output is the time-averaged amplitude of the output pulses of U2, as shown in Figure 7-33 (a and b).

Figure 7-33(a) shows when the value of Cx is small the duty cycle is relatively low. The output pulses are narrow and produce a lower average dc voltage level at the output of U3. As the capacitance value of Cx increases, the duty cycle increases making the output pulses at U2 wider and the average dc level output at U3 increases.

As an example, the graph in Figure 7-34 illustrates capacitance values of 0.01 μF to 0.1 μF plotted against the output voltage of U3. Notice the excellent linearity and direct one-to-one scale calibration of the meter. If this does not occur with your design, the 100 kΩ resistor, R1, can be replaced with a potentiometer which can be adjusted to the proper value for the meter being used.

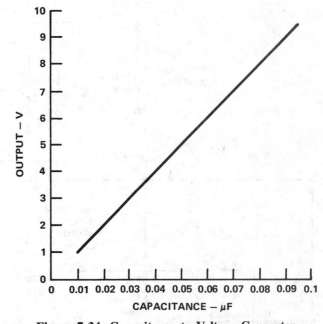

**Figure 7-34. Capacitance-to-Voltage Converter**

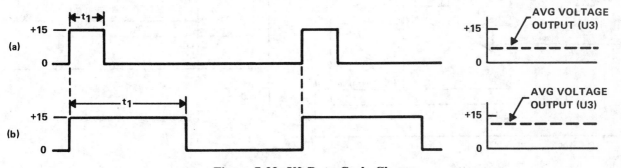

**Figure 7-33. U2 Duty Cycle Change**

## TLC555 PWM MOTOR CONTROLLER

The speed of a dc motor is proportional to the applied voltage, but the torque diminishes at low voltages. Low speed performance is usually erratic when analog controllers are used, especially under changing load conditions. Pulse-width-modulated (PWM) controllers offer superior control and operate efficiently at low speeds.

The PWM controller shown in Figure 7-35 uses complementary half-H peripheral drivers (SN75603, SN75604) with totem-pole outputs rated at 40 V and 2.0 A. These drivers effectively place the motor in a full bridge configuration which has the ability to provide bidirectional control.

Timer U1 operates in the astable mode at a frequency of 80 Hz. The 100 Ω discharge resistor results in an 8 μs trigger pulse which is coupled to the trigger input of timer U2. Timer U2 serves as the PWM generator. Capacitor C1 is charged linearly with a constant current of 1 mA from the IN5297, which is an FET current regulator diode.

Motor speed is controlled by feeding a dc voltage of 0 to 10 V to the control input (pin 5) of U2. As the control voltage increases, the width of the output pulse (pin 3) also increases. These pulses control the on/off time of the two motor drivers. Note that the trigger pulse width of timer U1 limits the minimum possible duty cycle from U2. Figure 7-36 illustrates the analog control voltage versus drive motor pulse width.

Figure 7-37 illustrates the output waveforms of U1 with respect to the output of U2. The maximum duty cycle that may be achieved is about 98% at which time the control voltage is 12.5 V.

CAUTION: Careful grounding is required to prevent motor-induced noise from interfering with the proper operation of the U1 and U2 timer circuits. Supply lines must be bypassed and decoupled at each timer to prevent transients from causing circuit instability. Separate power supplies should be used for the motor and the timer circuits.

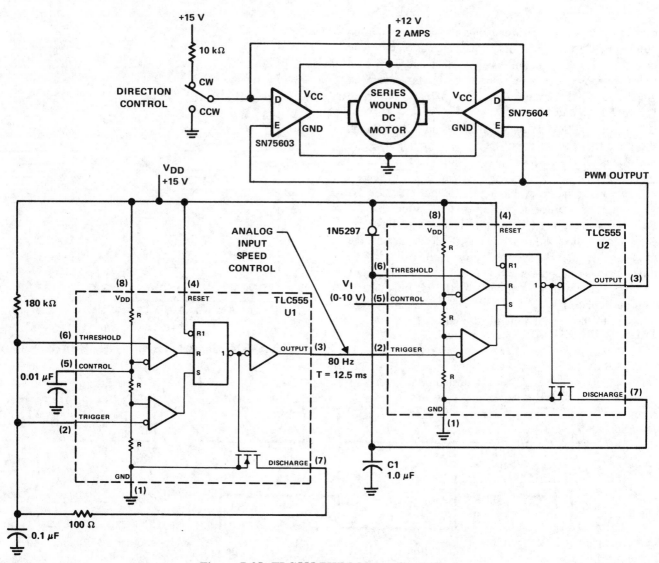

**Figure 7-35. TLC555 PWM Motor Controller**

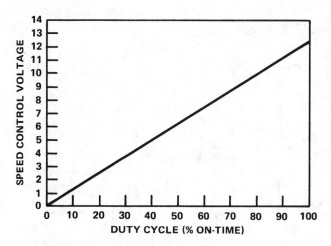

Figure 7-36. Control Voltage Versus Duty Cycle

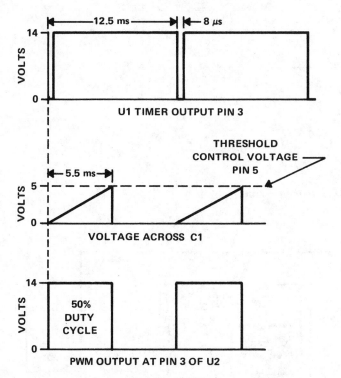

Figure 7-37. PWM Controller Waveforms

## TELEPHONE CONTROLLED NIGHT LIGHT

This application is a useful addition for the bedroom telephone stand. When the telephone rings, or when the handset is lifted, the night light is turned on and remains on while the conversation takes place. When the handset is replaced in the cradle, the light remains on for about 11 s. This circuit is illustrated in Figure 7-38.

Operationally the circuit may be divided into four sections.

1. U1 — TCM1520 Ring Detector
2. U2 — TLC555 Timer
3. U3 — TLC271 End-of-Call Detector
4. U4 — MOC3011 Light Switch

During standby conditions, the −48 V dc bias on the phone line maintains the output of U3 in a high state.

Also the timer discharge transistor is on, preventing the charging of timer capacitor C1. When the ac ring signal is applied to the phone line, it is processed by the ring detector U1, producing a negative output pulse at pin 2 for each ring. These pulses are applied to the trigger input (pin 2 of U2) and trigger U2 causing its output to go high and the discharge transistor to turn off. The high output of U2 activates opto-isolator U4 which turns on the night light. The discharge transistor, being off, allows C1 to begin charging. Each ring retriggers the timer and discharges C1 preventing it from reaching 2/3 $V_{DD}$ threshold level. Thus the night light will remain on while the phone is ringing and for about 11 s after the last ring. After 11 s C1 will be charged to the U2 threshold level (2/3 $V_{DD}$) resulting in the U2 output returning to a low level and its discharge output turning on discharging C1. At this time the lamp will turn off if the phone is not answered.

When the phone is answered, a 1 kΩ load is placed across the phone line (tip and ring in Figure 7-38). This removes the differential input to operational amplifier U3, causing its output to go low and capacitor C1 starts discharging through R1. As long as the voltage across C1 remains low, timer U2 cannot start its cycle and the lamp will remain on.

When the phone is hung up, the low impedance is removed from the phone line and the differential voltage across the line causes the U3 output to go high. This allows C1 to start charging, initiating the timing that will turn off the night light.

## PROGRAMMABLE VOLTAGE CONTROLLED TIMER

The uA2240 may easily be configured as a programmable voltage controlled timer with a minimum number of external components. The basic programmable timer circuit is shown in Figure 7-39, including the functional clock diagram of the uA2240. Counter outputs Q2 through Q6 are not shown in Figure 7-39.

A useful feature of the uA2240 timer is the modulation input (pin 12), which allows external adjustment of the input threshold level. A variable voltage is applied to pin 12 from the arm of a 10 kΩ potentiometer connected from $V_{CC}$ to ground. A change in the modulation input voltage will result in a change in the time base oscillator frequency and the period of the time base output (TBO). The time-base period may be trimmed via the modulation input to supply the exact value desired, within the limits determined by the values of R1 and C1. In this application, the basic time-base period set by R1 and C1 is 0.5 ms.

The effect of the voltage modulation input on the time-base oscillator period is shown in Figure 7-40. Although the voltage that can be safely applied to pin 12 may range from $V_{CC}$ to ground, oscillator operation may cease near $V_{CC}$ (within 0.5 V). Note that the chart also shows TBO operation inhibited with modulation inputs below approximately 2 V. With a modulation input voltage

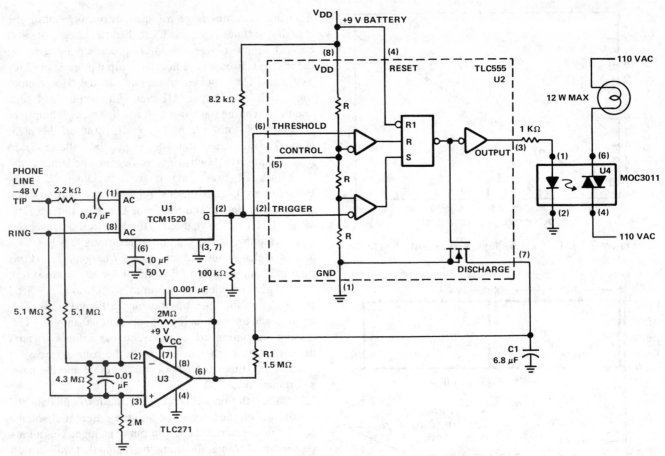

**Figure 7-38. Telephone Controlled Night Light**

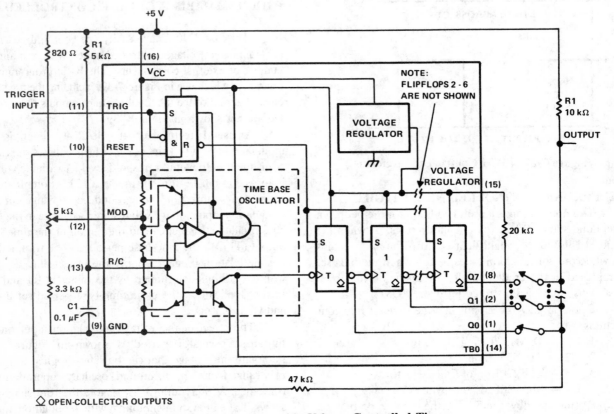

◇ OPEN-COLLECTOR OUTPUTS

**Figure 7-39. Programmable Voltage Controlled Timer**

of 3.5 V, the Q5 connection gives an active low output for 32 cycles of the time base oscillator, or 16 ms in the case of the circuit shown in Figure 7-39.

The TBO has an open-collector output that is connected to the regulator output via a 20 kΩ pull-up resistor. The output of the TBO drives the input to the 8-stage counter section.

At start-up, a positive trigger pulse starts the TBO and sets all counter outputs to a low state. The trigger pulse duration must be at least 2 µs with a voltage level exceeding 2 V. Once the uA2240 is initially triggered, any further trigger inputs are ignored until it is reset.

The binary outputs are open-collector stages that may be connected together to the 10 kΩ pull-up resistor to provide a "wired-OR" output function. The combined output is low if any single connected counter output is low. In this application, the output is connected to the reset input through a 47 kΩ resistor.

This circuit may be used to generate 255 discrete time delays that are integer multiples of the time-base period. The total delay is the sum of the number of time-base periods, which is the binary sum of the Q outputs connected. For example, if only Q5 is connected to the reset input, each trigger pulse generates an active-low output for 32 periods of the time-base oscillator. If Q0, Q2 and Q3 are connected together, the binary count is: $1 + 4 + 8 = 13$. Thus, 255 discrete time delays are available with the eight counter outputs, Q0 through Q7. Delays from 200 µs to 0.223 s are possible with this configuration.

## FREQUENCY SYNTHESIZER

The uA2240 may easily be connected to operate as a programmable voltage controlled frequency synthesizer as shown in Figure 7-41. The uA2240 consists of four basic circuit elements: (1) a time-base oscillator, (2) an eight-bit counter, (3) a control flip-flop, and (4) a voltage regulator.

The basic frequency of the time-base oscillator (TBO) is set by the external time constant determined by the values of R1 and C1 ($1/R1C1 = 2$ kHz). The basic frequency may be changed by varying the modulation input voltage supplied to terminal 12. With a modulation voltage range of 2 to 4.5 V, the basic frequency multiplier is changed from 0.4 to 1.75 nominally with a $V_{CC}$ of 5 V. See Figure 7-40.

The open-collector output of the TBO is connected to the regulator output via a 20 kΩ pull-up resistor, and drives the input to the eight-bit counter. Each counter output is an open-collector stage that may be connected to the 10 kΩ load pull-up resistor to provide a "wired-OR" function. The combined output is low if any single counter output is low.

At power-up, a positive trigger pulse is detected across C2 which starts the TBO and sets all counter outputs to a low state. Once the uA2240 is initially triggered, any further trigger inputs are ignored until it is reset. In this astable operation, the uA2240 will free-run from the time it is triggered until it receives an external reset signal.

Up to 255 discrete frequencies may be synthesized by connecting different counter outputs. For example, connecting the counter outputs of Q0, Q2, and Q3 supplies the output waveform shown in Figure 7-42. if the modulation voltage is set at 3.5 V, the TBO frequency is 2 kHz, then the output frequency will be 125 Hz. By adjusting the modulation voltage, the TBO frequency may be trimmed from 800 Hz to 3.5 kHz. A wide range of basic time-base frequencies are also available to the designer through the selection of different values of R1 and C1. This includes time-base frequencies as high as 100 kHz. The RC and modulation inputs, pins 12 and 13, have high speed capability and sensitivity for accurate, repeatable performance. It is essential, therefore, that high frequency layout and lead dress techniques be used to avoid noise problems which could result in undesirable jitter on the output pulse.

## CASCADED TIMERS FOR LONG TIME DELAYS

Two uA2240 timers may be cascaded to provide long time delays as shown in Figure 7-43. Each uA2240 counter consists of a time-base oscillator, an eight-bit counter, a control flip-flop, and a voltage regulator. The frequency of the time-base oscillator (TBO) is set by the time constant of an external resistor and capacitor.

The open-collector output of the TBO drives the internal eight-bit counter if the TBO output is connected to the regulator output via a pull-up resistor. Otherwise, an external source can be connected to the TBO terminal to supply the input to the eight-bit counter. The open-collector counter outputs Q0 through Q7 provide a "wired-OR" function. The combined output is low if any of the connected counter outputs is low.

The trigger and reset inputs to the internal control flip-flop determine the uA2240 operational state. Once the positive trigger pulse starts the TBO and resets all counter outputs to a low level, further trigger signals are ignored until a reset pulse is received. The reset input inhibits the TBO output and sets all counter outputs to a high level.

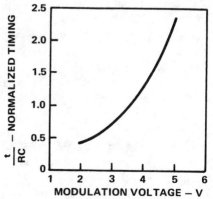

**Figure 7-40. Modulation Voltage Control of Time-Base Period**

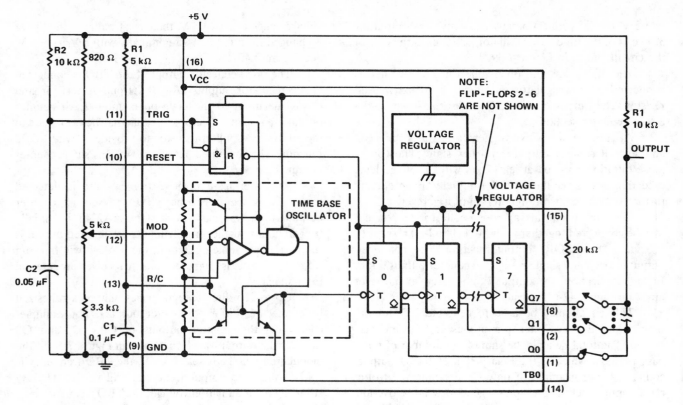

**Figure 7-41. Programmable Voltage Controlled Frequency Synthesizer**

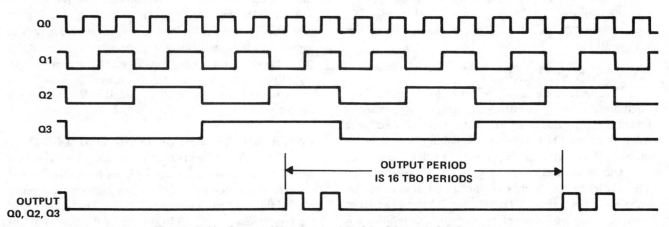

**Figure 7-42. Output Waveform with Q0, Q2, and Q3 Connected**

In this application, the TBO frequency of U1 is set at 2 kHz by the time constant of R1 and C1. This provides a circuit time-base period of 0.5 ms that drives the internal eight-bit counter of U1.

When the trigger switch is momentarily closed, the trigger input starts the U1 TBO and sets all outputs low. The U1 TBO output is connected to its regulator output through the 30 kΩ pull-up resistor. At the end of 256 U1 time-base periods, the U1 Q7 counter output generates a negative-going transition that supplies the active time-base (clock) input for U2. This clock input has a period of 128 ms and is active until a reset is generated by a high U2 output. The U2 time-base oscillator is inhibited by connecting its trigger input (pin 13) to ground through a 1 kΩ resistor.

The U2 counter outputs are connected together resulting in a continuous low U2 output until its final count of 256. At this time, all U2 outputs are high. This ends the output pulse period and resets both uA2240 counters. Thus, the output period is low for about 33 s (256 × 128 ms). If the values of R1 and C1 are changed to 4.8 MΩ and 100 μF, respectively, the output period duration will be about 1 year.

## uA2240 OPERATION WITH EXTERNAL CLOCK

The uA2240 programmable timer/counter may be operated by an external clock as shown in Figure 7-44. The internal time-base oscillator is disabled by connecting the trigger input (pin 13) to ground through a 1 kΩ resistor. An external clock is applied to the time-base output

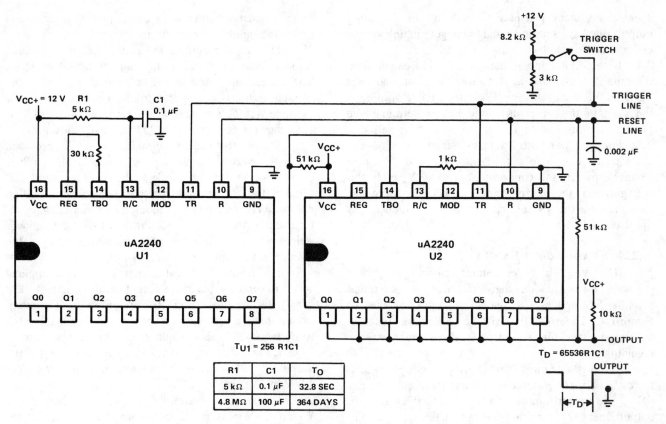

**Figure 7-43. Cascaded Operation for Long Delays**

| R1 | C1 | $T_O$ |
|-----|--------|----------|
| 5 kΩ | 0.1 μF | 32.8 SEC |
| 4.8 MΩ | 100 μF | 364 DAYS |

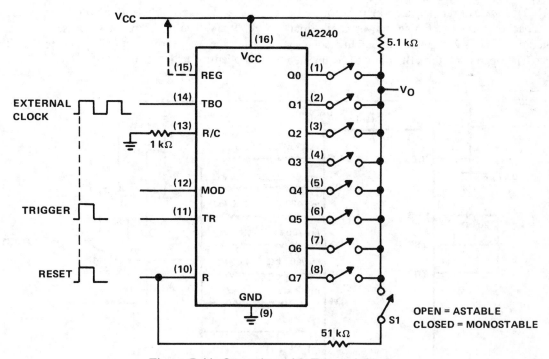

**Figure 7-44. Operation with External Clock**

(TBO), pin 14. For proper operation, the minimum clock amplitude and pulse-duration are 3 V and 1 μs respectively.

In this application the uA2240 consists of an eight-bit counter, a control flip-flop, and a voltage regulator. The external clock triggers the eight-bit counter on the negative-going edge of the clock pulse. The open-collector counter outputs are connected together to the 5.1 kΩ pull-up resistor to provide a "wired-OR" function where the combined output is low if any one of the outputs is low.

This arrangement provides time delays or frequency outputs that have a period equal to integer multiples of the external clock time-base period.

In the astable mode, the uA2240 will free-run from the time it is triggered until it receives an external reset signal. If the monostable mode is selected, one or more of the counter outputs is connected to the reset terminal, and provides the reset at the end of the pulse delay period.

For operation with a supply voltage of 6 V or less, the internal time-base can be powered down by open-circuiting pin 16 and connecting pin 15 to $V_{CC}$. In this configuration, the internal time-base does not draw any current, and the overall current drain is reduced by approximately 3 mA.

## uA2240 STAIRCASE GENERATOR

The uA2240 timer/counter combined with a precision resistor ladder network and an operational amplifier form the staircase generator shown in Figure 7-45. The uA2240 consists of a time-base oscillator, an eight-bit counter, a control flip-flop, and a voltage regulator.

In the astable mode, once a trigger pulse is applied, the uA2240 operates continuously until it receives a reset pulse. The trigger input (pin 11) is tied to the time base output (pin 14) resulting in automatic starting and continuous operation. The frequency of the time-base oscillator (TBO) is set by the time constant of R1 and C1 (f = 1/R1C1). for this example, a 10 kΩ resistor and a 0.01 µF capacitor form the timing network. The total ramp generation time is 25.6 ms for an output frequency of 39.1 Hz. The open-collector TBO output is connected

to the regulator output via a 20 kΩ pull-up resistor, and drives the input to the eight-bit counter.

The counter outputs are connected to a precision resistor ladder network with binary weighted resistors. The current sink through the resistors connected to the counter outputs correspond to the count number. For example, the current sink at Q7 (most significant bit) is 128 times the current sink at Q0 (least significant bit).

The positive bias of approximately 0.5 V applied to the non-inverting input of the operational amplifier generates a current feedback at the inverting input that supplies the current sink for the open-collector pull-up resistors. As the count is generated by the uA2240 eight-bit counter, the current sink through each active binary weighted resistor decreases the positive output of the operational amplifier in discrete steps.

The feedback potentiometer is set at a nominal 10 kΩ to supply a maximum output voltage range. A 12 V supply was used to allow a 10 V output swing. Operation from a single 5 V supply will require an adjustment of the gain (feedback resistor) and reference voltage. With a feedback resistance of 4.5 kΩ and a reference of 0.4 V, the output will allow a 3.6 V output change from 0.4 V to 4.0 V in 14.1 mV steps.

The staircase waveform is shown in Figure 7-46. With a 0.5 V input reference on pin 3 of the TLC271, the output will change from 10.46 V maximum, in 256 steps of 38.9 mV per step, to a 0.5 V minimum. Each step has a pulse duration of 100 µs and an amplitude decrease of 38.9 mV. The period of the staircase waveform is 25.6 ms and the waveform output is repeated until a reset is applied to the uA2240.

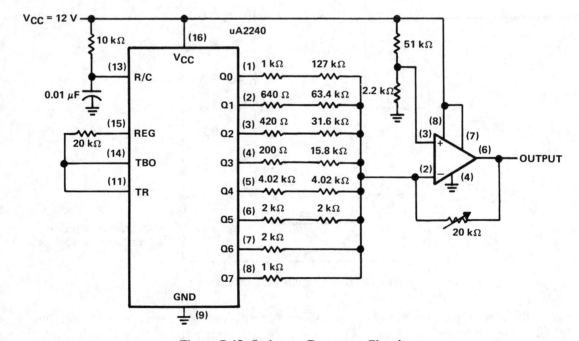

**Figure 7-45. Staircase Generator Circuit**

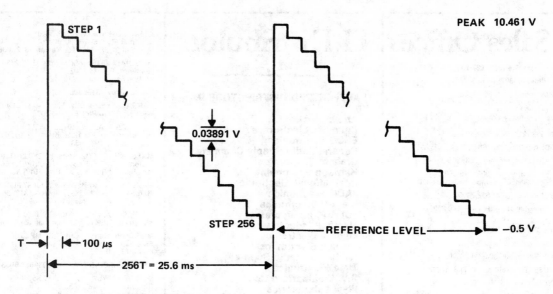

Figure 7-46. Staircase Generator Voltage Waveforms

# TI Sales Offices

**ALABAMA: Huntsville** (205) 837-7530.

**ARIZONA: Phoenix** (602) 995-1007.

**CALIFORNIA: Irvine** (714) 660-1200;
**Sacramento** (916) 929-1521;
**San Diego** (619) 278-9601;
**Santa Clara** (408) 980-9000;
**Torrance** (213) 217-7010;
**Woodland Hills** (213) 704-7759.

**COLORADO: Aurora** (303) 368-8000.

**CONNECTICUT: Wallingford** (203) 269-0074.

**FLORIDA: Ft. Lauderdale** (305) 973-8502;
**Maitland** (305) 660-4600; **Tampa** (813) 870-6420.

**GEORGIA: Norcross** (404) 662-7900.

**ILLINOIS: Arlington Heights** (312) 640-2925.

**INDIANA: Ft. Wayne** (219) 424-5174;
**Indianapolis** (317) 248-8555.

**IOWA: Cedar Rapids** (319) 395-9550.

**MARYLAND: Baltimore** (301) 944-8600.

**MASSACHUSETTS: Waltham** (617) 895-9100.

**MICHIGAN: Farmington Hills** (313) 553-1500.

**MINNESOTA: Eden Prairie** (612) 828-9300.

**MISSOURI: Kansas City** (816) 523-2500;
**St. Louis** (314) 569-7600.

**NEW JERSEY: Iselin** (201) 750-1050.

**NEW MEXICO: Albuquerque** (505) 345-2555.

**NEW YORK: East Syracuse** (315) 463-9291;
**Endicott** (607) 754-3900; **Melville** (516) 454-6600;
**Pittsford** (716) 385-6770;
**Poughkeepsie** (914) 473-2900.

**NORTH CAROLINA: Charlotte** (704) 527-0930;
**Raleigh** (919) 876-2725.

**OHIO: Beachwood** (216) 464-6100;
**Dayton** (513) 258-3877.

**OKLAHOMA: Tulsa** (918) 250-0633.

**OREGON: Beaverton** (503) 643-6758.

**PENNSYLVANIA: Ft. Washington** (215) 643-6450;
**Coraopolis** (412) 771-8550.

**PUERTO RICO: Hato Rey** (809) 753-8700

**TEXAS: Austin** (512) 250-7655;
**Houston** (713) 778-6592; **Richardson** (214) 680-5082;
**San Antonio** (512) 496-1779.

**UTAH: Murray** (801) 266-8972.

**VIRGINIA: Fairfax** (703) 849-1400.

**WASHINGTON: Redmond** (206) 881-3080.

**WISCONSIN: Brookfield** (414) 785-7140.

**CANADA: Nepean, Ontario** (613) 726-1970;
**Richmond Hill, Ontario** (416) 884-9181;
**St. Laurent, Quebec** (514) 334-3635.

# TI Regional Technology Centers

**CALIFORNIA: Irvine** (714) 660-8140,
**Santa Clara** (408) 748-2220.

**GEORGIA: Norcross** (404) 662-7945.

**ILLINOIS: Arlington Heights** (312) 640-2909.

**MASSACHUSETTS: Waltham** (617) 890-6671.

**TEXAS: Richardson** (214) 680-5066.

# TI Distributors

---

## TI AUTHORIZED DISTRIBUTORS IN USA

**Arrow Electronics**
**Diplomat Electronics**
**ESCO Electronics**
**General Radio Supply Company**
**Graham Electronics**
**Harrison Equipment Co.**
**International Electronics**
**JACO Electronics**
**Kierulff Electronics**
**LCOMP, Incorporated**
**Marshall Industries**
**Milgray Electronics**
**Newark Electronics**
**Rochester Radio Supply**
**Time Electronics**
**R.V. Weatherford Co.**
**Wyle Laboratories**

## TI AUTHORIZED DISTRIBUTORS IN CANADA

**CESCO Electronics, Inc.**
**Future Electronics**
**ITT Components**
**L.A. Varah, Ltd.**

---

**ALABAMA: Arrow** (205) 882-2730;
Kierulff (205) 883-6070; Marshall (205) 881-9235.

**ARIZONA: Arrow** (602) 968-4800;
Kierulff (602) 243-4101; Marshall (602) 968-6181;
Wyle (602) 249-2232.

**CALIFORNIA: Los Angeles/Orange County:**
Arrow (818) 701-7500, (714) 838-5422;
Kierulff (213) 725-0325, (714) 731-5711, (714) 220-6300;
Marshall (213) 999-5001, (818) 442-7204,
(714) 660-0951; R.V. Weatherford (714) 634-9600,
(213) 849-3451, (714) 623-1261; Wyle (213) 322-8100,
(714) 863-9953; **Sacramento:** Arrow (916) 925-7456;
Wyle (916) 638-5282; **San Diego:**
Arrow (619) 565-4800; Kierulff (619) 278-2112;
Marshall (619) 578-9600; Wyle (619) 565-9171;
**San Francisco Bay Area:** Arrow (408) 745-6600;
(415) 487-4600; Kierulff (408) 971-2600;
Marshall (408) 732-1100; Wyle (408) 727-2500;
**Santa Barbara:** R.V. Weatherford (805) 965-8551.

**COLORADO: Arrow** (303) 696-1111;
Kierulff (303) 790-4444; Wyle (303) 457-9953.

**CONNECTICUT: Arrow** (203) 265-7741;
Diplomat (203) 797-9674; Kierulff (203) 265-1115;
Marshall (203) 265-3822; Milgray (203) 795-0714.

**FLORIDA: Ft. Lauderdale:** Arrow (305) 429-8200;
Diplomat (305) 974-8700; Kierulff (305) 486-4004;
**Orlando:** Arrow (305) 725-1480;
Milgray (305) 647-5747; **Tampa:**
Arrow (813) 576-8995; Diplomat (813) 443-4514;
Kierulff (813) 576-1966.

**GEORGIA: Arrow** (404) 449-8252;
Kierulff (404) 447-5252; Marshall (404) 923-5750.

**ILLINOIS: Arrow** (312) 397-3440;
Diplomat (312) 595-1000; Kierulff (312) 640-0200;
Marshall (312) 490-0155; Newark (312) 638-4411.

**INDIANA: Indianapolis:** Arrow (317) 243-9353;
Graham (317) 634-8202;
**Ft. Wayne:** Graham (219) 423-3422.

**IOWA: Arrow** (319) 395-7230.

**KANSAS: Kansas City:** Marshall (913) 492-3121;
**Wichita:** LCOMP (316) 265-9507.

**MARYLAND: Arrow** (301) 247-5200;
Diplomat (301) 995-1226; Kierulff (301) 636-5800;
Milgray (301) 793-3993.

**MASSACHUSETTS: Arrow** (617) 933-8130;
Diplomat (617) 935-6611; Kierulff (617) 667-8331;
Marshall (617) 272-8200; Time (617) 935-8080.

**MICHIGAN: Detroit:** Arrow (313) 971-8220;
Marshall (313) 525-5850; Newark (313) 967-0600;
**Grand Rapids:** Arrow (616) 243-0912.

**MINNESOTA: Arrow** (612) 830-1800;
Kierulff (612) 941-7500; Marshall (612) 559-2211.

**MISSOURI: Kansas City:** LCOMP (816) 221-2400;
**St. Louis:** Arrow (314) 567-6888;
Kierulff (314) 739-0855.

**NEW HAMPSHIRE: Arrow** (603) 668-6968.

**NEW JERSEY: Arrow** (201) 575-5300, (609) 596-8000;
Diplomat (201) 785-1830;
General Radio (609) 964-8560; Kierulff (201) 575-6750;
(609) 235-1444; Marshall (201) 882-0320,
(609) 234-9100; Milgray (609) 983-5010.

**NEW MEXICO: Arrow** (505) 243-4566;
International Electronics (505) 345-8127.

**NEW YORK: Long Island:** Arrow (516) 231-1000;
Diplomat (516) 454-6400; JACO (516) 273-5500;
Marshall (516) 273-2053; Milgray (516) 420-9800;
**Rochester:** Arrow (716) 275-0300;
Marshall (716) 235-7620;
Rochester Radio Supply (716) 454-7800;
**Syracuse:** Arrow (315) 652-1000;
Diplomat (315) 652-5000; Marshall (607) 754-1570.

**NORTH CAROLINA: Arrow** (919) 876-3132,
(919) 725-8711; Kierulff (919) 872-8410.

**OHIO: Cincinnati:** Graham (513) 772-1661;
**Cleveland:** Arrow (216) 248-3990;
Kierulff (216) 587-6558; Marshall (216) 248-1788.
**Columbus:** Graham (614) 895-1590;
**Dayton:** Arrow (513) 435-5563;
ESCO (513) 226-1133; Kierulff (513) 439-0045;
Marshall (513) 236-8088.

**OKLAHOMA: Arrow** (918) 665-7700;
Kierulff (918) 252-7537.

**OREGON: Arrow** (503) 684-1690;
Wyle (503) 640-6000; Marshall (503) 644-5050.

**PENNSYLVANIA: Arrow** (412) 856-7000,
(215) 928-1800; General Radio (215) 922-7037.

**TEXAS: Austin:** Arrow (512) 835-4180;
Kierulff (512) 835-2090; Marshall (512) 458-5654;
Wyle (512) 834-9957; **Dallas:** Arrow (214) 380-6464;
International Electronics (214) 233-9323;
Kierulff (214) 343-2400; Marshall (214) 233-5200;
Wyle (214) 235-9953;
**El Paso:** International Electronics (915) 598-3406;
**Houston:** Arrow (713) 530-4700;
Marshall (713) 789-6600;
Harrison Equipment (713) 879-2600;
Kierulff (713) 530-7030; Wyle (713) 879-9953.

**UTAH: Diplomat** (801) 486-4134;
Kierulff (801) 973-6913; Wyle (801) 974-9953.

**VIRGINIA: Arrow** (804) 282-0413.

**WASHINGTON: Arrow** (206) 643-4800;
Kierulff (206) 575-4420; Wyle (206) 453-8300; Marshall (206) 747-9100.

**WISCONSIN: Arrow** (414) 764-6600;
Kierulff (414) 784-8160.

**CANADA: Calgary:** Future (403) 259-6408; Varah
(403) 230-1235; **Edmonton:** Future (403) 486-0974;
**Montreal:** CESCO (514) 735-5511; Future
(514) 694-7710; ITT Components (514) 735-1177;
**Ottawa:** CESCO (613) 226-6903; Future
(613) 820-8313; ITT Components (613) 226-7406;
Varah (613) 726-8884; **Quebec City:** CESCO
(418) 687-4231; **Toronto:** CESCO (416) 661-0220;
Future (416) 638-4771; ITT Components
(416) 630-7971; Varah (416) 516-9311;
**Vancouver:** Future (604) 438-5545; Varah
(604) 873-3211; ITT Components (604) 270-7805;
**Winnipeg:** Varah (204) 633-6190

BK

# TEXAS INSTRUMENTS

Creating useful products
and services for you.